W9-BNQ-234

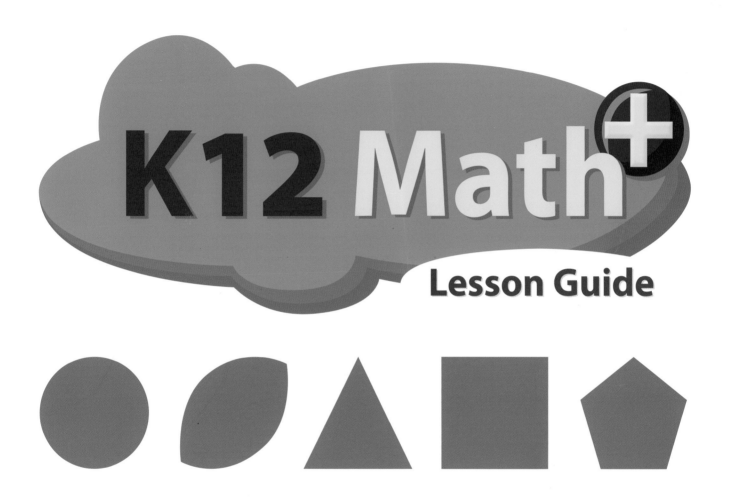

K12 Math+

Lesson Guide

Illustrations Credits
All illustrations © K12 unless otherwise noted

All photographs are royalty-free. © Alamy, © Artville,
© BigStockPhoto.com, © Digital Vision, © Dreamstime.com,
© Fotolia, © Index Open, © iStockphoto.com, © Jupiterimages,
© K12 Inc., © Photodisc, © Photoobjects.net

About K12 Inc.
K12 Inc. (NYSE: LRN) drives innovation and advances the quality of education by delivering
state-of-the-art digital learning platforms and technology to students and school districts
around the world. K12 is a company of educators offering its online and blended curriculum
to charter schools, public school districts, private schools, and directly to families. More
information can be found at K12.com.

ISBN: 978-1-60153-078-3
Printed by Bradford & Bigelow, Newburyport, MA, USA, October 2020

Contents

Numbers Through 10

Calendar and Time

Data and Graphs

Numbers Through 20

Introduction to Addition

Problem Solving with Addition

Introduction to Subtraction

Problem Solving with Subtraction

Subtraction as Comparison

Comparison Subtraction: Story Problems

Add or Subtract: Problem Solving

Measurement

Numbers Through 30

Solid Figures

Program Overview

Lesson Overview

The table at the beginning of each lesson tells you what activities are in the lesson and whether students are on the computer (**ONLINE**) or at a table or desk (**OFFLINE**). The expected time for each activity is given.

Objectives and Prerequisite Skills

Each lesson teaches the Lesson Objectives. The lesson assumes that students know the Prerequisite Skills from their previous math experience. The Get Ready activity is designed to remind students of the prerequisite skills, and to prepare them for the lesson.

Common Errors and Misconceptions

Research shows that students might misunderstand certain concepts, which then leads to misunderstanding of more advanced concepts. When certain research applies to a lesson, the lesson has a Common Errors and Misconceptions section.

Content Background

The Content Background tells you what the students will learn in the lesson, and it explains any complex math concepts, putting the lesson into perspective with wider math knowledge.

Materials

This box tells you what materials students will need in this lesson. More information about the materials is included on page x.

Keywords

Definitions of keywords are included in the lesson in which the math term is introduced. The Unit Review includes of a list of all keywords for the unit.

Advance Preparation

Some lessons require preparation that extends beyond gathering materials. In these cases, the lesson includes an Advance Preparation section.

Count Through 20

Lesson Overview

Skills Update	5 minutes	ONLINE
GET READY Shape Count	5 minutes	ONLINE
LEARN Sort and Count	15 minutes	OFFLINE
TRY IT Count in Nature	10 minutes	OFFLINE
CHECKPOINT	10 minutes	OFFLINE

▶ Lesson Objectives
- Count aloud a number of objects up through 20.
- Demonstrate that counting 20 or fewer objects can occur from left to right, right to left, or in any order as long as all the items are counted once.

▶ Prerequisite Skills
- Count aloud a number of objects up through 10.
- Demonstrate that counting 10 or fewer objects can occur from left to right, right to left, or in any order as long as all the items are counted once.

▶ Common Errors and Misconceptions
- Students might start counting before or after pointing to the first object in a group. Or they might stop counting before or after they point to the last object. Students should point to each object as they count it.
- Students might say more than one number for each object when counting objects in a group. Or they might skip objects. Students should point to each object and say exactly one number. Then they should point to the next object and say exactly one number, and so on.
- Students might use an incorrect counting sequence, such as "one, two, four, six, ten."

▶ Advance Preparation
Prepare six bags with the following numbers of counting objects (for example, dry macaroni and dry beans): 12, 14, 15, 16, 18, and 20. Be sure to include some of each type of counting object in each bag.

▶ Content Background
Students will count groups with up through 20 objects. Students will learn that they can count in any order as long as they count each object exactly one time.

Keywords   **count** – to say each number according to a defined sequence, such as consecutively, by 2s, or backward

COUNT THROUGH 20 **193**

Materials to Gather

SUPPLIED
Numbers Through 20 activity page
Checkpoint (printout)

ALSO NEEDED
counting objects – 50 of one type, 45 of another type
resealable plastic bags, medium – 7
crayons

Materials

K^{12} supplies math materials, including this Lesson Guide and the Activity Book, the student practice book.

The **block set** includes various counters as well as 2-D and 3-D shapes. Note that the blocks are labeled with letters. The materials lists in each lesson refer to these blocks by their letter (for instance, B blocks or BB blocks or C blocks). The O blocks refer to the cubes. These blocks aren't labeled with the letter O, but the hole in each block resembles this letter. Within the lesson, you might see a more descriptive term, such as "circles" for the B blocks.

Printouts, Plastic Sheet Cover, and Dry-Erase Markers

A lesson may ask you to print a document showing a number line, place-value chart, or other math tool. These documents will be reused throughout the course. We recommend that you obtain a plastic sheet cover and dry-erase markers so students can place the sheet over the printout and write answers on the sheet. They can then erase the answers and reuse the printout multiple times.

Number Cards

Index cards labeled with numbers are frequently called for in the lessons. We recommend that you create a set of index cards numbered 0–30, and use them throughout the course.

Paper and Pencil

Students should always have notebook paper and a pencil handy. These materials are not listed in each lesson.

Also Needed

Other common items are called for in lessons, designated in the materials list as "Also Needed." Common items include, but are not limited to, the following: calendar, containers, craft sticks, crayons, fingerpaints, glue, glue stick, index cards, markers (permanent and coloring), paper (construction, drawing, poster, and wide-line handwriting), pencils (coloring), pipe cleaners, scissors (adult and round-end safety), sticky notes, tape (clear, double-stick, and masking), and yarn.

Working Through a Lesson

When you go online with students to do a math lesson, you will see a list of the activities that are included in the lesson. In the first four units, students will warm up for their math lesson by completing an online calendar or time activity. In the fifth unit, students will take an assessment on calendar and time. In subsequent units, students will warm up for their math lesson by answering questions in an online Skills Update. Answers will be shown as students work through each question.

The Lesson Guide will give you an overview of the entire lesson.

Instructions for online activities are online, so you should expect to work at the computer with your students, reading instructions and activities to them as necessary. The Lesson Guide may, however, include a teaching tip or other information. In some cases, such as when an open-ended Learning Tool is used, there will be instructions to follow in the Lesson Guide. The online screen will guide you to follow the instructions in the Lesson Guide.

Instructions for offline activities are in the Lesson Guide. These activities may use supplied or common materials, and some include pages from the Activity Book.

Types of Activities

Skills Update Short online problem set for warm-up. These problems should take about 5 minutes to complete.

Get Ready Review of previous math knowledge that will be needed for this lesson. The Get Ready can be online or offline.

Learn Presentation of math concepts, or guided practice. The Learn activities can be online or offline.

Try It Students practice what they have just learned, without guidance. The Try It activities are usually found in the Activity Book.

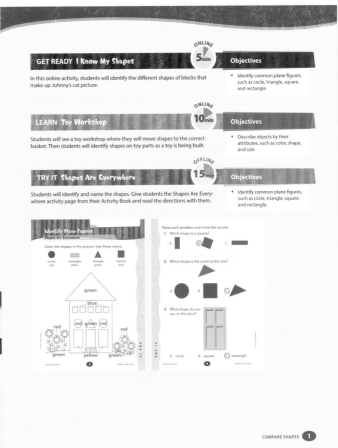

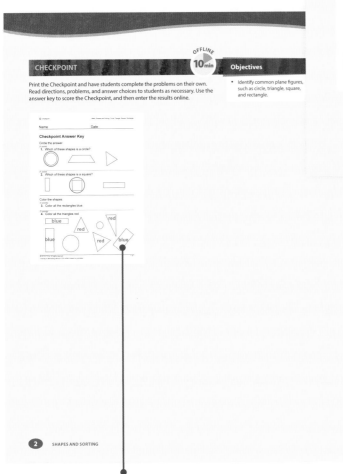

The Lesson Guide includes the answers, shown in magenta, to the Activity Book pages and offline Checkpoints.

Checkpoint Assessments of whether students have learned the objectives taught in the lesson or lessons. Not every lesson has a Checkpoint. In some Checkpoints, students show or explain their answers, and you record their performance.

In addition to the regular Checkpoints, **Unit Reviews** and **Unit Checkpoints** are lessons at the end of each unit.

Online Activities

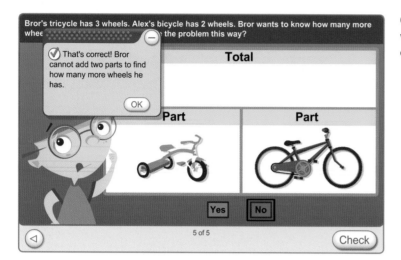

Online activities will show whether students answer correctly.

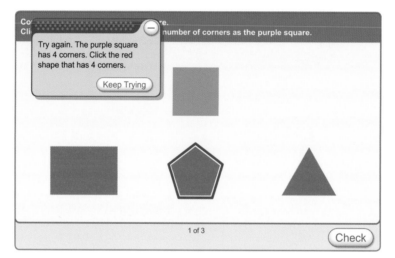

If students answer incorrectly, they will see feedback. They should click Keep Trying to try again. If they answer incorrectly a second time, they can click Show Me to see the correct answer.

Learning Tools are online activities that you set up to give students math exercises that will apply to what they are learning in a specific lesson.

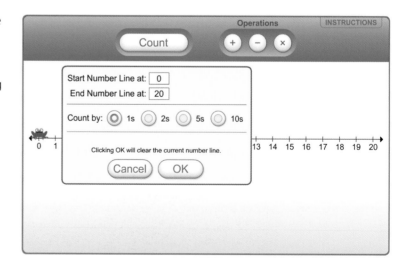

Shapes and Sorting

▶ Unit Objectives

- Identify common plane figures, such as circle, triangle, square, and rectangle.
- Describe objects by their attributes, such as color, shape, and size.
- Sort and classify objects by one attribute, such as color, shape, or size.

▶ Big Ideas

- Geometric figures can be described and classified by the shapes of their faces and by how many faces, sides, edges, or vertices they have.
- Common geometric objects can be identified, described, and compared.

▶ Unit Introduction

In this unit, students will describe the color, shape, and size of objects. Then they will sort and classify objects by these features, or attributes.

Students will learn about the attributes of geometric shapes, such as circles, triangles, squares, and rectangles. They will also describe, sort, and classify everyday objects, such as beads, stuffed animals, and fruit.

Identify Plane Figures

Lesson Overview

Meet the Characters	5 minutes	ONLINE
LEARN Look for Shapes	15 minutes	OFFLINE
LEARN Name That Shape	15 minutes	OFFLINE
TRY IT Shapes Are Everywhere	10 minutes	OFFLINE

▶ Lesson Objectives

Identify common plane figures, such as circle, triangle, square, and rectangle.

▶ Common Errors and Misconceptions

Students might not recgonize that a shape might be positioned different ways. For example, students might not recognize that the second shape is a square:

▶ Advance Preparation

Place a variety of circle, square, rectangle, and triangle blocks in a paper bag.

▶ Safety

Supervise students to make sure they use their scissors safely and stay seated.

▶ Content Background

In this lesson, students will use blocks and drawings to identify and describe circles, triangles, squares, and rectangles.

A square is mathematically defined as a special type of rectangle. So, if students were sorting shapes and called a square a rectangle, they would be mathematically correct. However, in the very early grades, students are asked to differentiate between the more traditional rectangle that has two longer sides and two shorter sides and a square that has all sides equal. Therefore, the square is given its own category for sorting in earlier grades.

The term *diamond*, often used by young children for a square rotated onto one of its corners, is not a standard geometric term and will not be used in this course. Students should understand that a square rotated in any direction is still a square.

Materials to Gather

SUPPLIED

Look for Shapes activity page

Shapes Are Everywhere activity page

blocks – AA, BB, CC, DD, EE, FF, GG, HH (all colors)

ALSO NEEDED

scissors, round-end safety

crayons

paper bag

circle – a plane figure with no straight sides or corners; the edge of a circle is a curve with all points the same distance from the center

orientation – the position of an object, such as rotated or flipped

rectangle – a plane figure with 4 sides and 4 square corners with opposite sides of equal length

shape – a closed outline or form, such as a square or hexagon

square – a plane figure with 4 sides of equal length and 4 square corners

triangle – a plane figure with 3 sides and 3 corners

LEARN Look for Shapes

OFFLINE
15min

Objectives

- Identify common plane figures, such as circle, triangle, square, and rectangle.

Students will identify circles, triangles, squares, and rectangles. They will learn that a shape may vary in size, color, or orientation. For example, a small blue rectangle that is oriented vertically and a big red rectangle that is oriented horizontally are both rectangles.

Gather the Look for Shapes activity page, crayons, and round-end scissors.

1. Have students complete the activity page.

2. Hold up a circle from the activity page and say the name of the shape.

   Say: Ask students to repeat the word *circle*. Then ask students to hold up another circle. Point out that even though the circles are not the same size and color, they are both circles. Have students look around the room and find circles (for example, buttons, knobs, CDs, clocks).

3. Repeat Step 2 with a triangle.

4. Repeat Step 2 with a rectangle.

5. Hold up two squares. Rotate one of the squares at a 45° angle. Ask students what shapes you are holding. Emphasize that both shapes are squares even though they are positioned differently. Continue with Step 2, asking students to find a third square and identify squares in the room.

6. Have students identify the remaining shapes. Then ask them to sort the shapes—all circles in one group, and so on.

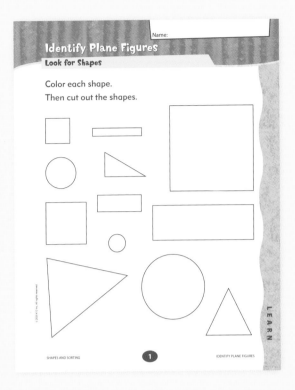

Identify Plane Figures
Look for Shapes

Name:

Color each shape.
Then cut out the shapes.

SHAPES AND SORTING
1
IDENTIFY PLANE FIGURES

L E A R N

OFFLINE
15 min

LEARN Name That Shape

Objectives

- Identify common plane figures, such as circle, triangle, square, and rectangle.

Students will identify circles, triangles, squares, and rectangles. Students will learn that a shape may vary in size, color, and orientation.

Gather the paper bag that you have filled with blocks.

1. Show students the paper bag. Tell students to reach into the bag and pull out a shape.

2. Have students pull out a shape, name the shape, and place it to the side. As they continue to pull out shapes, tell students to make a separate pile for each shape.

3. When the bag is empty, ask students to tell how the shapes are alike and different. If students need help, ask questions to guide them.

   Ask: How is a triangle like the other shapes? How is it different?

TRY IT Shapes Are Everywhere

Objectives

Students will identify and name the shapes. Give students the crayons and Shapes Are Everywhere activity page from their Activity Book. Read the directions with them.

- Identify common plane figures, such as circle, triangle, square, and rectangle.

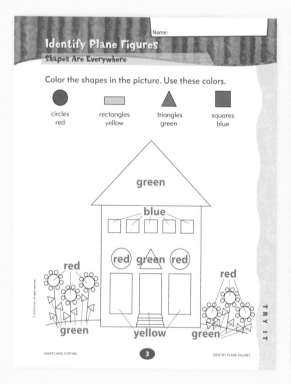

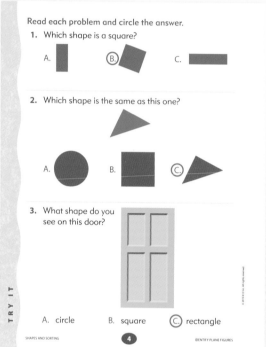

Circle, Triangle, Square, Rectangle

Lesson Overview

CALENDAR Where Is the Calendar?		5 minutes	ONLINE
GET READY Find the Shape		5 minutes	ONLINE
LEARN Shape Puppet		15 minutes	OFFLINE
TRY IT Common Shapes		10 minutes	OFFLINE
CHECKPOINT		10 minutes	OFFLINE

▶ Lesson Objectives

- Identify common plane figures, such as circle, triangle, square, and rectangle.
- Identify tools that measure time of at least a day, such as a calendar, and describe what those tools measure (for example, a calendar measures days and weeks).

▶ Common Errors and Misconceptions

- Students might have heard some geometric vocabulary words, but their definitions of these words might be incorrect.
- Students might not recognize that a shape might be positioned different ways.
- Students might not understand why circles—which have no sides—are grouped with triangles, squares, and rectangles. By definition, a circle is a plane figure because it is an enclosed two-dimensional, or flat, shape.

▶ Safety

Supervise students to make sure they use their scissors safely and stay seated.

▶ Content Background

Students will contine to practice identifying shapes. They will use circles, triangles, squares, and rectangles to create a puppet.

A square is mathematically defined as a special type of rectangle. So, if students were sorting shapes and called a square a rectangle, they would be mathematically correct. However, in the very early grades, students are asked to differentiate between the more traditional rectangle that has two longer sides and two shorter sides and a square that has all sides equal. Therefore, the square is given its own category for sorting in earlier grades.

The term *diamond*, often used by young children for a square rotated onto one of its corners, is not a standard geometric term and will not be used in this course. Students should understand that a square rotated in any direction is still a square.

Materials to Gather

SUPPLIED

Shape Puppet activity page
Common Shapes activity page
Checkpoint (printout)

ALSO NEEDED

paper bag
glue
scissors, round-end safety
crayons

GET READY Find the Shape

Students will identify circles, squares, rectangles, and triangles online.

Objectives

- Identify common plane figures, such as circle, triangle, square, and rectangle.

Tips

For students still struggling to identify shapes, point to each shape and say its name. Have students repeat the names.

LEARN Shape Puppet

Students will use circles, triangles, squares, and rectangles to create a puppet. As they make their puppets, students will discuss what they know about shapes.
Gather the paper bag, scissors, glue, crayons, and Shape Puppet activity page.

1. Place a paper bag on your hand to show how to make a puppet. Point out that the bottom of the bag is the face, and the rest of the bag is the body.

2. Beginning with the eyes, have students choose the shapes from the Shape Puppet activity page to use for each part of the puppet. Have students color and cut out the shapes as they choose them.

3. Have students glue their shapes onto the puppet. As they glue each shape, ask students to say the shape's name.

4. When they finish making their puppets, ask students to tell about the shapes they used to make their puppets. (An example of what an assembled puppet might look like is shown.)

Objectives

- Identify common plane figures, such as circle, triangle, square, and rectangle.

Tips

When telling about the shapes they used in their puppets, students may not recognize that a shape may be positioned different ways. For example, in the puppet shown, students may not recognize that the arms are rectangles. Hold the puppet at different angles to show that you can rotate a shape without changing what shape it is.

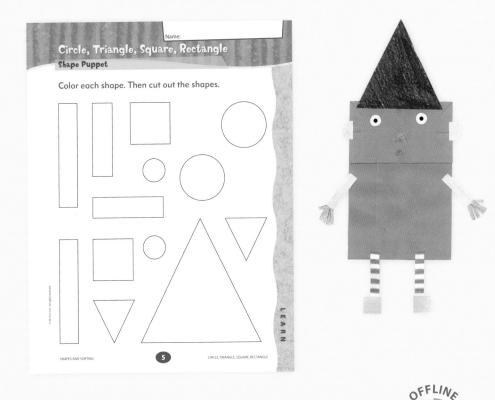

OFFLINE
10 min

TRY IT Common Shapes

Students will identify circles, triangles, squares, and rectangles. Give students the Common Shapes activity page from their Activity Book and read the directions with them.

Objectives

- Identify common plane figures, such as circle, triangle, square, and rectangle.

Tips

In the Activity Book and Checkpoints, students will see multiple choice questions. Explain that students will hear you read a question and three answer choices. Only one of the three answers is correct. Students should circle the correct answer.

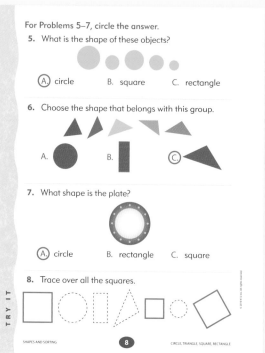

CHECKPOINT

OFFLINE
10 min

Objectives

Print the Checkpoint and have students complete the problems on their own. Read the directions, problems, and answer choices to students as necessary. Use the answer key to score the Checkpoint, and then enter the results online.
Gather the crayons. Students will need the crayons for Problems 3 and 4.

- Identify common plane figures, such as circle, triangle, square, and rectangle.

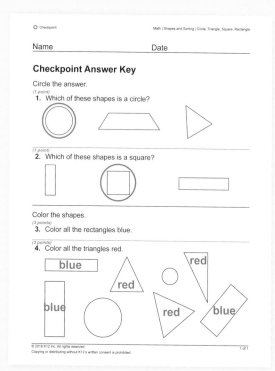

Compare Shapes

CALENDAR Find the Month	5 minutes	ONLINE
GET READY I Know My Shapes	5 minutes	ONLINE
LEARN Toy Workshop	10 minutes	ONLINE
LEARN Shapes: The Same or Different?	15 minutes	OFFLINE
TRY IT Shape Match	10 minutes	OFFLINE

▶ **Lesson Objectives**

- Describe objects by their attributes, such as color, shape, and size.
- Identify tools that measure time of at least a day, such as a calendar, and describe what those tools measure (for example, a calendar measures days and weeks).

▶ **Prerequisite Skills**

Identify common plane figures, such as circle, triangle, square, and rectangle.

▶ **Common Errors and Misconceptions**

- Students might have heard some geometric vocabulary words, but their definitions of these words might be incorrect.
- Students might not recognize that a shape might be positioned different ways.

▶ **Content Background**

In this lesson, students will use blocks to describe whether shapes are the same or different.

A square is mathematically defined as a special type of rectangle. So, if students were sorting shapes and called a square a rectangle, they would be mathematically correct. However, in the very early grades, students are asked to differentiate between the more traditional rectangle that has two longer sides and two shorter sides and a square that has all sides equal. Therefore, the square is given its own category for sorting in earlier grades.

The term diamond, often used by young children for a square rotated onto one of its corners, is not a standard geometric term and will not be used in this course. Students should understand that a square rotated in any direction is still a square.

Materials to Gather

SUPPLIED

blocks – AA, CC, EE, FF (yellow, blue, green)

Shape Match activity page

ALSO NEEDED

paper bag

Keywords

attribute – a characteristic, such as size, shape, or color

GET READY I Know My Shapes

ONLINE 5min

In this online activity, students will identify the different shapes of blocks that make up Johnny's cat picture.

Objectives

- Identify common plane figures, such as circle, triangle, square, and rectangle.

LEARN Toy Workshop

ONLINE 10min

Students will see a toy workshop where they will move shapes to the correct basket. Then students will identify shapes on toy parts as a toy is being built.

Objectives

- Describe objects by their attributes, such as color, shape, and size.

LEARN Shapes: The Same or Different?

OFFLINE 15min

Students will describe the shapes that they've learned. They will describe sets of blocks as having the same or different shapes. Gather the blocks and paper bag. Lay out the blocks in a random arrangement. Do not group the shapes together.

Objectives

- Describe objects by their attributes, such as color, shape, and size.

1. Hold up a triangle block. Ask students to name the shape and find two more blocks with the same shape.

   Ask: How do you know these are triangles?
   ANSWER: They have three sides. They have three corners.

2. Repeat this step with circles, squares, and rectangles. Important things to point out if students do not mention them: Circles are round, or have a curved edge. Squares have 4 sides that are all the same length. Rectangles have 2 longer sides and 2 shorter sides.

3. Place one circle, one square, one rectangle and one triangle block in the paper bag. Tell students they will try to find shapes by feeling them without looking.

4. Hold up a shape and have students find the matching shape in the bag using only their hands. Then hold up a shape and have them find a shape that does not match your shape using only their hands. Repeat with all of the shapes.

TRY IT Shape Match

Students will practice identifying shapes of objects. Give student the Shape Match activity page from their Activity Book, and read the directions with them. Use the answer key to check students' answers, and then enter the results online.

Objectives

- Describe objects by their attributes, such as color, shape, and size.

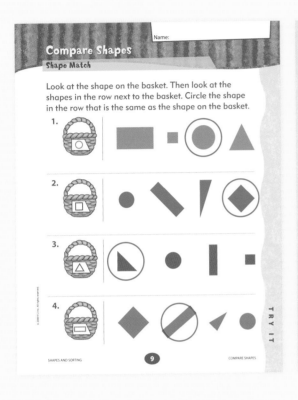

Compare Shapes
Shape Match

Name:

Look at the shape on the basket. Then look at the shapes in the row next to the basket. Circle the shape in the row that is the same as the shape on the basket.

1.
2.
3.
4.

SHAPES AND SORTING   9   COMPARE SHAPES

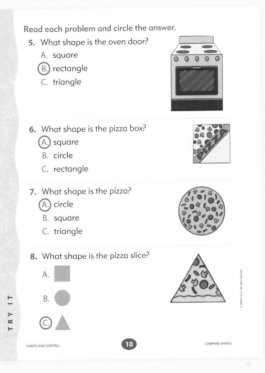

Read each problem and circle the answer.

5. What shape is the oven door?
   A. square
   B. rectangle
   C. triangle

6. What shape is the pizza box?
   A. square
   B. circle
   C. rectangle

7. What shape is the pizza?
   A. circle
   B. square
   C. triangle

8. What shape is the pizza slice?
   A.
   B.
   C.

TRY IT

SHAPES AND SORTING   10   COMPARE SHAPES

Compare Colors

Lesson Overview		
CALENDAR Find Weeks on a Calendar	5 minutes	ONLINE
GET READY Color Concentration	5 minutes	ONLINE
LEARN I Know My Colors	10 minutes	ONLINE
LEARN Pick That Color	15 minutes	OFFLINE
TRY IT Same Colors	10 minutes	OFFLINE

▶ Lesson Objectives

- Describe objects by their attributes, such as color, shape, and size.
- Identify tools that measure time of at least once a day, such as a calendar, and describe what those tools measure (for example, a calendar measures days and weeks).

▶ Prerequisite Skills

Identify common plane figures, such as circle, triangle, square, and rectangle.

▶ Common Errors and Misconceptions

- Students might have heard some geometric vocabulary words, but their definitions of these words might be incorrect.
- Students might not recognize that a shape might be positioned different ways.

▶ Advance Preparation

Label four sheets of paper as follows: write **blue** with a blue crayon on one; write **yellow** with a yellow crayon on one; write **red** with a red crayon on one; write **green** with a green crayon on one.

▶ Content Background

In this lesson, students will identify and sort objects by color. Color is an important way to describe objects. By learning about color, students will become better able to talk about and categorize objects in the world around them.

Materials to Gather

SUPPLIED

blocks – AA, BB, CC, DD, EE, FF, GG, HH (all colors)

Same Colors activity page

ALSO NEEDED

crayons

GET READY Color Concentration

ONLINE
5min

Students will sort by color. They will match objects that are the same color in a memory game.

Objectives

- Describe objects by their attributes, such as color, shape, and size.

LEARN I Know My Colors

ONLINE
10min

Students will continue to practice sorting by color. They will find flowers and vegetables in Alexander's garden that are the same color as Alexander's crayon.

Objectives

- Describe objects by their attributes, such as color, shape, and size.

LEARN Pick That Color

OFFLINE
15min

Students will identify objects that are given color. Gather the blocks and the sheets of paper labeled blue, yellow, red, and green.
  For each of the labeled pieces of paper:

1. Place the paper in front of students and ask what color the word is.
   Tell students that they will be finding things of that color.
2. Have students find the blocks of the given color.
3. Have students find something in the room that is the given color.
4. Review the color of the blocks, and the object.

Objectives

- Describe objects by their attributes, such as color, shape, and size.

TRY IT Same Colors

OFFLINE
10min

Students will circle objects that are the same color. They will also apply what they learned about colors to answer questions. Give students the Same Colors activity page from their Activity Book and read the directions with them. Use the answer key to check students' answers, and then enter the results online.

Objectives

- Describe objects by their attributes, such as color, shape, and size.

Compare Colors

Same Colors

Look at the objects in each row.
Circle the objects that are the same color.

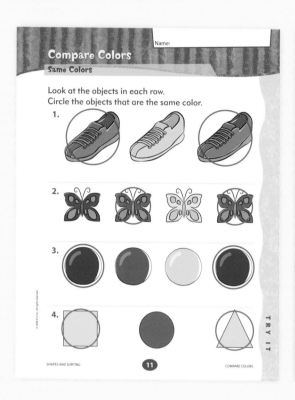

1.

2.

3.

4.

T R Y   I T

T R Y   I T

Read each problem and circle the answer.

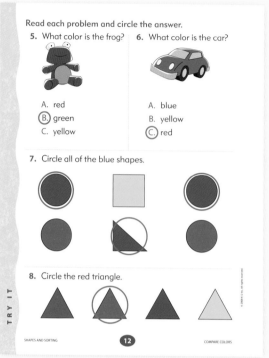

5. What color is the frog?

A. red
B. green
C. yellow

6. What color is the car?

A. blue
B. yellow
C. red

7. Circle all of the blue shapes.

8. Circle the red triangle.

Compare Sizes

Lesson Overview

CALENDAR Find the Days	5 minutes	ONLINE
GET READY Spaceship Sizes	5 minutes	ONLINE
LEARN Large and Small Animals	10 minutes	ONLINE
LEARN I Know Large and Small	15 minutes	OFFLINE
TRY IT Compare Large and Small	10 minutes	OFFLINE

▶ Lesson Objectives

- Describe objects by their attributes, such as color, shape, and size.
- Identify tools that measure time of at least once a day, such as a calendar, and describe what those tools measure (for example, a calendar measures days and weeks).

▶ Prerequisite Skills

Identify common plane figures, such as circle, triangle, square, and rectangle.

▶ Common Errors and Misconceptions

- Students might have heard some geometric vocabulary words, but their definitions of these words might be incorrect.
- Students might not recognize that a shape might be positioned different ways.

▶ Advance Preparation

- Label one index card **large** and another index card **small**. You may also draw a large dot on the **large** card and a small dot on the **small** card.
- Gather four large and four small household objects for the Learn: I Know Large and Small activity. Use objects similar in size to those listed here:

Large	Small
large bowl	pencil
textbook	circular button
adult shoe	eraser
picture book	dry macaroni noodle

▶ Content Background

In this lesson, students will identify large and small objects and sort them by size. They will also compare objects by size, telling which objects are larger and smaller.

   Size is an important way to describe objects. By learning to compare by size, students will become better able to talk about and categorize objects in the world around them.

Materials to Gather

SUPPLIED

blocks – AA, BB, CC, DD, EE, FF, GG, HH (all colors)

Compare Large and Small activity page

ALSO NEEDED

household objects – 4 large and 4 small

index cards – labeled **large** and **small**

crayons

large – big in amount or size
larger – bigger in amount or size in relation to another amount or size
small – little in amount or size
smaller – littler in amount or size in relation to another amount or size

GET READY Spaceship Sizes

ONLINE
5min

Students will practice sorting by size. They will identify spaceships as large or small and place the spaceships onto shelves according to size.

Objectives

- Describe objects by their attributes, such as color, shape, and size.

LEARN Large and Small Animals

ONLINE
10min

Students will compare animals by size. They will look at a picture of two animals and follow instructions to choose either the larger or smaller animal.

Objectives

- Describe objects by their attributes, such as color, shape, and size.

Tips

Use the words *large* and *small* to describe size.

LEARN I Know Large and Small

OFFLINE
15min

Students will compare the sizes and shapes of objects. Gather the blocks, index cards, and household objects. Lay out the blocks in a random arrangement.

1. Hold up one small red circle and one large red circle.

   Say: Here are two red circles. What is different about them?
   ANSWER: One is large and one is small.

2. Have students find all the other circles that are the same size as the large circle. Tell them the circles do not need to be red, they just need to be large.

3. **Say:** We have large circles and small circles. We also have large squares and small squares, large triangles and small triangles, and large rectangles and small rectangles. Find all the large shapes and put them in a group.

   Students should group all the large squares, triangles, and rectangles.

4. Clear the work area.

5. Give students the index cards and read the words *large* and *small* with students. Explain that you will show them two objects. Students will use the cards to tell you which object is large and which is small.

6. Place one large household object and one small household object, such as a picture book and a circular button, in the work area.

Objectives

- Describe objects by their attributes, such as color, shape, and size.

Tips

If students have difficulty identifying sizes of objects in a group, use a reference object. For example, if students are identifying fruit as large or small, use an apple as a reference object. Tell students to compare each fruit to the apple: If fruit is smaller than an apple, it is small. If fruit is larger than an apple, it is large.

7. **Say:** Place the "large" index card next to the large object. Place the "small" index card next to the small object.

Students should place the "large" index card next to the book and the "small" index card next to the button.

8. Repeat Steps 7 and 8 with the remaining three pairs of large and small objects.

Extend the activity: Mix the blocks and lay them out in a random arrangement. Hold up two blocks that are either both large or both small. Ask students to find a third block of the same size. Discuss whether shape or color affects size.

TRY IT Compare Large and Small

Students will color shapes based on their size. Then they will answer questions about sizes of objects. Give students the crayons and the Compare Large and Small activity page from their Activity Book. Read the directions with them.

Objectives

- Describe objects by their attributes, such as color, shape, and size.

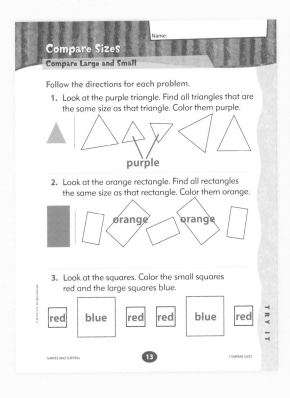

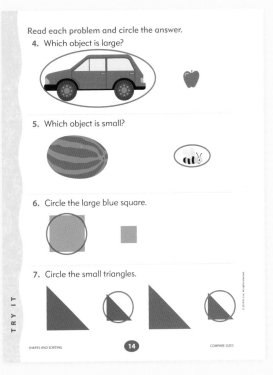

Sizes, Shapes, and Colors

Lesson Overview

CALENDAR Days of the Week	5 minutes	**ONLINE**
GET READY Play the Matching Game	5 minutes	**ONLINE**
LEARN Rosa's Colorful Shape Necklace	10 minutes	**ONLINE**
TRY IT Do You Know Colors, Shapes, and Sizes?	5 minutes	**ONLINE**
TRY IT Beary Large	10 minutes	**OFFLINE**
CHECKPOINT	10 minutes	**OFFLINE**

▶ Lesson Objectives

- Describe objects by their attributes, such as color, shape, and size.
- Name the days of the week.

▶ Prerequisite Skills

Identify common plane figures, such as circle, triangle, square, and rectangle.

▶ Common Errors and Misconceptions

- Students might have heard some geometric vocabulary words, but their definitions of these words might be incorrect.
- Students might not recognize that a shape might be positioned in different ways.

▶ Content Background

In this lesson, students will identify, compare, and describe the shape, size, and color of plane figures and common objects by engaging in online and offline activities.

Materials to Gather

SUPPLIED
Beary Large activity page
Checkpoint (printout)

ALSO NEEDED
crayons

GET READY Play the Matching Game

ONLINE
5 min

Objectives

Students will match plane figures with words that describe their color, shape, and size. By matching the shapes to the correct words, students will create a picture.

- Describe objects by their attributes, such as color, shape, and size.

LEARN Rosa's Colorful Shape Necklace

ONLINE 10 min

Students will identify the color, shape, and size of beads to help Rosa make a necklace.

Objectives

- Describe objects by their attributes, such as color, shape, and size.

Tips

If students struggle, help them focus on one attribute of a bead at a time. Ask, "What color is this bead?" Once they identify the color, ask about shape.

TRY IT Do You Know Colors, Shapes, and Sizes?

ONLINE 5 min

Students will answer questions online to demonstrate how well they can identify colors, shapes, and sizes.

Objectives

- Describe objects by their attributes, such as color, shape, and size.

TRY IT Beary Large

OFFLINE 10 min

Students will follow directions to color a shape picture. Then they will answer questions about shapes. Give students the crayons and the Beary Large activity page from their Activity Book. Read the directions with them.

Objectives

- Describe objects by their attributes, such as color, shape, and size.

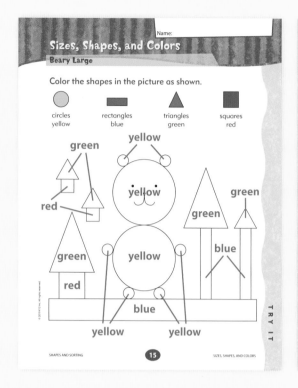

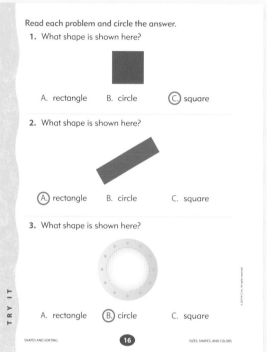

CHECKPOINT

Objectives

Print the Checkpoint and have students complete it on their own. Read the directions, problems, and answer choices to students as necessary. Use the answer key to score the Checkpoint, and then enter the results online.

You will need to display a blue crayon for Problem 3. Show students the blue crayon as you read the problem aloud.

- Describe objects by their attributes, such as color, shape, and size.

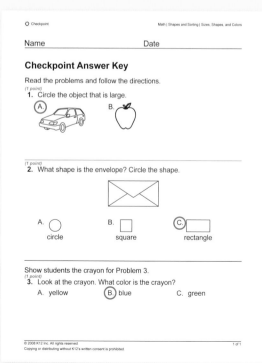

Sort by Color

▶ Lesson Objectives

- Sort and classify objects by one attribute, such as color, shape, or size.
- Name the days of the week.

▶ Prerequisite Skills

Describe objects by their attributes, such as color, shape, and size.

▶ Content Background

In this lesson, students will sort objects by color. They will sort color tiles as well as everyday objects.

Materials to Gather

SUPPLIED

Color Sort activity page

blocks – E (all colors)

Keywords

sort – to put objects into categories on the basis of a particular set of characteristics

---

ONLINE
10 min

GET READY Shape Hunt

Students will use clues to determine which shape Rosa wants them to choose. To choose the correct shapes, students must know common shapes, sizes, and colors.

Objectives

- Describe objects by their attributes, such as color, shape, and size.

LEARN Toy Cleanup

Students will practice sorting online by placing toys onto shelves according to their color.

Objectives

- Sort and classify objects by one attribute, such as color, shape, or size.

LEARN Sort Tiles

Students will sort blocks by color. Sorting blocks helps link students' senses of sight and touch. Gather the blocks.

Objectives

- Sort and classify objects by one attribute, such as color, shape, or size.

1. Select 2–4 squares of each color to place in front of students. Ask students to identify the color of each square.

2. **Say:** Let's sort the red squares. Put all of the red squares in a group.

3. Next tell students to put all of the yellow squares in a group.

4. Ask students to sort the remaining squares by color. If students struggle, tell them to put all of the green squares in a group.

   Ask: How many groups did you make?
   ANSWER: 4

5. Point to the group of blue squares.

   Ask: Why are these squares in this group together?
   ANSWER: They are all blue.

6. Gather a handful of additional color squares. Give the squares to students one at a time. Tell students to put each square into the correct color group.

7. Ask students to point to and name each group.

TRY IT **Color Sort**

Students will practice sorting by color by choosing objects from a group that are a specific color. Give students the Color Sort activity page from their Activity Book and read the directions with them.

Use the answer key to check students' answers, and then enter the results online.

Objectives

- Sort and classify objects by one attribute, such as color, shape, or size.

Tips

Have students cross out objects that are not the sorting color (for example, in Problem 5, students should cross out the gray mug). This extra step will ensure that students consider each object.

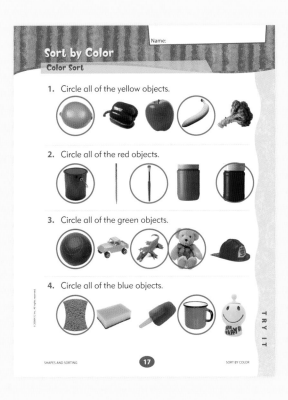

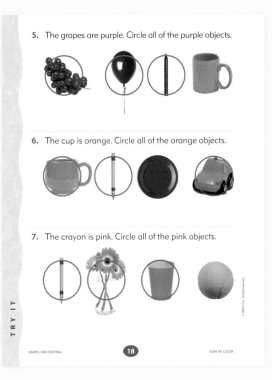

Sort by Shape

CALENDAR Days of the Week on the Calendar	5 minutes	**ONLINE**
GET READY Find the Shape	10 minutes	**ONLINE**
LEARN Click and Sort	10 minutes	**ONLINE**
TRY IT Sort Blocks	10 minutes	**OFFLINE**
TRY IT Sort Shapes	10 minutes	**OFFLINE**

▶ Lesson Objectives

- Sort and classify objects by one attribute, such as color, shape, or size.
- Name the days of the week.

▶ Prerequisite Skills

Describe objects by their attributes, such as color, shape, and size.

▶ Common Errors and Misconceptions

Students might not recognize that a shape might be positioned different ways.

▶ Advance Preparation

Cut out each card from the Sort Shapes activity page.

▶ Content Background

In this lesson, students will sort blocks and everyday objects by shape.

A square is mathematically defined as a special type of rectangle. So if students call a square a rectangle, they are mathematically correct. However, in the very early grades, we teach students that a rectangle has two longer sides and two shorter sides and that a square has four equal sides. When sorting, students should separate squares from more traditional rectangles.

The term *diamond*, often used by young children for a square rotated onto one of its corners, is not a standard geometric term and will not be used in this course. Students should understand that a square rotated in any direction is still a square.

Materials to Gather

SUPPLIED

blocks – AA, BB, CC, DD, EE, FF, GG, HH (all colors)

Sort Shapes activity page

ALSO NEEDED

scissors, adult

GET READY Find the Shape

ONLINE
10min

Objectives

Students will identify shapes. They will find objects of different shapes in a picture of a room.

- Describe objects by their attributes, such as color, shape, and size.

LEARN Click and Sort

Objectives

Students will sort triangles, rectangles, and squares.

DIRECTIONS FOR USING THE ATTRIBUTE BLOCKS LEARNING TOOL

1. Click Single Attribute Mode and choose the following:
   - Sort by: Shape
   - Shapes: 20
   - Containers: 4
   - Options: Visual Cues and Rotate Shapes
2. Click Start Sorting.
3. Have students sort the shapes.

- Sort and classify objects by one attribute, such as color, shape, or size.

TRY IT Sort Blocks

Objectives

Students will practice sorting by shape. Gather the blocks. Lay out the blocks in a random arrangement. Do not group shapes together.

Ask students to sort the blocks by shape. Note how students perform, and enter the results online.

- Sort and classify objects by one attribute, such as color, shape, or size.

TRY IT Sort Shapes

Objectives

Students will practice sorting by shape. Gather the cut-out cards from the Sort Shapes activity page. Lay out the cards in a random arrangement. Do not group shapes together.

Ask students to sort the cards by shape. Note how students perform, and enter the results online.

- Sort and classify objects by one attribute, such as color, shape, or size.

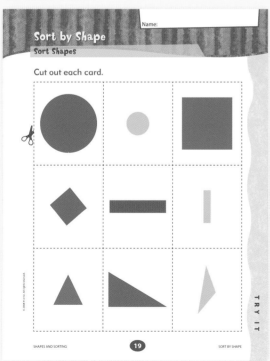

Sort by Size

CALENDAR Today and Tomorrow	5 minutes	ONLINE
GET READY Same Size	10 minutes	ONLINE
LEARN Sorting by Size	10 minutes	ONLINE
LEARN Compare and Sort	10 minutes	OFFLINE
TRY IT Size Roundup	10 minutes	OFFLINE

▶ Lesson Objectives

- Sort and classify objects by one attribute, such as color, shape, or size.
- Demonstrate an understanding of the concepts of today, yesterday, and tomorrow.

▶ Prerequisite Skills

Describe objects by their attributes, such as color, shape, and size.

▶ Advance Preparation

You will need four types of household objects for the Learn: Compare and Sort activity. For each object, you will need a small version and a large version. Suggestions are listed here:

Large	Small
serving spoon	teaspoon
child's shoe	doll's shoe
paper dinner plate	paper saucer
printer paper	index card

▶ Content Background

Students will sort blocks and everyday objects by size. When students sort by size, encourage them to use the words *large*, *small*, *larger*, and *smaller*.

Materials to Gather

SUPPLIED

blocks – AA, BB, CC, DD, EE, FF, GG, HH (red)

Size Roundup activity page

ALSO NEEDED

household objects – 4 types of objects, small and large versions of each

crayons

ONLINE
10 min

GET READY Same Size

Students will review the concepts *larger* and *smaller* by identifying shoes and hats that are the same size as a given shoe or hat.

Objectives

- Describe objects by their attributes, such as color, shape, and size.

LEARN Sorting by Size

Students will sort items by size. First they will compare the sizes of two groups of balls. Then they will sort clothes, placing smaller items on one shelf and larger items on another shelf.

Objectives

- Sort and classify objects by one attribute, such as color, shape, or size.

LEARN Compare and Sort

Students will sort blocks and household objects by size. Gather the blocks and the household objects. Lay out the small red shapes and large red shapes in a random arrangement. Do not group sizes together.

Objectives

- Sort and classify objects by one attribute, such as color, shape, or size.

1. Display the two red squares.

    Ask: How are these blocks the same? How are they different?
    ANSWER: They are the same color and shape. They are different sizes.

2. **Say:** Let's start two groups for sorting: one small and one large.

    As you say *small*, place the small square to the left. As you say *large*, place the large square to the right.

3. Have students finish sorting the blocks into two groups by size.

    Ask: What's another way we could sort the blocks?
    ANSWER: We could sort by shape.

4. Clear the work area, and lay out the household objects in a random arrangement. Ask students to sort the objects into two groups by size. If students have difficulty, follow the procedure in Step 2 and begin the groups for them.

TRY IT Size Roundup

Objectives

- Sort and classify objects by one attribute, such as color, shape, or size.

Students will practice identifying smaller and larger objects in groups. Give students the crayons and Size Roundup activity page from their Activity Book. Read the directions with them. Use the answer key to check students' answers, and then enter the results online.

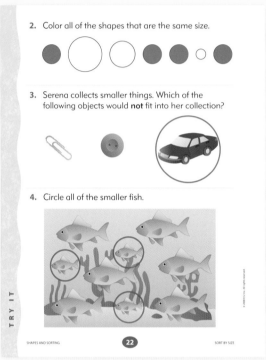

Sort Different Ways

Lesson Overview

CALENDAR Today and Yesterday	5 minutes	ONLINE
GET READY Sort by Shape	5 minutes	ONLINE
LEARN Sort Different Ways	15 minutes	OFFLINE
TRY IT Different Groups	10 minutes	OFFLINE
CHECKPOINT	10 minutes	OFFLINE

▶ Lesson Objectives

- Sort and classify objects by one attribute, such as color, shape, or size.
- Demonstrate an understanding of the concepts of today, yesterday, and tomorrow.

▶ Prerequisite Skills

Describe objects by their attributes, such as color, shape, and size.

▶ Common Errors and Misconceptions

- Students might have heard some geometric vocabulary words, but their definitions of these words might be incorrect.
- Students might not recognize that a shape might be positioned different ways.
- Students might misinterpret which characteristics define a shape. For example, they may see a triangle that has three equal sides and think that all triangles must have three equal sides. Actually, any shape with only three sides is a triangle.

▶ Advance Preparation

Cut out the shapes from the last page of the Different Groups activity page.

▶ Content Background

In this lesson students will sort objects by color, shape, and size. In some activities, they will choose which way to sort. When students sort, have them tell you what they are sorting by and have them describe the groups accordingly. For example, "I am sorting by shape. This group is the triangles."

Materials to Gather

SUPPLIED

blocks – AA, BB, CC, DD, EE, FF, GG, HH (red, yellow, blue)

Different Groups activity page

Checkpoint (printout)

ALSO NEEDED

crayons

glue stick

scissors, adult

GET READY Sort by Shape

ONLINE 5 min

Students will sort blocks onto shelves according to shape.

Objectives

- Sort and classify objects by one attribute, such as color, shape, or size.

LEARN Sort Different Ways

Students will learn that there are different ways to sort the same group of objects. They will sort the same group of blocks by color, shape, and size.

Gather the blocks. Lay out the blocks in a random arrangement. Do not group colors, shapes, or sizes together.

Ask: What are some ways we can sort these blocks?
ANSWER: color, shape, and size

SORT BY COLOR

1. **Say:** Let's sort by color. What groups will we make?
   ANSWER: red, blue, and yellow

2. Ask students how many groups they will make. (3)

3. Have students choose one red block, one blue block, and one yellow block to start each group. Have students sort the remaining blocks by color.

4. Ask students to describe each group. If students need help, ask questions to guide them.

   Ask: What color are the blocks in this group? What shape? What size?

5. Combine the groups. Lay out blocks in a random arrangement.

SORT BY SHAPE

6. **Say:** Let's sort by shape. What groups will we make?
   ANSWER: circle, square, triangle, and rectangle

7. Ask students how many groups they will make. (4)

8. Have students choose one circle, one square, one rectangle, and one tri-angle to start each group. Have students sort the remaining blocks by shape.

9. Ask students to describe each group. If students need help, ask questions to guide them.

   Ask: What color are the blocks in this group? What shape? What size?

10. Combine the groups. Lay out blocks in a random arrangement.

SORT BY SIZE

11. **Say:** Let's sort by size. What groups will we make?
    ANSWER: large and small

12. Ask students how many groups they will make. (2)

13. Have students choose one large block and one small block to start each group. Have students sort remaining blocks by shape.

14. Ask students to describe each group. If students need help, ask questions to guide them.

    Ask: What color are the blocks in this group? What shape? What size?

15. Tell students they have sorted the same set of blocks three ways: by color, shape, and size.

TRY IT Different Groups

Students will practice sorting by color, shape or size. Give students the cut-out shapes, crayons, glue stick, and Different Groups activity page from their Activity Book. Read the directions with them.

Use the answer key to check students' answers, then enter the results online.

Objectives

- Sort and classify objects by one attribute, such as color, shape, or size.

Tips

Check that students have sorted the cut-outs shapes correctly before they glue the shapes to the page.

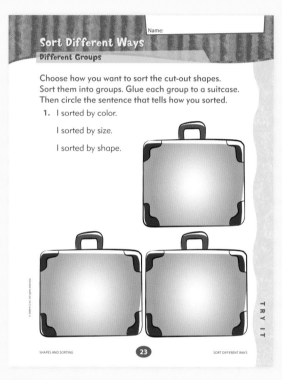

CHECKPOINT

Objectives

- Sort and classify objects by one attribute, such as color, shape, or size.

Print the Checkpoint. Students will take a performance-based assessment. Read the directions and problems to students. Use the answer key to score the Checkpoint, and then enter the results online.

Gather the blocks and crayons. Have students use the materials as directed.

⚙ Checkpoint   Math | Shapes and Sorting | Sort Different Ways

Name _____ Date _____

Checkpoint Answer Key

Use your blocks for Problems 1 and 2.
(1 point)
Use the circles for Problem 1.

1. Put the blocks in groups of the same size.

(1 point)
Use all the shapes for Problem 2.

2. Put the blocks in groups of the same shape.

(1 point)
Use your crayons for Problems 3 and 4.

3. Color all the larger shapes red.
4. Color all the smaller shapes yellow.

red   yellow   red   yellow   red   red

Unit Review

UNIT REVIEW Look Back	20 minutes	**ONLINE**
UNIT REVIEW Checkpoint Practice	10 minutes	**OFFLINE**
⏩ **UNIT REVIEW** Prepare for the Checkpoint		

▶ Unit Objectives

This lesson reviews the following objectives:

- Identify common plane figures, such as circle, triangle, square, and rectangle.
- Describe objects by their attributes, such as color, shape, and size.
- Sort and classify objects by one attribute, such as color, shape, or size.

Materials to Gather

SUPPLIED

Checkpoint Practice activity page

ALSO NEEDED

crayons

▶ Advance Preparation

In this lesson, students will have an opportunity to review previous activities in the Shapes and Sorting unit. Look at the suggested activities in Unit Review: Prepare for the Checkpoint online and gather any needed materials.

Keywords

attribute	shape
circle	small
large	smaller
larger	sort
orientation	square
rectangle	triangle

UNIT REVIEW Look Back

ONLINE 20 min

In this unit, students have learned to identify and describe circles, squares, triangles, and rectangles. Students have also learned to sort and describe objects by color, shape, and size. Students will review these concepts to prepare for the Unit Checkpoint.

Objectives

- Review unit objectives.

UNIT REVIEW Checkpoint Practice

OFFLINE 10 min

Students will complete a Checkpoint Practice activity page to prepare for the Unit Checkpoint. If necessary, read the directions, questions, and answer choices to students. Have students answer the problems on their own. Carefully review the answers with students.

Give students the crayons to use as directed.

Objectives

- Review unit objectives.

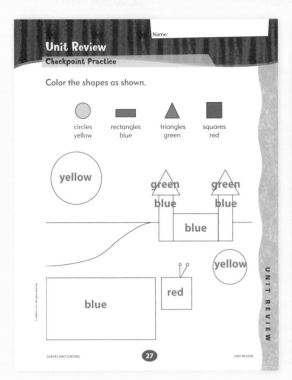

Unit Review
Checkpoint Practice

Color the shapes as shown.

circles
yellow

rectangles
blue

triangles
green

squares
red

yellow

green
blue

green
blue

blue

yellow

blue

red

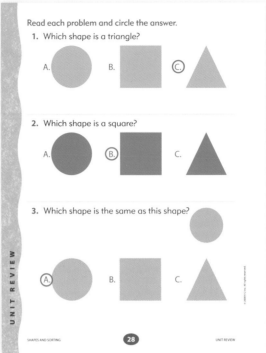

Read each problem and circle the answer.

1. Which shape is a triangle?

A. B. C.

2. Which shape is a square?

A. B. C.

3. Which shape is the same as this shape?

A. B. C.

4. Which object is smaller?

A. B.

5. Which object is larger?

A. B.

6. Look at the bird.
   What color is the bird?
   A. red
   B. blue
   C. yellow

7. Look at the clock.
   What shape is the clock?
   A. circle
   B. square
   C. triangle

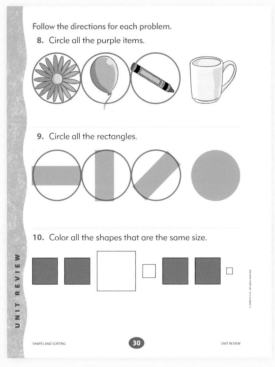

Follow the directions for each problem.

8. Circle all the purple items.

9. Circle all the rectangles.

10. Color all the shapes that are the same size.

➡ UNIT REVIEW Prepare for the Checkpoint

What you do next depends on how students performed in the previous activity,
Unit Review: Checkpoint Practice. If students had difficulty with any of the
problems, complete the appropriate review activity listed in the table online.

Unit Checkpoint

Lesson Overview

UNIT CHECKPOINT Online	15 minutes	**ONLINE**
UNIT CHECKPOINT Offline	25 minutes	**OFFLINE**

Unit Objectives

This Unit Checkpoint assesses the following objectives:

- Identify common plane figures, such as circle, triangle, square, and rectangle.
- Describe objects by their attributes, such as color, shape, and size.
- Sort and classify objects by one attribute, such as color, shape, or size.

Materials to Gather

SUPPLIED

Unit Checkpoint (printout)

ALSO NEEDED

crayons

UNIT CHECKPOINT Online

ONLINE 15min

Objectives

- Assess unit objectives.

Students will complete this part of the Unit Checkpoint online. Read the directions, problems, and answer choices to students. If necessary, help students with keyboard or mouse operations.

UNIT CHECKPOINT Offline

OFFLINE 25min

Objectives

- Assess unit objectives.

Students will complete this part of the Unit Checkpoint offline. Print the Checkpoint and have students complete it on their own. Read the directions, problems, and answer choices to students, if necessary. Use the answer key to score the Checkpoint, and then enter the results online.

For Problems 6 and 7, students will need crayons.

Name _____ Date _____

Unit Checkpoint Answer Key

For Problems 1–5, circle the correct answer.

(1 point)
1. Which of these shapes is a circle?

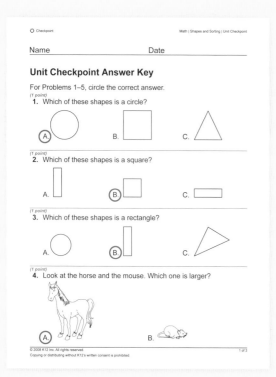

A. (circled)   B.   C.

(1 point)
2. Which of these shapes is a square?

A.   B. (circled)   C.

(1 point)
3. Which of these shapes is a rectangle?

A.   B. (circled)   C.

(1 point)
4. Look at the horse and the mouse. Which one is larger?

A. (circled)   B.

Name _____ Date _____

(1 point)
5. Look at the two balloons. Which one is smaller?

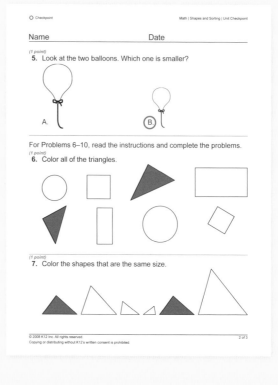

A.   B. (circled)

For Problems 6–10, read the instructions and complete the problems.

(1 point)
6. Color all of the triangles.

(1 point)
7. Color the shapes that are the same size.

Name _____ Date _____

(1 point)
8. What is the name of this shape? Circle the answer.

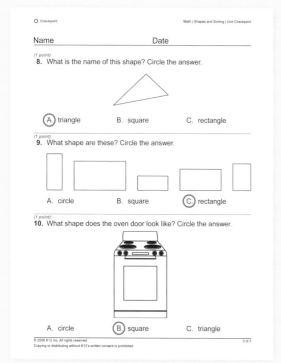

A. (circled) triangle   B. square   C. rectangle

(1 point)
9. What shape are these? Circle the answer.

A. circle   B. square   C. (circled) rectangle

(1 point)
10. What shape does the oven door look like? Circle the answer.

A. circle   B. (circled) square   C. triangle

Shapes and Patterns

▶ Unit Objectives

- Given a group of plane figures, identify which figure does not belong according to color, shape, or size.
- Identify and describe AB and ABB patterns of colors, shapes, or sizes.
- Extend AB and ABB patterns of colors, shapes, or sizes.
- Identify and describe AAAB and AAB patterns of colors, shapes, or sizes.
- Extend AAAB and AAB patterns of colors, shapes, or sizes.
- Identify and describe ABCC and ABC patterns of colors, shapes, or sizes.
- Extend ABCC and ABC patterns of colors, shapes, or sizes.

▶ Big Ideas

Rules can be used to generate number patterns.

▶ Unit Introduction

Students have learned to sort and classify objects by shape, size, and color. In this unit, students will learn to identify which object in a group does not belong based on color, shape, or size. Students will also learn about patterns. They will use the letters A, B, and C to describe pattern cores: AB, ABB, AAAB, AAB, ABB, ABCC, and ABC. They will identify and extend these patterns with blocks and other objects.

Which Object Is Different?

Lesson Overview

CALENDAR Today and Tomorrow	5 minutes	ONLINE
GET READY Sort Blocks	5 minutes	ONLINE
LEARN Which Block Is Different?	15 minutes	OFFLINE
TRY IT Does It Belong?	10 minutes	OFFLINE
CHECKPOINT	10 minutes	ONLINE

▶ Lesson Objectives

- Given a group of plane figures, identify which figure does not belong according to color, shape, or size.

- Demonstrate an understanding of the concepts of today, yesterday, and tomorrow.

▶ Prerequisite Skills

Sort and classify objects by one attribute, such as color, shape, or size.

▶ Content Background

Students know how to sort and classify objects by shape, size, and color. Students will use this knowledge in this lesson. They will determine which object in a group does not belong based on color, shape, and size.

Keywords **attribute** – a characteristic, such as size, shape, or color

Materials to Gather

SUPPLIED

blocks – A, AA, B, BB, C, CC, D, DD, E, EE, F, FF, G, GG, H, HH (all colors)

Does It Belong? activity page

ONLINE
5 min

GET READY Sort Blocks

Students will review sorting. They will sort blocks by color.
   After students complete the activity, ask them the question on the screen.

Objectives

- Sort and classify objects by one attribute, such as color, shape, or size.

LEARN Which Block Is Different?

Students will identify the block in a group that does not belong based on color, shape, or size. Gather the blocks.

- Given a group of plane figures, identify which figure does not belong according to color, shape, or size.

1. Lay out these blocks in a random arrangement: 1 large red circle, 1 large red triangle, 1 small red square, 1 small red rectangle.

   Ask: What is the same about these blocks?
   ANSWER: They are all red.

   Explain that the blocks belong in the group because they are the same color.

2. Add these blocks to the group: 1 small red circle, 1 large blue square, 1 large red rectangle.

   Ask: Which block doesn't belong with this group now?
   ANSWER: the blue square

   Explain that the blue square does not belong in the group because it is a different color from the other blocks.

3. Lay out these blocks in a random arrangement: 3 small blue triangles, 1 small blue circle.
   Have students name the shapes in the group.

   Ask: Which block doesn't belong in the group?
   ANSWER: circle

   Ask: Why doesn't the circle belong?
   ANSWER: It is a different shape from the other blocks.

4. Lay out these blocks in a random arrangement: 3 small red circles, 1 large red circle.

   Ask: What is the same about these blocks?
   ANSWER: They are all red, and they are all circles.
   Tell students that one block has something different about it. Ask them to hold up the block that does not belong. (Students should hold up the large circle.)

   Ask: Why doesn't this block belong to the group?
   ANSWER: It is a different size from the other blocks.

5. Tell students that it's their turn to make a group of four blocks in which one block doesn't belong.

   Say: Choose four blocks. Three blocks should be the same color. One block should be a different color.

   After students make the group, have them tell you which block doesn't belong and explain why.

6. Repeat Step 5 with the attributes *shape* and *size*.

TRY IT Does It Belong?

Students will practice choosing the object in a group that doesn't belong. Give students the Does It Belong? activity page from their Activity Book, and read the directions with them.

Objectives

• Given a group of plane figures, identify which figure does not belong according to color, shape, or size.

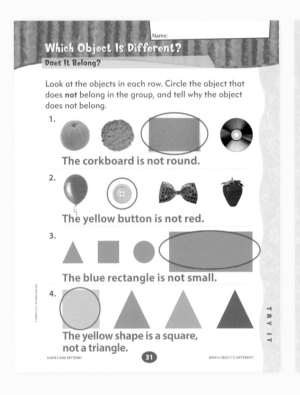

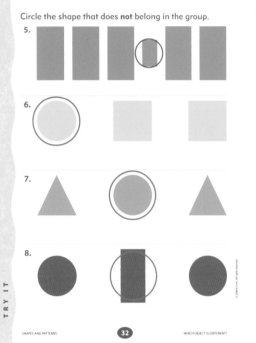

CHECKPOINT

Students will complete an online Checkpoint. Read the directions, problems, and answer choices to students. If necessary, help students with keyboard or mouse operations.

Objectives

• Given a group of plane figures, identify which figure does not belong according to color, shape, or size.

AB and ABB Patterns

Lesson Overview

TIME Where Is the Clock?	5 minutes	ONLINE
GET READY What Is the Pattern?	10 minutes	ONLINE
LEARN What Kind of Pattern?	10 minutes	ONLINE
LEARN Extend the Pattern	10 minutes	OFFLINE
TRY IT Patterns Are Fun	5 minutes	OFFLINE

▶ Lesson Objectives

- Identify and describe AB and ABB patterns of colors, shapes, or sizes.
- Extend AB and ABB patterns of colors, shapes, or sizes.
- Identify tools that measure time within a day, such as a clock, and describe what those tools measure (for example, a clock measures minutes and hours).

▶ Prerequisite Skills

Sort and classify objects by one attribute, such as color, shape, or size.

▶ Advance Preparation

Label 12 index cards with a capital **A**. Label 12 other index cards with a capital **B**.

▶ Content Background

Students will learn about patterns. They will learn that the part of a pattern that repeats is called the *pattern core*. They will also extend patterns. Identifying pattern cores will help students extend patterns.

Pattern cores are often described with letters.

- **AB pattern:** In an AB pattern, each object repeats once. Example: triangle, square, triangle, square
- **ABB pattern:** An ABB pattern, the first object repeats once and the second object repeats twice. Example: moon, star, star, moon, star, star

The part of the pattern that repeats is called the pattern core.

- **AB pattern:** TLTLTLTLTL   **Pattern core:** TL
- **ABB pattern:** 133133133133   **Pattern core:** 133

Materials to Gather

SUPPLIED

blocks – B, E, K

Patterns Are Fun activity page

ALSO NEEDED

index cards – 12 labeled **A**, 12 labeled **B**

extend - to continue, such as to extend a pattern by adding on the next object in the pattern

pattern – a sequence of objects and/or numbers with attributes that are repeated in a predictable way

pattern core – the repeating portion that defines a pattern; AB is the pattern core for the pattern ABABAB

GET READY What Is the Pattern?

ONLINE 10min

Students will learn that a *pattern* is something that repeats. They will look at patterns of bee stripes, flowers, butterflies, and suns and clouds.

Objectives

- Identify and describe AB and ABB patterns of colors, shapes, or sizes.

LEARN What Kind of Pattern?

ONLINE 10min

Students will learn that a *pattern core* is the part of a pattern that repeats. They will learn how to use the letters A and B to describe pattern cores. They will explore patterns with AB and ABB pattern cores.

Objectives

- Identify and describe AB and ABB patterns of colors, shapes, or sizes.

LEARN Extend the Pattern

OFFLINE 10min

Students will look at patterns of blocks. They will identify the core of these patterns as AB or ABB. Then they will extend the patterns.

Gather the blocks and the index cards you labeled A and B.
Lay out blocks and cards as shown below. Place the cards below each block.

Objectives

- Extend AB and ABB patterns of colors, shapes, or sizes.

A   B   A   B   A   B   A   B

1. Show students the row of blocks and the letter cards below each block.

2. **Ask:** What is the pattern of the blocks?
   ANSWER: triangle, circle, triangle, circle, triangle, circle, triangle, circle

   Point to the first triangle and circle blocks as you explain that the pattern core is *triangle, circle*. Ask students to use letters to tell you the core. (AB)

3. Explain that you can extend the pattern, or add another block.

   Say: Let's extend the pattern. What block should we put next?
   ANSWER: triangle

   Have students explain why a triangle comes next. (It's the first block in the core.)

4. Have students place a triangle block at the end of the pattern. Then ask students to place the block that comes next. (Students should place a circle.)

5. Have students place letter cards below the new blocks. (Students should place the letter cards in this order: A, B.)

6. Have students place 4 more blocks and letter cards at the end of the pattern.

   Clear the work area. Lay out blocks and cards as shown below. Place the cards below each block.

   A   B   B   A   B   B   A   B   B

7. Show students the row of blocks and the letter cards below each block.

8. Ask students to tell you the core of this pattern. (ABB or red, blue, blue) Pointing to each letter as you say it, say, "The core that repeats is ABB."

9. **Say:** Let's extend the pattern. What color block should we put next?
   ANSWER: red

   Have students explain why red comes next. (The first block in the core is red.)

10. Have students place a red block at the end of the pattern. Then ask students to place the two blocks that come next. (Students should place two blue blocks.)

11. Have students place letter cards below the new blocks. (Students should place the letter cards in this order: A, B, B.)

12. Have students place 4 more blocks and letter cards at the end of the pattern.

13. Clear the work area. Have students use the blocks to create their own pattern. They may use any blocks in the set. Ask them to use letters to name the pattern and to extend the pattern.

TRY IT Patterns Are Fun

OFFLINE
5 min

Objectives

Students will practice identifying pattern cores. Give students the Patterns Are Fun activity page from their Activity Book and read the directions with them.

- Identify and describe AB and ABB patterns of colors, shapes, or sizes.
- Extend AB and ABB patterns of colors, shapes, or sizes.

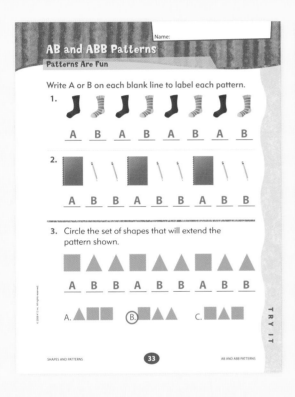

AB and ABB Patterns

Name: _____

Patterns Are Fun

Write A or B on each blank line to label each pattern.

1. A B A B A B A B

2. A B B A B B A B B

3. Circle the set of shapes that will extend the pattern shown.

    A B B A B B A B B

    A. ▲■■   (B.) ■▲▲   C. ■▲■

SHAPES AND PATTERNS   33   AB AND ABB PATTERNS

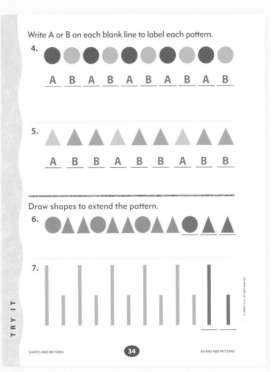

Write A or B on each blank line to label each pattern.

4. A B A B A B A B A B

5. A B B A B B A B B

Draw shapes to extend the pattern.

6. ___ ___

7. ___ ___

SHAPES AND PATTERNS   34   AB AND ABB PATTERNS

AAAB and AAB Patterns

Lesson Overview

TIME The Hands on a Clock	5 minutes	ONLINE
GET READY Clothing Patterns	5 minutes	ONLINE
LEARN Alexander's Flower Garden	10 minutes	ONLINE
LEARN Pattern Necklaces	10 minutes	OFFLINE
TRY IT Baseball Patterns	10 minutes	OFFLINE

▶ Lesson Objectives

- Identify and describe AAAB and AAB patterns of colors, shapes, or sizes.
- Extend AAAB and AAB patterns of colors, shapes, or sizes.
- Identify tools that measure time within a day, such as a clock, and describe what those tools measure (for example, a clock measures minutes and hours).

▶ Prerequisite Skills

- Identify and describe AB and ABB patterns of colors, shapes, or sizes.
- Extend AB and ABB patterns of colors, shapes, or sizes.

▶ Common Errors and Misconceptions

- Students might have difficulty recognizing patterns in which more than one attribute changes.
- Students might have difficulty replicating patterns that are flipped 180 degrees.

▶ Advance Preparation

Cut two 12-inch lengths of string. Tie a knot at one end of each string.

▶ Content Background

Students will identify and describe repeating AAAB and AAB patterns of colors, shapes, and sizes.

Materials to Gather

SUPPLIED

Baseball Patterns activity page

ALSO NEEDED

beads – 20 to 30 of various colors, shapes, and sizes

string – two 12-inch pieces

GET READY Clothing Patterns

ONLINE 5 min

Students will extend AB and ABB patterns of clothing hanging on a clothesline.

Objectives

- Identify and describe AB and ABB patterns of colors, shapes, or sizes.
- Extend AB and ABB patterns of colors, shapes, or sizes.

LEARN Alexander's Flower Garden

ONLINE
10min

Students will learn about the AAAB and AAB pattern cores. They will identify and describe AAAB and AAB patterns in a flower garden.

Objectives

- Identify and describe AAAB and AAB patterns of colors, shapes, or sizes.

Tips

To reinforce the rhythm of a pattern, have students hop for each A element and clap for each B element.

LEARN Pattern Necklaces

OFFLINE
10min

Students will use colored beads to identify and describe a pattern, and then extend the pattern. Gather the beads and the string that you cut into 12-inch lengths.

1. Put 8 beads on one string in an AAAB color pattern. Example: yellow, yellow, yellow, red, yellow, yellow, yellow, red

   Ask: What is the pattern core for this pattern?
   ANSWER: yellow, yellow, yellow, red or AAAB

2. If necessary, remind students that each yellow bead can be represented by the letter A, and each red bead can be represented by the letter B.

   Ask: What bead comes next in the pattern?
   ANSWER: yellow

   Ask: How do you know?
   ANSWER: A yellow bead is the first bead in the pattern core.

3. Have students add beads to the string to continue the pattern. When the necklace is complete, have students say the pattern aloud in two ways. First have them name the color of each bead. Then have them say "A" or "B" to describe each bead.

4. Put 6 beads on the second string in an AAB size or shape pattern. Example: large, large, small, large, large, small

5. Repeat Steps 2 and 3 with the second string of beads.

6. Have students choose their favorite pattern from the activity. Help students tie the ends of the string to make a necklace.

Objectives

- Extend AAAB and AAB patterns of colors, shapes, or sizes.

Tips

Practice reading patterns that are flipped 180 degrees. For example, after students say the AAAB pattern of yellow and red beads, flip the necklace 180 degrees and ask them to say the new pattern. The new pattern is ABBB—red is now "A," and yellow is "B."

TRY IT Baseball Patterns

Students will practice naming and extending patterns. Give students the Baseball Patterns activity page from their Activity Book and read the directions with them.

Objectives

- Identify and describe AAAB and AAB patterns of colors, shapes, or sizes.
- Extend AAAB and AAB patterns of colors, shapes, or sizes.

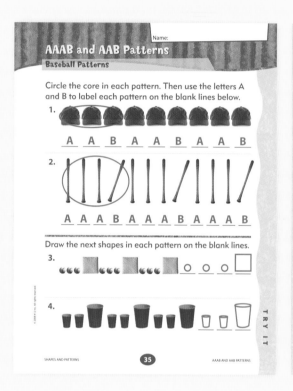

ABCC and ABC Patterns

Lesson Overview

TIME The Numbers on a Clock	5 minutes	**ONLINE**
GET READY Patterns Everywhere	5 minutes	**ONLINE**
LEARN Coin Patterns	10 minutes	**OFFLINE**
LEARN Picnic Patterns	10 minutes	**OFFLINE**
TRY IT Kitchen Patterns	10 minutes	**OFFLINE**
CHECKPOINT	5 minutes	**OFFLINE**

▶ Lesson Objectives

- Identify and describe ABCC and ABC patterns of colors, shapes, or sizes.
- Extend ABCC and ABC patterns of colors, shapes, or sizes.
- Identify tools that measure time within a day, such as a clock, and describe what those tools measure (for example, a clock measures minutes and hours).

▶ Prerequisite Skills

- Identify and describe AAAB and AAB patterns of colors, shapes, or sizes.
- Extend AAAB and AAB patterns of colors, shapes, or sizes.

▶ Advance Preparation

- Label 6 index cards with a capital **A**, 6 other index cards with a capital **B**, and 6 other index cards with a capital **C**.
- You can substitute blocks for plastic cups and utensils if these materials are unavailable.

▶ Safety

- Supervise students when they work with coins to ensure they do not put the coins in their mouths.
- Caution students to handle utensils carefully. Show them how to hold the utensils so pointed ends face away from them.

▶ Content Background

Students will identify and describe repeating ABCC and ABC patterns of colors, shapes, and sizes. Students will explore ABCC and ABC patterns of coins and kitchen objects.

Materials to Gather

SUPPLIED

Kitchen Patterns activity page

Checkpoint (printout)

ALSO NEEDED

index cards – 6 labeled **A**, 6 labeled **B**, 6 labeled **C**

crayons

coins – 6 pennies, 6 nickels, 3 dimes

plastic utensils – 6 spoons, 6 forks, 6 knives

plastic cups – 6 red, 6 yellow, 6 blue

GET READY Patterns Everywhere

Students will see AAAB and AAB patterns. They will decide what objects come next in each pattern.

LEARN Coin Patterns

Students will use letters to describe the core, or repeating part, of ABCC and ABC patterns.

Gather the coins and the index cards you labeled A, B, and C. Lay out coins in the following pattern: nickel, dime, penny, penny, nickel, dime, penny, penny, nickel, dime, penny, penny.

1. Ask students to say the coin pattern aloud. (nickel, dime, penny, penny,…)
2. **Say:** Let's use letters to name the pattern core.
   Put an A card below the nickel and a B card below the dime.

   Ask: Can we put an A card below the penny? Why?
   ANSWER: No; the A in this pattern is a nickel.

   Ask: Can we put a B card below the penny? Why?
   ANSWER: No; the B in this pattern is a dime.

   Explain that because the penny is a different type of coin, it needs a new letter. Have students put a C card below the penny.
3. Have students place letter cards below the remaining coins in the pattern. Then have them read the pattern using the letters. (A B C C A B C C A B C C)
4. **Ask:** What is the pattern core in this pattern?
   ANSWER: ABCC

   Explain that this type of pattern is called an ABCC pattern.

   Clear the work area. Lay out coins in the following pattern: dime, nickel, penny, dime, nickel, penny, dime, nickel, penny.
5. Repeat Steps 1–4 with the new pattern, which is an ABC pattern.

   Clear the work area. Lay out coins in the following patterns: (1) penny, dime, nickel, nickel, penny, dime, nickel, nickel, penny, dime, nickel, nickel; (2) nickel, dime, penny, nickel, dime, penny, nickel, dime, penny.

Objectives

- Identify and describe AAAB and AAB patterns of shapes, sizes, or colors.
- Extend AAAB and AAB patterns of colors, shapes or sizes.

Tips

Encourage students to say the patterns aloud, using descriptive words or letters, so that they hear the repeated rhythm of the pattern.

Objectives

- Identify and describe ABCC and ABC patterns of colors, shapes, or sizes.

Tips

If students do not know the names of the coins, have them describe the coins by color and size when talking about the patterns (for example, "large silver coin").

Tips

For additional practice, create ABC and ABCC patterns with the index cards. Have students place coins or blocks above the cards to make ABC and ABCC patterns.

6. Ask students to point to the ABC pattern. (Students should point to the second pattern.) Then have them point to the ABCC pattern. (Students should point to the first pattern.)

   Ask: How did you know which pattern was which?
   ANSWER: In the ABC pattern, each coin repeated only once in the pattern core. In the ABCC pattern, the nickel repeated twice in the pattern core.

LEARN Picnic Patterns

Students will extend ABC and ABCC patterns.

Gather the plastic cups and utensils. Lay out utensils in the following pattern: knife, fork, spoon, spoon, knife, fork, spoon, spoon.

1. **Say:** Let's point to each utensil and say the pattern together. Point to each utensil and say pattern with students. (knife, fork, spoon, spoon,…)

2. **Ask:** How can we say this pattern using letters?
   ANSWER: ABCC. The knife is A. The fork is B. The two spoons are CC.

   Explain to students that they can use the pattern core to extend the pattern. They can keep placing objects in the order ABCC.

   Ask: What objects come next in the pattern?
   ANSWER: knife, fork, spoon, spoon

   Ask: How do you know?
   ANSWER: The pattern core is ABCC, or knife, fork, spoon, spoon.

3. Give students 2 spoons, 1 fork, and 1 knife. Have students extend the pattern using these objects. Then have students say the pattern aloud.

   Clear the work area. Lay out cups in the following pattern: red, yellow, blue, red, yellow, blue, red, yellow, blue.

4. Repeat Steps 1–3 with the new pattern, which is an ABC pattern.

   Clear the work area. Continue making ABCC and ABC patterns with the utensils and cups. Have students extend the patterns.

   For more practice identifying pattern cores and building and extending patterns, have students use the Patterns Learning Tool online. This learning tool has audio. Make sure your speakers are turned up.

Tips

For additional practice:

• Make a noise pattern: clap, snap, stomp. Repeat three times. Have students extend the pattern.

• Create an ABCC pattern with blocks. Have students extend the pattern.

TRY IT Kitchen Patterns

Objectives

Students will practice naming and extending patterns. Give students the crayons and Kitchen Patterns activity page from their Activity Book. Read the directions with them.

- Identify and describe ABCC and ABC patterns of colors, shapes, or sizes.
- Extend ABCC and ABC patterns of colors, shapes, or sizes.

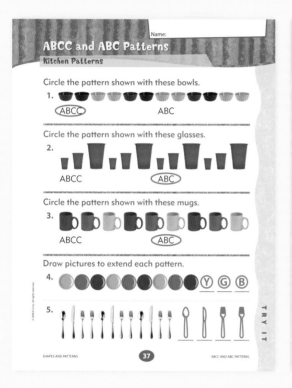

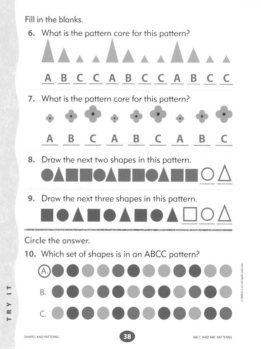

CHECKPOINT

Objectives

Print the Checkpoint and have students complete it on their own. Read the directions, problems, and answer choices to students, if necessary. Use the answer key to score the Checkpoint, and then enter the results online.

- Identify and describe ABCC and ABC patterns of colors, shapes, or sizes.
- Extend ABCC and ABC patterns of colors, shapes, or sizes.

Checkpoint   Math | Shapes and Patterns | ABCC and ABC Patterns

Name _____ Date _____

Checkpoint Answer Key

Choose the answer.
(1 point)
1. Which set of shapes is in an ABB pattern?

 A.   (B.)   C.

(1 point)
2. What is the next shape in this pattern?

 A. ☐ B. △ (C.) ◯

(1 point)
3. Which pattern do these shapes make?

 (A.) AAAB B. ABB C. AAB

Checkpoint   Math | Shapes and Patterns | ABCC and ABC Patterns

Name _____ Date _____

Read each problem and follow the directions.
(1 point)
4. Draw the next two shapes in this pattern.

◯ ☐ ☐ ◯ ☐ ☐ ◯ ☐ ☐ ◯ ☐

(1 point)
5. Which of the patterns below is most similar to the pattern shown here? Circle the answer.

☐ ◯ △ △ ☐ ◯ △ △ ☐ ◯ △ △

 (A.) ▭ △ ◯ ◯ ▭ △ ◯ ◯ ▭ △ ◯ ◯

 B. ▭ ◯ ▭ ◯ ▭ ◯

 C. ▭ ☐ △ ▭ ☐ △ ▭ ☐ △

(1 point)
6. What are the next two objects in this pattern? Circle the answer.

☐ ☐ ☐ ☐ ☐ ☐ ☐ ☐ _____ _____

 A. ☐ ☐ (B.) ☐ ☐ C. ☐ ☐

Unit Review

Lesson Overview

UNIT REVIEW Look Back	20 minutes	ONLINE
UNIT REVIEW Checkpoint Practice	10 minutes	OFFLINE
⇥ UNIT REVIEW Prepare for the Checkpoint		

▶ Unit Objectives

This lesson reviews the following objectives:

- Given a group of plane figures, identify which figure does not belong according to color, shape, or size.
- Identify and describe AB and ABB patterns of colors, shapes, or sizes.
- Extend AB and ABB patterns of colors, shapes, or sizes.
- Identify and describe AAAB and AAB patterns of colors, shapes, or sizes.
- Extend AAAB and AAB patterns of colors, shapes, or sizes.
- Identify and describe ABCC and ABC patterns of colors, shapes, or sizes.
- Extend ABCC and ABC patterns of colors, shapes, or sizes.

▶ Advance Preparation

In this lesson, students will have an opportunity to review previous activities in the Shapes and Patterns unit. Look at the suggested activities in Unit Review: Prepare for the Checkpoint online and gather any needed materials.

Keywords	attribute	pattern
	extend	pattern core

Materials to Gather

SUPPLIED

Checkpoint Practice activity page

UNIT REVIEW Look Back

ONLINE 20min

Objectives

- Review unit objectives.

In this unit, students have learned to identify which object in a group does not belong based on color, shape, or size. Students have also learned about patterns. They have learned that the repeating part of a pattern is called the *pattern core*. They have used the letters A, B, and C to describe pattern cores: AB, ABB, AAAB, AAB, ABCC, and ABC. They have identified and extended these patterns with blocks and other objects. Students will review these concepts to prepare for the Unit Checkpoint.

UNIT REVIEW Checkpoint Practice

Objectives

- Review unit objectives.

Students will complete a Checkpoint Practice activity page to prepare for the Unit Checkpoint. If necessary, read the directions, questions, and answer choices to students. Have students answer the problems on their own. Carefully review the answers with students.

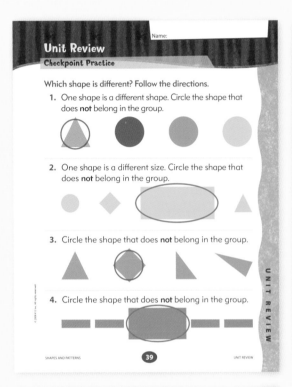

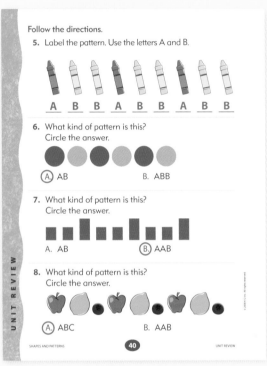

➡ UNIT REVIEW Prepare for the Checkpoint

What you do next depends on how students performed in the previous activity, Unit Review: Checkpoint Practice. If students had difficulty with any of the problems, complete the appropriate review activity listed in the table online.

Unit Checkpoint

Lesson Overview

UNIT CHECKPOINT Online	15 minutes	**ONLINE**
UNIT CHECKPOINT Offline	25 minutes	**OFFLINE**

▶ Unit Objectives

This Unit Checkpoint assesses the following objectives:

- Given a group of plane figures, identify which figure does not belong according to color, shape, or size.
- Identify and describe AB and ABB patterns of colors, shapes, or sizes.
- Extend AB and ABB patterns of colors, shapes, or sizes.
- Identify and describe AAAB and AAB patterns of colors, shapes, or sizes.
- Extend AAAB and AAB patterns of colors, shapes, or sizes.
- Identify and describe ABCC and ABC patterns of colors, shapes, or sizes.
- Extend ABCC and ABC patterns of colors, shapes, or sizes.

Materials to Gather

SUPPLIED

Unit Checkpoint (printout)

ONLINE
15min

UNIT CHECKPOINT Online

Students will complete this part of the Unit Checkpoint online. Read the directions, problems, and answer choices to students. If necessary, help students with keyboard or mouse operations.

Objectives

- Assess unit objectives.

UNIT CHECKPOINT Offline

Objectives

- Assess unit objectives.

Students will complete this part of the Unit Checkpoint offline. Print the Checkpoint and have students complete it on their own. Read the directions, problems, and answer choices to students, if necessary. Use the answer key to score the Checkpoint, and then enter the results online.

○ Checkpoint   Math | Shapes and Patterns | Unit Checkpoint

Name _____ Date _____

Unit Checkpoint Answer Key

For Problems 1–3, circle the answer.
(1 point)
1. Which shape does not belong in this group?

A. △   (B.) ○   C. ◁   D. ◣

(1 point)
2. What is the next shape in this pattern?

□ ○ □ ○ □ ○ □ ___

A. □   B. △   (C.) ○

(1 point)
3. What are the next two objects in this pattern?

∘○ ○∘ ○∘ ○∘ ∘ ___ ___

A. ∘○   (B.) ○○   C. ○∘

© 2008 K12 Inc. All rights reserved.   1 of 2
Copying or distributing without K12's written consent is prohibited.

○ Checkpoint   Math | Shapes and Patterns | Unit Checkpoint

Name _____ Date _____

For Problems 4–6, say the answer aloud.   **Answers vary; examples given.**
(1 point)
4. What is the core for this pattern?

○ ○ □ ○ ○ □ ○ ○ □

circle, circle, square, or AAB

(1 point)
5. Describe this pattern.

tall, medium, short, short, or ABCC

(1 point)
6. Describe this pattern.

small, large, large, or ABB

(1 point)
7. Draw the next two shapes in this pattern.

□ ○ □ ○ □ □ ○ □ ○ **□ ○**

© 2008 K12 Inc. All rights reserved.   2 of 2
Copying or distributing without K12's written consent is prohibited.

Numbers Through 5 and Plane Figures

TRY IT **Numbers 0 Through 5**

Students will practice counting the objects in a group and drawing a given number of objects. Give students the crayons and Numbers 0 Through 5 activity page from their Activity Book. Read the directions with them.

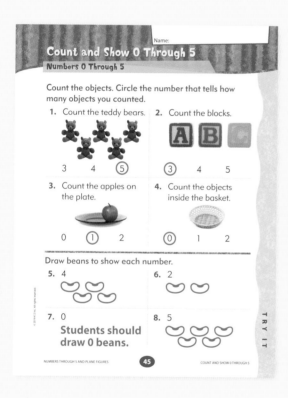

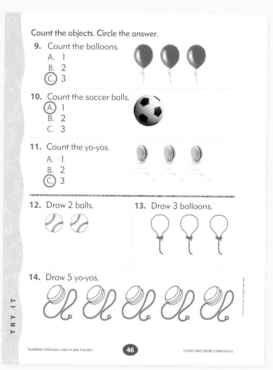

CHECKPOINT

OFFLINE
5 min

Objectives

Print the Checkpoint and have students complete it on their own. Read the directions, problems, and answer choices to students if necessary. Use the answer key to score the Checkpoint, and then enter the results online.

- Count aloud a number of objects up through 5.
- Use concrete objects or sketches to represent a quantity up through 5.

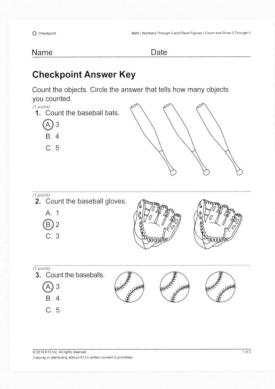

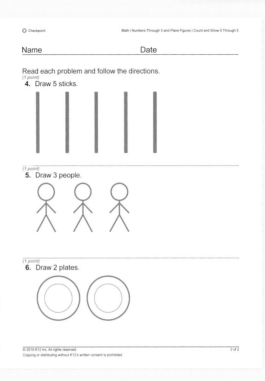

Write Numerals Through 5

Lesson Overview

TIME My Day Book	5 minutes	ONLINE
GET READY Count Aloud	5 minutes	ONLINE
LEARN Follow the Pencil	10 minutes	ONLINE
TRY IT Write 0 Through 5	10 minutes	OFFLINE
LEARN Count and Write Numerals	5 minutes	OFFLINE
TRY IT Count and Write 0 Through 5	10 minutes	OFFLINE

▶ **Lesson Objectives**

- Write numerals from 1 through 5.
- Demonstrate an understanding of the concepts of morning, afternoon, and evening.

▶ **Prerequisite Skills**

Count aloud a number of objects up through 5.

▶ **Advance Preparation**

Print the Numeral Writing Guide.

▶ **Content Background**

Students will learn to write the numbers 0 through 5. Students will first watch numbers being written, then trace numbers, and finally write numbers on handwriting paper.

In mathematics, the word *number* represents the quantity, and the word *numeral* represents the written symbol. So numerals, such as 0, 1, 2, and 3, symbolically represent numbers, or quantities. In everyday language, we say *number* to describe both the symbol and the quantity. As you speak with students, you may use *number* only. This lesson is titled "Write Numerals Through 5" to convey correct mathematical terminology.

A *set* is a group of objects. *Set* is a mathematical term for *group*. You may use *set* or *group* interchangeably in conversation with students.

Materials to Gather

SUPPLIED

Numeral Writing Guide (printout)

Count and Write Numerals activity page

Count and Write 0 Through 5 activity page

ALSO NEEDED

paper, wide-line handwriting

GET READY Count Aloud

ONLINE
5min

Students will practice counting aloud groups of up through 5 objects.

Objectives

- Count aloud a number of objects up through 5.

Tips

Listen to ensure students count aloud in the correct order.

LEARN Follow the Pencil

ONLINE
10min

Students will learn how to write the numbers 0 through 5 by watching a virtual pencil write each number.

Objectives

- Write numerals from 1 through 5.

TRY IT Write 0 Through 5

OFFLINE
10min

Students will practice writing each number on wide-line handwriting paper. Gather the Numeral Writing Guide and wide-line handwriting paper.

1. Tell students they will practice writing the numbers 0 through 5.
2. Write each number. As students watch you write, have them use their finger to trace each number in the Numeral Writing Guide.
3. Have students write each number 5 times on the wide-line handwriting paper. As students write each number, check that they have written it correctly.

Objectives

- Write numerals from 1 through 5.

Tips

If students have difficulty writing numbers, place your hand over theirs and write the numbers with them.

LEARN Count and Write Numerals

Students will practice counting and writing the numbers 0 through 5. Give students the Count and Write Numerals activity page from their Activity Book and read the directions with them.

Objectives

- Write numerals from 1 through 5.

Tips

If students still have difficulty writing the numbers 0 through 5, their motor coordination skills might not be fully developed. If possible, give students a thicker pencil to use.

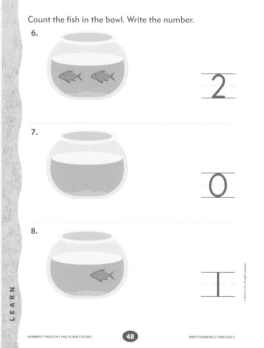

Objectives

- Write numerals from 1 through 5.

Students will practice counting and writing the numbers 0 through 5. Give students the Count and Write 0 Through 5 activity page from their Activity Book and read the directions with them.

Write Numerals Through 5

Count and Write 0 Through 5

Name: _____

Look at the picture and write the number for the objects you are counting.

1. Count the trees.

   5

2. Count the birds.

   2

3. Count the clouds.

   3

4. Count the flowers.

   4

5. Count the suns.

   1

6. Count the bunnies.

   0

NUMBERS THROUGH 5 AND PLANE FIGURES   49   WRITE NUMERALS THROUGH 5

Read each problem, and then write the number.

7. Write the number zero.

   0

8. Write the number one.

   1

9. Write the number two.

   2

10. Write the number three.

    3

11. Write the number four.

    4

12. Write the number five.

    5

NUMBERS THROUGH 5 AND PLANE FIGURES   50   WRITE NUMERALS THROUGH 5

Sides of a Shape

Lesson Overview

TIME Rosa's Morning, Afternoon, and Evening	5 minutes	**ONLINE**
GET READY Which Shape Does Not Belong?	5 minutes	**ONLINE**
LEARN Count the Sides	10 minutes	**OFFLINE**
LEARN Which Shape?	10 minutes	**OFFLINE**
TRY IT How Many Sides?	10 minutes	**OFFLINE**

▶ Lesson Objectives

- Compare plane figures by common attributes, such as number of sides and number of corners of triangles, rectangles, squares, pentagons, and circles.
- Demonstrate an understanding of the concepts of morning, afternoon, and evening.

▶ Prerequisite Skills

Given a group of plane figures, identify which figure does not belong according to color, shape, or size.

▶ Advance Preparation

Cut out each shape from the Count the Sides activity page.

▶ Content Background

Students will learn to count the number of sides of a shape. They will learn that rectangles and squares have the same number of sides. They will also choose the shape in a group that has the most sides.

Materials to Gather

SUPPLIED
Count the Sides activity page
How Many Sides? activity page

ALSO NEEDED
paper bag
scissors, adult

Keywords

circle – a plane figure with no straight sides or corners; the edge of a circle is a curve with all points the same distance from the center
pentagon – a 5-sided plane figure
rectangle – a plane figure with 4 sides and 4 square corners with opposite sides of equal length
shape – a closed outline or form, such as a square or hexagon
side – a segment that forms the edge of a shape
square – a plane figure with 4 sides of equal length and 4 square corners
triangle – a plane figure with 3 sides and 3 corners

GET READY Which Shape Does Not Belong?

ONLINE
5min

Students will look at a group of blocks. They will identify which block in the group is a different shape.

Objectives

- Given a group of plane figures, identify which figure doesn't belong, according to color, shape, or size.

Tips

Students might not recognize a shape positioned in different ways. Use blocks to show students that, for example, a rectangle can be positioned vertically or horizontally.

LEARN Count the Sides

OFFLINE
10min

Students will review the names of basic shapes. They will learn that some shapes have sides. Students will also compare shapes based on number of sides.

Gather the cut-out shapes from the Count the Sides activity page. Lay out the shapes in a random arrangement.

1. Have students find a triangle. Tell them that a triangle has 3 sides. Trace each side with your finger. Then have students trace each side with their finger.

   Ask: How many sides does a triangle have?
   ANSWER: 3

2. Place the triangle in the work area. To the right of the triangle, place the other triangle, a square, and a pentagon.

   Say: Count the sides on each shape.

   Watch students as they count the sides on each shape. Make sure they count each side exactly one time.

3. **Say:** Hold up the shape that has the same number of sides as the triangle.

   If students choose the wrong shape, point out how many sides that shape has. For example, if they choose the pentagon, say, "This shape has 5 sides. The triangle has 3 sides. Find the shape that has the same number of sides as the triangle."

   Students should hold up the second triangle. Explain that both shapes are triangles. Even though the two triangles are different sizes and colors, they both have 3 sides.

4. Clear the work area, and place a pentagon. To the right of the pentagon, place a rectangle, a square, the other pentagon, and a circle.

   Say: Count the sides on the pentagon. Then hold up the shape that has the same number of sides as the pentagon.
   ANSWER: Students should hold up the other pentagon.

Objectives

- Compare plane figures by common attributes, such as number of sides and number of corners of triangles, rectangles, squares, pentagons, and circles.

Tips

If students have difficulty identifying the circle as the shape with 0 sides, review the number 0. Place 2 cups in front of students. Place 4 objects in 1 cup. Have students describe the number of objects in each cup. Explain that the empty cup has 0 objects.

Ask: How do you know the shape you are holding has the same number of sides?
ANSWER: I counted 5 sides on this shape and on the pentagon.

Explain that both shapes are pentagons. Even though the two pentagons are different sizes and colors, they both have 5 sides.

5. Clear the work area, and place a rectangle. To the right of the rectangle, place a square, a triangle, and a pentagon. Point to the rectangle, and ask students to name the shape.

   Say: Count the sides of the rectangle. Then hold up the shape that has the same number of sides as the rectangle.
   ANSWER: Students should hold up the square.
   Ask students to name the shape.

   Ask: How do you know that the square and the rectangle have the same number of sides?
   ANSWER: I counted. They both have 4 sides.

6. Clear the work area, and place a circle. To the right of the circle, place a pentagon, a triangle, and the other circle.

   Say: A circle has no sides. Hold up another shape that has no sides.
   ANSWER: Students should hold up the other circle.

   Explain that both shapes are circles. Even though the two circles are different sizes and colors, they both have 0 sides.

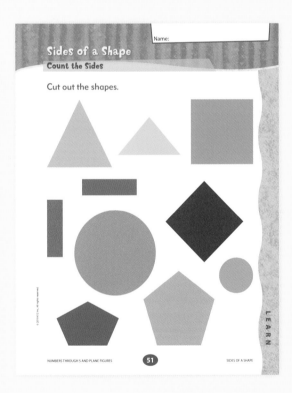

LEARN Which Shape?

Students will determine which shape has more sides than other shapes.
  Gather the paper bag and cut-out shapes from the Count the Sides activity page.

1. Place a circle, rectangle, and triangle in the work area.

    Ask: How many sides does a circle have?
    ANSWER: 0

    Ask: How many sides does a rectangle have?
    ANSWER: 4

    Ask: How many sides does a triangle have?
    ANSWER: 3

2. **Ask:** Which shape has the most sides?
    ANSWER: rectangle

3. **Ask:** How do you know the rectangle has the most sides?
    ANSWER: 4 sides is more than 3 sides or 0 sides.

4. Clear the work area, and place a square, rectangle, triangle, and pentagon.

    Say: Count the sides on each shape.

    Watch students as they count the sides on each shape. Make sure they
    count each side exactly one time.

    Say: Hold up the shape that has the most sides.
    ANSWER: Students should hold up the pentagon.

    If necessary, tell students that this shape is called a pentagon.

5. **Ask:** How do you know the pentagon has the most sides?
    ANSWER: 5 sides is more than 4 sides or 3 sides.

6. Place the shapes in the paper bag.

    Say: Pull out three shapes. Tell which shape has the most sides.

    If there is more than one shape with the most sides in a group, have students
    identify all the shapes that have the most sides.

Objectives

- Compare plane figures by
  common attributes, such as
  number of sides and number of
  corners of triangles, rectangles,
  squares, pentagons, and circles.

Tips

As students count the sides of a shape,
have them trace each side with their
finger.

Objectives

Students will practice counting the sides of shapes and choosing the shape with the most sides. Give students the How Many Sides? activity page from their Activity Book and read the directions with them.

- Compare plane figures by common attributes, such as number of sides and number of corners of triangles, rectangles, squares, pentagons, and circles.

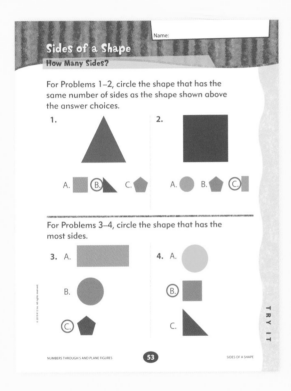

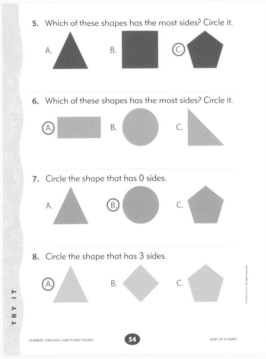

Corners of a Shape

Lesson Overview

TIME Look at Morning, Afternoon, and Evening	5 minutes	ONLINE
GET READY Which Cookie Is Different?	5 minutes	ONLINE
LEARN Count the Corners	10 minutes	ONLINE
LEARN Shape Poster	10 minutes	OFFLINE
TRY IT How Many Corners?	10 minutes	OFFLINE

▶ Lesson Objectives

- Compare plane figures by common attributes, such as number of sides and number of corners of triangles, rectangles, squares, pentagons, and circles.
- Demonstrate an understanding of the concepts of morning, afternoon, and evening.

▶ Prerequisite Skills

Given a group of plane figures, identify which figure does not belong according to color, shape, or size.

▶ Advance Preparation

Cut out each shape from the Shape Poster activity page. Divide the construction paper into 4 sections. Label the sections as follows: **0 corners**, **3 corners**, **4 corners**, **5 corners**. Keep the poster after students complete it—you will use this poster in the next lesson.

▶ Content Background

Students will learn the term *corner*. They will identify corners and count the number of corners on a shape. They will also compare the number of corners on shapes.

Rectangles and squares both have 4 sides. Rectangles have 2 long sides and 2 short sides, while squares have 4 sides of the same length.

Materials to Gather

SUPPLIED

Shape Poster activity page

How Many Corners? activity page

blocks – A, C, G, H (1 of any color)

ALSO NEEDED

scissors, adult

paper, construction – 1 light-colored sheet

glue

Keywords

corner – the point where two segments, lines, surfaces, or edges meet

sort – to put objects into categories on the basis of a particular set of characteristics

GET READY Which Cookie Is Different?

ONLINE 5min

Students will identify which cookie is a different color, size, or shape from the others in a group.

Objectives

- Given a group of plane figures, identify which figure does not belong according to color, shape, or size.

LEARN Count the Corners

ONLINE 10min

Students will learn that two sides of a shape meet at a *corner*. They will count the number of corners on familiar shapes, including a circle, which has 0 corners. Then students will compare the number of corners on shapes.

Objectives

- Compare plane figures by common attributes, such as number of sides and number of corners of triangles, rectangles, squares, pentagons, and circles.

LEARN Shape Poster

OFFLINE 10min

Students will sort and compare shapes by the number of corners.

Gather the cut-out shapes from the Shape Poster activity page, glue, and the construction paper that you labeled. Display the construction paper. Lay out the shapes in a random arrangement.

1. **Say:** You will sort shapes and make a poster that shows the number of corners on each shape.
2. Explain that the poster has 4 sections. Point to the section labeled "0 corners."
   Say: This section is for shapes with 0 corners.
   Point to and describe each section in this way.
3. Show students the shapes. Ask them to find a triangle.
   Ask: How many corners does a triangle have?
   ANSWER: 3
4. **Ask:** Where will you glue the triangle on the poster?
   ANSWER: in the "3 corners" section

Objectives

- Compare plane figures by common attributes, such as number of sides and number of corners of triangles, rectangles, squares, pentagons, and circles.

Tips

When students count corners, have them place a finger on the corner they start with to help them keep track of which corners they have counted.

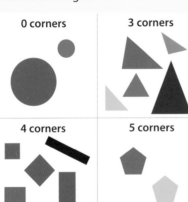

0 corners 3 corners

4 corners 5 corners

5. Have students glue the triangle onto their poster.

   Ask: Are there other shapes that have 3 corners?
   Have students find all the shapes with 3 corners.
   Say: Place the shapes with 3
   corners on your poster, but don't glue them yet.

   Check that students have placed the correct shapes in the "3 corners" section.
   Have them count the corners of any shapes that do not belong. Once
   students have found all the triangles, have them glue them to the poster.

6. **Ask:** Does the color and size of a shape change the number of corners it has?
   ANSWER: No

7. Have students sort the remaining shapes and glue them onto their poster.
   When the poster is complete, ask them the following questions.

   Ask: What shapes have 4 corners?
   ANSWER: squares and rectangles

   Ask: What shapes have 0 corners?
   ANSWER: circles

   Ask: What shape has the most corners?
   ANSWER: pentagon

TRY IT How Many Corners?

Students will practice identifying the number of corners on shapes.

Before students complete the activity page, use the blocks to review that a corner is the place where two sides meet. Have students point to and count the corners on each block.

Give students the How Many Corners? activity page from their Activity Book and read the directions with them.

Objectives

- Compare plane figures by common attributes, such as number of sides and number of corners of triangles, rectangles, squares, pentagons, and circles.

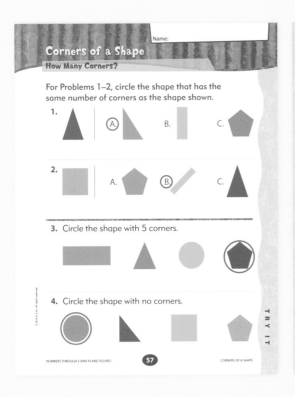

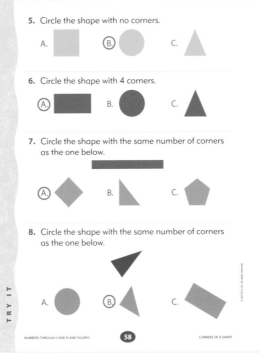

Sides and Corners of Shapes

Lesson Overview

CALENDAR What's in a Day?	5 minutes	**ONLINE**
GET READY Count Animals	5 minutes	**ONLINE**
LEARN Practice Writing Numerals	5 minutes	**OFFLINE**
TRY IT Write Numerals 0 Through 5	5 minutes	**OFFLINE**
LEARN Count the Corners and Sides	5 minutes	**OFFLINE**
TRY IT How Many Corners and Sides?	10 minutes	**ONLINE**
CHECKPOINT	10 minutes	**OFFLINE**

▶ Lesson Objectives

- Write numerals from 1 through 5.
- Compare plane figures by common attributes, such as number of sides and number of corners of triangles, rectangles, squares, pentagons, and circles.
- Demonstrate an understanding of the concepts of day, week, and year.

▶ Prerequisite Skills

- Count aloud a number of objects up through 5.
- Given a group of plane figures, identify which figure does not belong according to color, shape, or size.

▶ Advance Preparation

- Gather the completed shape poster from the Corners of a Shape lesson. If you do not have the poster, refer to the Corners of a Shape lesson in the Lesson Guide for instructions on how to create it.
- Print the Numeral Writing Guide.

▶ Content Background

Students will write the numerals 0 through 5. They will then count the corners and sides of various shapes to learn that a shape has the same number of sides and corners.

Materials to Gather

SUPPLIED

Write Numerals 0 Through 5 activity page

Numeral Writing Guide (printout)

Checkpoint (printout)

ALSO NEEDED

paper, wide-line handwriting

completed shape poster from the Corners of a Shape lesson

GET READY Count Animals

ONLINE 5min

Students will practice counting aloud groups of up through 5 animals.

Objectives

- Count aloud a number of objects up through 5.

Tips

To prevent students from counting too many or too few animals, have students point to each animal as they count it.

LEARN Practice Writing Numerals

OFFLINE 5min

Students will write the numerals 0 through 5.
  Gather the Numeral Writing Guide and the wide-line handwriting paper. Refer to the Numeral Writing Guide as needed throughout the activity.

1. On the wide-line handwriting paper, model how to write the numeral 0.
2. Have students write the numeral 0 five times on the handwriting paper.
3. Repeat Steps 1 and 2 for the numerals 1 through 5.

Objectives

- Write numerals from 1 through 5.

Tips

If students have difficulty writing a numeral, show them the numeral in the Numeral Writing Guide and have them trace it with their finger.

TRY IT Write Numerals 0 Through 5

OFFLINE 5min

Students will practice writing the numerals 0 through 5. Give students the Write Numerals 0 Through 5 activity page and read the directions with them.

Objectives

- Write numerals 1 through 5.

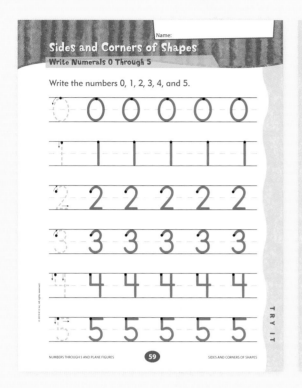

Sides and Corners of Shapes
Write Numerals 0 Through 5

Name: _____

Write the numbers 0, 1, 2, 3, 4, and 5.

0 0 0 0 0
1 1 1 1 1
2 2 2 2 2
3 3 3 3 3
4 4 4 4 4
5 5 5 5 5

T R Y   I T

T R Y   I T

Read each problem, and then write the number.

1. Write the number five.

     5

2. Write the number four.

     4

3. Write the number three.

     3

4. Write the number two.

     2

5. Write the number one.

     1

6. Write the number zero.

     0

OFFLINE
5 min

LEARN Count the Corners and Sides

Students will count the corners and sides of various shapes to learn that a shape has the same number of sides and corners.

Gather the completed shape poster from the Corners of a Shape lesson.

1. Point to the section labeled "5 corners."

   Ask: What shapes are in this section?
   ANSWER: pentagons

   Ask: How many corners does a pentagon have?
   ANSWER: 5

   Ask: How many sides does a pentagon have?
   ANSWER: 5

   Ask: What do you notice about the number of sides and corners of a pentagon?
   ANSWER: They are both 5.

2. Repeat Step 1 with each section of the poster.

3. Tell students to think about the shapes on the poster.

   Ask: What can you tell about the number of sides and corners of a shape?
   ANSWER: For each shape, the number of sides and corners are the same.

Objectives

- Compare plane figures by common attributes, such as number of sides and number of corners of triangles, rectangles, squares, pentagons, and circles.

Tips

Before students begin the activity, remind them that a corner is where two sides meet.

Tips

When discussing the section labeled "4 corners," point out that although squares have sides that are the same length and rectangles have sides that are different lengths, both shapes have 4 sides.

TRY IT How Many Corners and Sides?

Objectives

Students will complete an online Try It. Read the directions, problems, and answer choices to students. If necessary, help students with keyboard or mouse operations.

- Compare plane figures by common attributes, such as number of sides and number of corners of triangles, rectangles, squares, pentagons, and circles.

CHECKPOINT

Objectives

Print the Checkpoint and have students complete it on their own. Read the directions, problems, and answer choices to students if necessary. Use the answer key to score the Checkpoint, and then enter the results online.

- Compare plane figures by common attributes, such as number of sides and number of corners of triangles, rectangles, squares, pentagons, and circles.
- Write numerals from 1 through 5.

Checkpoint   Math | Numbers Through 5 and Plane Figures | Sides and Corners of Shapes

Name _____ Date _____

Checkpoint Answer Key

Circle the answer.

1. Which of these shapes has the most sides?
   A.   B.   C.

2. Circle the shape that has 0 corners.
   A.   B.   C.

3. Count the corners on the shape to the right. Choose the shape that has the same number of corners as the one to the right.
   A.   B.   C.

4. Circle the two shapes that have the same number of sides.

1 of 2

Checkpoint   Math | Numbers Through 5 and Plane Figures | Sides and Corners of Shapes

Name _____ Date _____

5. Write the number two.   2

6. Write the number five.   5

7. Write the number three.   3

8. Write the number four.   4

2 of 2

Unit Review

Lesson Overview

UNIT REVIEW Look Back	20 minutes	**ONLINE**
UNIT REVIEW Checkpoint Practice	10 minutes	**OFFLINE**
⊡ **UNIT REVIEW** Prepare for the Checkpoint		

▶ Unit Objectives

This lesson reviews the following objectives:

- Count aloud a number of objects up through 5.
- Use concrete objects or sketches to represent a quantity up through 5.
- Write numerals from 1 through 5.
- Compare plane figures by common attributes, such as number of sides and number of corners of triangles, rectangles, squares, pentagons, and circles.

▶ Advance Preparation

In this lesson, students will have an opportunity to review previous activities in the Numbers Through 5 and Plane Figures unit. Look at the suggested activities in Unit Review: Prepare for the Checkpoint online and gather any needed materials.

Materials to Gather

SUPPLIED

Checkpoint Practice activity page

Keywords

circle	set
corner	shape
count	side
numeral	sort
number	square
pentagon	triangle
rectangle	

ONLINE
20min

UNIT REVIEW Look Back

In this unit, students have learned about the numbers 0 through 5. They have counted through 5, made groups of up through 5 objects, and written the numerals 0 through 5. Students have also learned about sides and corners of shapes. They have counted sides and corners and compared shapes based on the number of sides and corners they have. Students will review these concepts to prepare for the Unit Checkpoint.

Objectives

- Review unit objectives.

UNIT REVIEW Checkpoint Practice

Objectives

- Review unit objectives.

Students will complete a Checkpoint Practice activity page to prepare for the Unit Checkpoint. If necessary, read the directions, questions, and answer choices to students. Have students answer the problems on their own. Carefully review the answers with students.

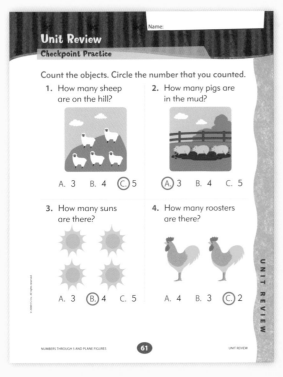

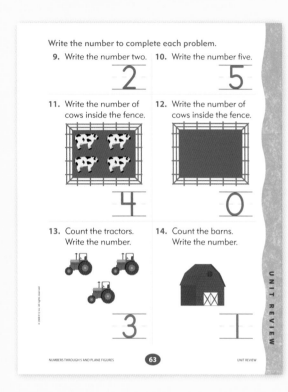

Write the number to complete each problem.

9. Write the number two.

2

10. Write the number five.

5

11. Write the number of cows inside the fence.

4

12. Write the number of cows inside the fence.

0

13. Count the tractors. Write the number.

3

14. Count the barns. Write the number.

1

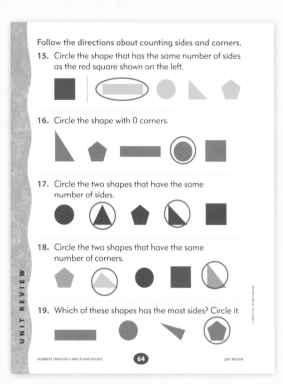

Follow the directions about counting sides and corners.

15. Circle the shape that has the same number of sides as the red square shown on the left.

16. Circle the shape with 0 corners.

17. Circle the two shapes that have the same number of sides.

18. Circle the two shapes that have the same number of corners.

19. Which of these shapes has the most sides? Circle it.

⇥ UNIT REVIEW Prepare for the Checkpoint

What you do next depends on how students performed in the previous activity, Unit Review: Checkpoint Practice. If students had difficulty with any of the problems, complete the appropriate review activity listed in the table online.

Unit Checkpoint

UNIT CHECKPOINT Online	10 minutes	**ONLINE**
UNIT CHECKPOINT Offline	30 minutes	**OFFLINE**

▶ Unit Objectives

This Unit Checkpoint assesses the following objectives:

- Count aloud a number of objects up through 5.
- Use concrete objects or sketches to represent a quantity up through 5.
- Write numerals from 1 through 5.
- Compare plane figures by common attributes, such as number of sides and number of corners of triangles, rectangles, squares, pentagons, and circles.

Materials to Gather

SUPPLIED
Unit Checkpoint (printout)
blocks – O (5 of any color)

UNIT CHECKPOINT Online

ONLINE
10min

Objectives

- Assess unit objectives.

Students will complete this part of the Unit Checkpoint online. Read the directions, problems, and answer choices to students. If necessary, help students with keyboard or mouse operations.

UNIT CHECKPOINT Offline

Objectives

- Assess unit objectives.

Students will complete this part of the Unit Checkpoint offline. Print the Checkpoint and have students complete it on their own. Read the directions, problems, and answer choices to students, if necessary. Use the answer key to score the Checkpoint, and then enter the results online.

Gather the blocks. For Problems 3 and 4, lay out the blocks in a random arrangement.

Name _____ Date _____

Unit Checkpoint Answer Key   **4 frogs**

(1 point)
1. Count aloud the frogs. Then say the number that tells how many.

(1 point)
2. Count aloud the apples. Then say the number that tells how many.

   5 apples

Use blocks for Problems 3 and 4.

(1 point)
3. Show 3 blocks.   **Students should show 3 blocks.**

(1 point)
4. Show 1 block.   **Students should show 1 block.**

(1 point)
5. Draw 2 lines.

Name _____ Date _____

(1 point)
6. Circle the shape that has no corners.

(1 point)
7. Circle the two shapes that have the same number of sides.

(1 point)
8. Write the number two.

   2

(1 point)
9. Write the number three.

   3

(1 point)
10. Write the number four.

   4

(1 point)
11. Write the number five.

   5

(1 point)
12. Count the dogs. Then write the number that tells how many.

   4

Numbers Through 10

▶ Unit Objectives

- Count aloud a number of objects up through 10.

- Demonstrate that counting 10 or fewer objects can occur from left to right, right to left, or in any order as long as all the items are counted once.

- Use concrete objects or sketches to represent a quantity up through 10.

- Order a group of no more than 10 objects, such as number tiles or stacks of counting blocks.

- Write numerals from 1 through 10.

- Given two or more sets that have 10 or fewer objects, identify which set has more or fewer objects than another set, or which sets have an equal number of objects

- Recognize that numbers with greater values describe sets with more objects in them than numbers with lesser values (for sets of 10 or fewer objects).

▶ Big Ideas

Numbers can represent basic counting results.

▶ Unit Introduction

Students will learn about numbers through 10. They will count through 10 and make groups of 0 through 10 objects. Students will learn that they can count objects in any order as long as they count each object exactly one time. They will also read and write the numerals through 10.

Students will compare and order groups of up through 10 objects. They will learn that greater numbers describe groups with more objects. Comparing and ordering groups of objects will help students learn to compare and order numbers.

Count Through 10

Lesson Overview

CALENDAR First and Last Day	5 minutes	ONLINE
GET READY Count Through 5	5 minutes	ONLINE
LEARN Count Dogs	10 minutes	ONLINE
LEARN How Many Objects?	10 minutes	OFFLINE
TRY IT Count Fruit	10 minutes	OFFLINE

▶ Lesson Objectives

- Demonstrate that counting 10 or fewer objects can occur from left to right, right to left, or in any order as long as all the items are counted once.
- Count aloud a number of objects up through 10.
- Demonstrate an understanding of the concepts of day, week, and year.

▶ Prerequisite Skills

Count aloud a number of objects up through 5.

▶ Common Errors and Misconceptions

- Students might start counting before or after pointing to the first object in a group. Or they might stop counting before or after they point to the last object. Students should point to each object as they count it.
- Students might say more than one number for each object when counting objects in a group. Or they might skip objects. Students should point to each object and say exactly one number. Then they should point to the next object and say exactly one number, and so on.
- Students might use an incorrect counting sequence, such as "one, two, four, six, ten."

▶ Content Background

In this lesson, students will count groups of up through 10 objects. They will learn that the order in which they count objects does not affect the number of objects.

When learning to count objects, students should point to and move each object as they say a number. Students will need to point to one object as they say exactly one number to count the objects correctly. Moving the counted object away from the others prevents students from counting too many or too few objects.

Materials to Gather

SUPPLIED

blocks – B (10 of any color)

Count Fruit activity page

ALSO NEEDED

paper, construction – 1 light-colored sheet

Keywords	**count** – to say each number according to a defined sequence, such as consecutively, by 2s, or backward **number** – a quantity or value

GET READY Count Through 5

Students will practice counting aloud groups of up through 5 objects in the garden with Alexander.

Objectives

- Count aloud a number of objects up through 5.

Tips

Guide students to count objects in the same sequence (for example, left to right) on each screen so that they don't skip an object or count an object twice.

LEARN Count Dogs

Students will listen as groups of up through 10 objects are counted. Then they will count aloud each group. They will watch as a group is counted in different sequences—left to right, then right to left, then randomly—to learn that the sequence in which they count does not affect the number of objects.

Objectives

- Demonstrate that counting 10 or fewer objects can occur from left to right, right to left, or in any order as long as all the items are counted once.

LEARN How Many Objects?

Students will count groups of up through 10 blocks. They will learn that the sequence in which they count the blocks does not affect the number of blocks.
  Gather the blocks and construction paper.

1. Place the construction paper in the work area in front of students.

   Say: This is your work mat. You will place the blocks on the paper as you count them.

2. **Ask:** Are there any blocks on the paper?
   ANSWER: No

   Say: There are no blocks on the paper, so there are 0 blocks.

3. Place 1 block in the work area in front of students but not on the paper.

   Say: Place the blocks on the paper, and count it.
   ANSWER: 1

4. Remove the block from the paper. Place 2 blocks in the work area in front of students. Ask students to count them, placing each block in a line on the paper as they count it.

5. Repeat Step 4 with groups of 3, 4, and 5 blocks in that order.

6. Place 6 blocks in the work area in front of students but not on the paper.

   Say: I am going to count these blocks. Place each block in a line on the paper as I count it.

7. Repeat Step 6 with groups of 7, 8, 9, and 10 blocks.

Objectives

- Demonstrate that counting 10 or fewer objects can occur from left to right, right to left, or in any order as long as all the items are counted once.
- Count aloud a number of objects up through 10.

Tips

Place the blocks in a plastic cup when they are not in the group that students are counting.

8. Clear the work area.

   Say: Now it's your turn to count groups of more than 5 blocks. Place each block in a line on the paper as you count it. Remember to say one number for each block.

9. Have students count groups of 6, 7, 8, 9, and 10 blocks. Check that they say the correct sequence of numbers. Tell them the next number if they need help. Remind students to move each block to the paper as they count it.

   After students count 10 blocks, do not clear the paper.

10. **Ask:** How did you know there were 10 blocks in this group?
    ANSWER: I put each block on the paper as I counted it. I said all the numbers from 1 to 10. The last number I said was 10.

11. Move the 10 blocks so they are in a horizontal line, with the blocks slightly separated form each other. Point to the first block on the left.

    Ask: Start with this block. Count the blocks. How many are there?
    ANSWER: 10

12. Point to the last block on the right. Motion from right to left across the row, as you say, "Count the blocks this way."

    Ask: Start with this block. Count the blocks this way. How many are there?
    ANSWER: 10

13. **Ask:** Does the number change when you count the blocks in a different order?
    ANSWER: No

14. Now rearrange the blocks so they are in a line with about $\frac{1}{2}$ inch of space between them.

    Ask: How many blocks are in the group now?
    ANSWER: 10

    If students answer incorrectly, have them count the blocks.

15. **Say:** We can rearrange the blocks. The number stays the same.

16. Have students arrange the blocks in a circle.

    Ask: Do you need to count to tell me how many are in the group? Why or why not?
    ANSWER: No. I moved the blocks around, but the number did not change.

17. If students answer the question in Step 16 incorrectly, rearrange the 10 blocks several more times. Each time ask students to count the blocks and then to tell you why the number did not change.

TRY IT Count Fruit

OFFLINE
10 min

This Try It activity has two parts.

Part 1
Students will practice counting objects in different orders.
Gather the blocks.

1. Place 7 blocks in a row.

2. Point to the first block on the left.

   Say: Starting with this block, count the blocks in this group.
   ANSWER: 7

3. Point to the last block on the right. As you say, "this way," motion from right to left.

   Say: Now start with this block, and count the blocks in this group this way.
   ANSWER: 7

4. **Ask:** Does the number change when you count the blocks in a different order?
   ANSWER: No

5. Repeat Steps 1–4 with 8 blocks and 10 blocks.

Part 2
Students will practice counting groups of up through 10 objects. Give students the Count Fruit activity page from their Activity Book and read the directions with them.

Objectives

- Demonstrate that counting 10 or fewer objects can occur from left to right, right to left, or in any order as long as all the items are counted once.

- Count aloud a number of objects up through 10.

Tips

To prevent students from counting the same object twice, have them cross out each object as they count it.

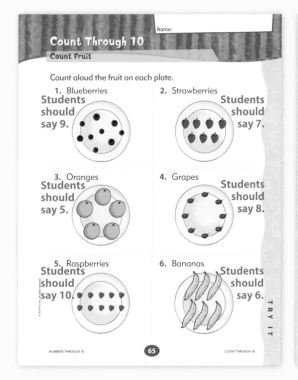

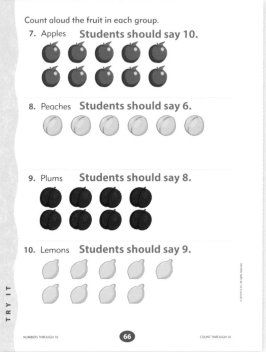

98 NUMBERS THROUGH 10

Show an Amount Through 10

CALENDAR One Week	5 minutes	ONLINE
GET READY Count Shapes	5 minutes	ONLINE
LEARN Build It or Draw It	10 minutes	ONLINE
LEARN Number Cards Through 10	10 minutes	OFFLINE
TRY IT Show an Amount	10 minutes	OFFLINE

▶ Lesson Objectives

- Use concrete objects or sketches to represent a quantity up through 10.
- Demonstrate an understanding of the concepts of day, week, and year.

▶ Prerequisite Skills

Use concrete objects or sketches to represent a quantity up through 5.

▶ Common Errors and Misconceptions

- Students might start counting before or after pointing to the first object in a group. Or they might stop counting before or after they point to the last object. Students should point to each object as they count it.
- Students might say more than one number for each object when counting objects in a group. Or they might skip objects. Students should point to each object and say exactly one number. Then they should point to the next object and say exactly one number, and so on.
- Students might say numbers and point to objects when counting, but they might not understand the connection between saying the numbers and pointing to the objects.
- Students might use an incorrect counting sequence, such as "one, two, four, six, ten."

▶ Content Background

In this lesson, students will use objects and pictures to show amounts through 10.

Keywords   **represent** – to symbolize or stand for something else

Materials to Gather

SUPPLIED

blocks – O (10 of any color)

Show an Amount activity page

ALSO NEEDED

crayons

index cards – 11

GET READY Count Shapes

Students will make groups of up through 5 shapes.

- Use concrete objects or sketches to represent a quantity up through 5.

LEARN Build It or Draw It

Objectives

Students will use blocks and drawings to represent numbers through 10. Gather the blocks and crayons.

Follow the directions on each screen. Students will need to either gather a certain number of blocks or draw a certain number of objects.

- Use concrete objects or sketches to represent a quantity up through 10.

LEARN Number Cards Through 10

Objectives

Students will make number cards to show each amount through 10.
Gather the blocks, crayons, index cards.

- Use concrete objects or sketches to represent a quantity up through 10.

1. Explain to students that they can use objects to show an amount.

   Give students an index card and 1 block.

   Ask: Count the blocks. Place each block on the card as you count it. How many blocks do you have?
   ANSWER: 1

2. **Say:** Draw 1 circle on the card to show that there is 1 block.

   Take the block off the card and set the card aside.

3. Give students a second card and 2 blocks.

   Ask: Count the blocks. Place each block on the card as you count it. How many blocks do you have?
   ANSWER: 2

4. **Say:** Draw 2 circles on the card to show that there are 2 blocks.
   Take the block off the card and set the card aside.

5. Repeat Steps 3 and 4 with 3, 4, 5, 6, 7, 8, 9, and 10 blocks.

6. Give students the last card.

   Ask: This card will show 0. How many circles will your draw on the card?
   ANSWER: none

7. Lay out the cards in a row, in order from 0 through 10.

8. Have students count from 0 through 10, pointing to each card as they count it.

9. **Say:** Pick up the card that shows 5 circles. Draw 5 squares on the back of the card.

10. Repeat Step 9 with each number, asking students to pick up each card in a random order. If students enjoy drawing, vary the objects that you ask them to draw on the back of the cards. Alternatively, students may choose what types of objects to draw.

Tips

As an alternative to drawing on the backs of the cards, students can place stickers or glue objects (such as beads and buttons) to represent each amount.

Tips

Students can refer to their number cards throughout the unit.

TRY IT Show an Amount

Students will practice showing amounts with blocks and drawings. Give students the blocks, crayons, and Show an Amount activity page from their Activity Book. Read the directions with them.

Objectives

- Use concrete objects or sketches to represent a quantity up through 10.

Tips

To prevent students from counting the same block twice, have them touch each block as they count it.

Show an Amount Through 10

Show an Amount

Use blocks to show each amount.

1. 8

2. 6

3. 10

4. 0

5. 7

6. 9

Draw the objects to show each amount.

7. 6 dots

8. 10 dots

9. 7 squares

10. 9 circles

Draw objects of your choice to show each amount.

11. 8 objects

Students should draw 8 objects.

12. 5 objects

Students should draw 5 objects.

Represent Amounts

Lesson Overview

CALENDAR A Week in Two Different Months	5 minutes	ONLINE
GET READY Amounts Through 5	5 minutes	ONLINE
LEARN Amounts Through 10	20 minutes	OFFLINE
TRY IT Show the Amount	10 minutes	OFFLINE

▶ Lesson Objectives

Use concrete objects or sketches to represent a quantity up through 10.

▶ Prerequisite Skills

Use concrete objects or sketches to represent a quantity up through 5.

▶ Common Errors and Misconceptions

- Students might start counting before or after pointing to the first object in a group. Or they might stop counting before or after they point to the last object. Students should point to each object as they count it.
- Students might say more than one number for each object when counting objects in a group. Or they might skip objects. Students should point to each object and say exactly one number. Then they should point to the next object and say exactly one number, and so on.
- Students might use an incorrect counting sequence, such as "one, two, four, six, ten."

▶ Advance Preparation

Fold a sheet of paper in half vertically and then in thirds horizontally, making 6 sections.

▶ Content Background

Students will use objects and drawings to represent amounts through 10.

It is important for students to understand that the same amount can be represented in different ways. For example, a drawing of 5 trees and a group of 5 blocks both represent the number 5.

Materials to Gather

SUPPLIED

blocks – B (10 of any color)
blocks – O (10 of any color)
Show the Amount activity page

ALSO NEEDED

crayons

GET READY Amounts Through 5

ONLINE 5 min

Students will represent amounts through 5. They will see a picture of up through 5 animals and choose the group of objects that shows the same number.

Objectives

- Use concrete objects or sketches to represent a quantity up through 5.

Tips

To motivate students, let them use stuffed animals or other toys to represent the animals online.

LEARN Amounts Through 10

OFFLINE 20 min

Students will use blocks and drawings to represent numbers through 10. Gather the cubes, crayons, and paper you folded into 6 sections. Place the cubes in a group in front of students.

1. **Say:** Show 6 with cubes. Count aloud as you place each cube in a group.

   Students should say one number as they move each cube into the group. After students make the group, combine all cubes into one group again.

2. Repeat Step 1 with the following numbers in this order: 8, 2, 7, 0, 5, 10, 3, 1, 9, 4.

3. **Say:** You have shown the numbers 0 through 10 with cubes. Now you will show 0 through 10 with pictures.

4. Give students the crayons and folder paper. Point out the sections of the paper. Students may trace the folds to outline each section.

5. **Say:** In the first box, draw 4 circles.

   If students have difficulty, have them first make a group of 4 cubes. Then ask them to draw 1 circle for each cube.

6. Have students check their work by taking 4 cubes and placing 1 cube on each circle.

7. Repeat Steps 5 and 6 for the remaining numbers through 10, using the order of the numbers given in Step 2. Rather than drawing circles each time, let students choose what to draw (for example, squares, sticks, flowers). Because of time constraints, make sure students' drawing choices are simple.

8. **Ask:** How does a drawing of a set of objects show a number?
   ANSWER: It helps me see the number, and I can count it.

Objectives

- Use concrete objects or sketches to represent a quantity up through 10.

Tips

For students having difficulty showing 0, offer examples, such as, "I have 0 books in my hand," or "There are 0 elephants in this room." Then have students give their own examples.

Objectives

- Use concrete objects or sketches to represent a quantity up through 10.

Students will practice using blocks and drawings to show amounts through 10. Give students the crayons, circle blocks, cubes, and Show the Amount activity page from their Activity Book. Read the directions with them.

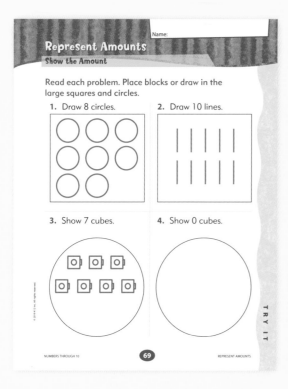

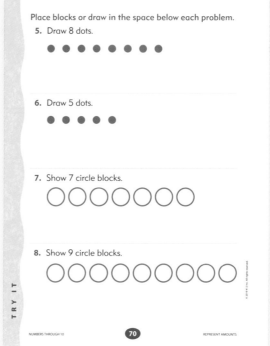

Count Aloud Through 10

Lesson Overview

CALENDAR Calendar Year	5 minutes	ONLINE
GET READY Count Aloud to 5	5 minutes	ONLINE
LEARN Count Aloud to 10	20 minutes	ONLINE
TRY IT Numbers Through 10	10 minutes	OFFLINE

▶ Lesson Objectives

- Count aloud a number of objects up through 10.
- Demonstrate that counting 10 or fewer objects can occur from left to right, right to left, or in any order as long as all the items are counted once.

▶ Prerequisite Skills

Use concrete objects or sketches to represent a quantity up through 5.

▶ Common Errors and Misconceptions

- Students might start counting before or after pointing to the first object in a group. Or they might stop counting before or after they point to the last object. Students should point to each object as they count it.
- Students might say more than one number for each object when counting objects in a group. Or they might skip objects. Students should point to each object and say exactly one number. Then they should point to the next object and say exactly one number, and so on.
- Students might use an incorrect counting sequence, such as "one, two, four, six, ten."

▶ Content Background

In this lesson, students will count groups of up through 10 objects. They will learn that the order in which they count objects does not affect the number of objects.

Materials to Gather

SUPPLIED
blocks – B (10 of any color)
Numbers Through 10 activity page

GET READY Count Aloud to 5

ONLINE 5 min

Students will practice counting aloud up through 5 objects on a playground.

Objectives

- Use concrete objects or sketches to represent a quantity up through 5.

LEARN Count Aloud to 10

Students will count groups of stamps. Emphasize to students that they can count the stamps in any order as long as they count each stamp one time.

First have students try the game in Practice mode. Then have them click Play to compete against a timer.

Objectives

- Count aloud a number of objects up through 10.
- Demonstrate that counting 10 or fewer objects can occur from left to right, right to left, or in any order as long as all the items are counted once.

TRY IT Numbers Through 10

This Try It activity has two parts.

Part 1
Students will practice counting in different orders.
  Gather the blocks.

1. Place 9 blocks in a row.
2. Point to the first block on the left.

   Say: Starting with this circle, count the circles in this group.

3. Point to the last circle in the row.

   Say: Now start with this circle. Count the circles in this group.

4. **Ask:** Did changing the direction that you counted change the number of circles?
   ANSWER: No

5. Repeat Steps 1–4 with 10 blocks.

Part 2
Students will practice counting groups of up through 10 objects. Give students the Numbers Through 10 activity page from their Activity Book and read the directions with them.

Objectives

- Count aloud a number of objects up through 10.
- Demonstrate that counting 10 or fewer objects can occur from left to right, right to left, or in any order as long as all the items are counted once.

Tips

To prevent students from counting the same block twice, have them touch each block as they count it.

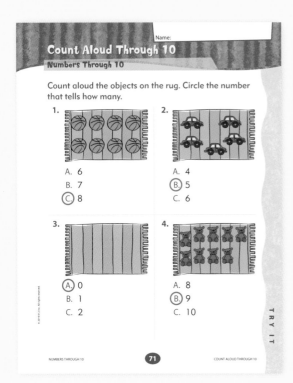

Count Aloud Through 10
Numbers Through 10

Count aloud the objects on the rug. Circle the number that tells how many.

1.
- A. 6
- B. 7
- **C. 8**

2.
- A. 4
- **B. 5**
- C. 6

3.
- **A. 0**
- B. 1
- C. 2

4.
- A. 8
- **B. 9**
- C. 10

TRY IT

TRY IT

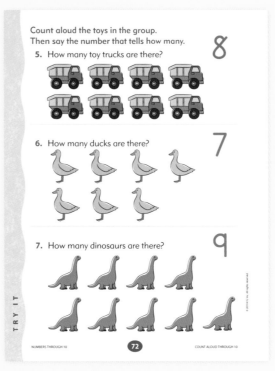

Count aloud the toys in the group.
Then say the number that tells how many.

5. How many toy trucks are there?

8

6. How many ducks are there?

7

7. How many dinosaurs are there?

9

Show Amounts in Different Ways

Lesson Overview

CALENDAR Compare Day, Week, Month, and Year	5 minutes	ONLINE
GET READY How Many Bears?	5 minutes	ONLINE
LEARN Match Amounts	15 minutes	OFFLINE
TRY IT Represent the Amount	5 minutes	OFFLINE
CHECKPOINT	10 minutes	OFFLINE

▶ Lesson Objectives

- Use concrete objects or sketches to represent a quantity up through 10.
- Demonstrate an understanding of the concepts of day, week, and year.

▶ Prerequisite Skills

Use concrete objects or sketches to represent a quantity up through 5.

▶ Advance Preparation

For 10 of the plastic bags, place an index card into each bag.

▶ Safety

Supervise students to make sure plastic bags are used only for the activity and for no other purpose.

Content Background

Students will use objects and drawings to represent amounts through 10.

Materials to Gather

SUPPLIED

blocks – O (10 of any color)
Represent the Amount activity page
Checkpoint (printout)

ALSO NEEDED

counting objects – 55
crayons
index cards – 20
paper, construction – 1 light-colored sheet
plastic sandwich bags – 20

GET READY How Many Bears?

ONLINE 5 min

Students will use blocks to represent amounts through 5. Gather the crayons, construction paper, and blocks.

1. Have students draw a large upside-down letter U with a crayon on the construction paper to make a cave. The cave should be large enough to fit 5 blocks inside of it.
2. Read the text above the first index card on the screen.
3. **Say:** Pretend that each block is a bear. Place the correct number of bears in your cave.

Objectives

- Use concrete objects or sketches to represent a quantity up through 5.

Tips

Give students a small container, such as a cup, to hold their blocks.

4. Have students click the icon on the upper right of the card to see if they have placed the correct number of blocks.

5. If necessary, help students correct their answer. Point to the bears on-screen as they place one block for each bear.

6. Click the Next Card arrow. Follow the on-screen directions and repeat Steps 3–5 for each card in the deck.

LEARN Match Amounts

Students will use objects and drawings to represent amounts through 10.

Gather the counting objects (for example, dry macaroni), crayons, bags with index cards inside them, and the remaining bags and index cards.

- Use concrete objects or sketches to represent a quantity up through 10.

1. **Say:** We are going to play a matching game. We need some objects and drawings to get started.

2. **Ask:** Let's start with 1. How many objects should you place in a bag to show 1?
ANSWER: 1

Have students place one object into one of the bags that has an index card in it. Set the bag aside.

3. Repeat Step 2 with the numbers 0 and 2–9. Have them place objects in front of the index cards.

4. **Say:** Now we need some drawings. Let's start with 1 again.
Ask: How many dots should you draw on the card to show 1?
ANSWER: 1

Have students draw 1 dot on an index card and place it into an empty bag.

5. Repeat Step 4 with the numbers 0 and 2–9. After students draw dots on a card, have them count the dots to check their work.

6. Gather all the bags. Turn over the bags so that the dots and objects are hidden. Randomly place the bags in a 5 by 4 arrangement.
Say: It's time to play the game.

7. Have students turn over two bags at a time to find two bags showing the same number. For example, if they turn over a bag with 3 objects and a bag with 3 dots, they have a match.

If the objects and dot cards match, students can keep the pair; if not, they must turn the bags back over and try again.

8. Have students turn over pairs until they've found all matches.

Students can save the bags and play again on their own for review.

Tips

If students have difficulty creating the bags to represent 0, remind them that 0 means "none." So 0 objects means "no objects" and 0 dots means "no dots."

Tips

For counting objects, use small, durable household items (for example, dry macaroni, shells, or twists).

TRY IT Represent the Amount

Students will use drawings and blocks to represent numbers through 10. Give students the blocks and the Represent the Amount activity page from their Activity Book. Read the directions with them.

Objectives

- Use concrete objects or sketches to represent a quantity up through 10.

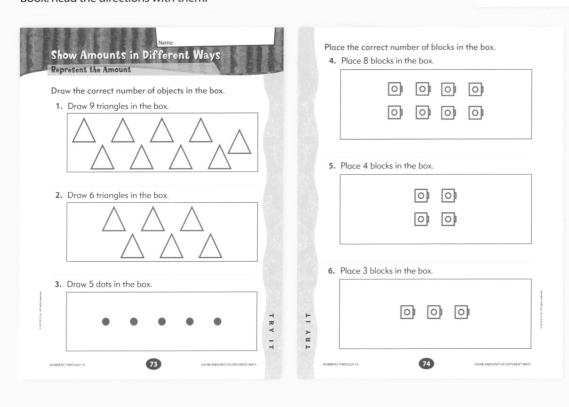

CHECKPOINT

Objectives

Print the Checkpoint. Students will take a performance-based assessment. Read the directions and problems to students. Use the answer key to score the Checkpoint, and then enter the results online.

Gather the blocks. For Problems 1–3, lay out 9 blocks in a row. For Problems 4–6, lay out 8 blocks in a row.

- Use concrete objects or sketches to represent a quantity up through 10.

Name _____ Date _____

Checkpoint Answer Key

Part 1

Read each problem and follow the directions

1. Count aloud starting with the first heart. Write the number of hearts in the group.
(1 point)

♡♡♡♡♡♡♡♡♡ **9** hearts

2. Count aloud starting with the last heart. Write the number of hearts in the group
(1 point)

9 hearts ♡♡♡♡♡♡♡♡♡

3. Did changing the counting direction change the number of hearts? Circle your answer.
(1 point)

A. Yes   (B) No

Name _____ Date _____

4. Count aloud starting with the first cube. Write the number of cubes in the group.
(1 point)

▱▱▱▱▱▱▱▱ **8** cubes

5. Count aloud starting with the last cube. Write the number of cubes in the group.
(1 point)

8 cubes ▱▱▱▱▱▱▱▱

6. Did changing the counting direction change the number of cubes? Circle your answer.
(1 point)

A. Yes   (B) No

Give students Part 2 of the assessment.

Name _____ Date _____

Part 2

Read each problem and follow the directions.

(1 point)
7. Count aloud. How many balloons are there?

🎈🎈🎈🎈🎈🎈🎈🎈

A. 7   (B) 8   C. 9

(1 point)
8. Count aloud the number of bugs.

Students count aloud from 1 to 7.

(1 point)
9. Count aloud. How many crayons are there?

Students count aloud from 1 to 6.

(1 point)
10. Draw 9 dots in the box.

● ● ● ● ● ● ● ● ●

Name _____ Date _____

(1 point)
11. Draw 7 dots in the box.

● ● ● ● ● ● ●

(1 point)
12. Show 5 snap cubes in the box.

(1 point)
13. Show 6 snap cubes in the box.

SHOW AMOUNTS IN DIFFERENT WAYS **111**

Write Numerals 1 Through 10

TIME What Do You Do?	5 minutes	ONLINE
GET READY Write Numerals Through 5	5 minutes	ONLINE
LEARN Write Numerals Through 10	15 minutes	ONLINE
LEARN Count and Write	5 minutes	OFFLINE
TRY IT Know Your Numerals Through 10	10 minutes	OFFLINE

▶ Lesson Objectives

- Write numerals from 1 through 10.
- Identify the time to the nearest hour of everyday events (for example, lunchtime is 12 o'clock; bedtime is 8 o'clock at night).

▶ Prerequisite Skills

Write numerals from 1 through 5.

▶ Content Background

Students will count and write numbers though 10.

In mathematics, the word *number* represents the quantity, and the word *numeral* represents the written symbol. So numerals, such as 0, 1, 2, and 3, symbolically represent numbers, or quantities. In everyday language, we say *number* to describe both the symbol and the quantity. As you speak with students, you may use *number* only. This lesson is titled "Write Numerals 1 Through 10" to convey correct mathematical terminology.

Keywords   **numeral** – a symbol that stands for a number

Materials to Gather

SUPPLIED

Count and Write activity page
Know Your Numerals Through 10
   activity page

ALSO NEEDED

paper, wide-line handwriting – 2 sheets

ONLINE
5min

GET READY Write Numerals Through 5

Students will practice counting sets of up through 5 objects. They will watch a virtual pencil write the number of objects in each set.

Objectives

- Write numerals from 1 through 5.

Tips

To prevent students from skipping an object or counting an object twice, have students touch each object on-screen as they count it.

LEARN Write Numerals Through 10

ONLINE 15min

Objectives

- Write numerals from 1 through 10.

Students will learn to write the numbers 1 through 10 by watching a virtual pencil write each number. Students will practice writing each number on handwriting paper.

Gather the wide-line handwriting paper.

1. Click Follow the Pencil and follow the on-screen directions.
2. After students watch the virtual pencil write the number on each screen, have students practice writing the number on the handwriting paper.

LEARN Count and Write

OFFLINE 5min

Objectives

- Write numerals from 1 through 10.

Students will practice writing numbers through 10. Give students the Count and Write activity page from their Activity Book and read the directions with them.

Tips

Check that students are gripping the pencil correctly and holding it at a slant when writing the numbers.

Name:

Write Numerals 1 Through 10

Count and Write

Write the number of objects shown in each picture.

1. 7
2. 5
3. 9
4. 10

NUMBERS THROUGH 10   75   WRITE NUMERALS 1 THROUGH 10

5. 6
6. 3
7. 8
8. 4

NUMBERS THROUGH 10   76   WRITE NUMERALS 1 THROUGH 10

OFFLINE
10min

Objectives

- Write numerals from 1 through 10.

Students will count objects in a picture and write the number that represents each amount. Give students the Know Your Numerals Through 10 activity page from their Activity Book and read the directions with them.

Name:

Write Numerals 1 Through 10
Know Your Numerals Through 10

Look at the picture. Write the answer to each problem.

1. Count the apples. Write the number.
    8

2. Count the chairs. Write the number.
    4

3. Count the empty plates. Write the number.
    3

4. Count the vases. Write the number.
    1

5. Count the flowers. Write the number.
    7

TRY IT

NUMBERS THROUGH 10   77   WRITE NUMERALS 1 THROUGH 10

Read each problem and write the answer.

6. Write the number zero.
    0

7. Write the number nine.
    9

8. Write the number two.
    2

9. Write the number five.
    5

10. Write the number six.
    6

TRY IT

NUMBERS THROUGH 10   78   WRITE NUMERALS 1 THROUGH 10

More, Fewer, and Equal

Lesson Overview		
TIME Order the Events in a Day	5 minutes	ONLINE
GET READY Show the Number	10 minutes	ONLINE
LEARN Count and Compare	15 minutes	OFFLINE
TRY IT Compare Objects in Groups	5 minutes	OFFLINE
CHECKPOINT	5 minutes	OFFLINE

▶ Lesson Objectives

- Given two or more sets that have 10 or fewer objects, identify which set has more or fewer objects than another set, or which sets have an equal number of objects.
- Identify the time to the nearest hour of everyday events (for example, lunchtime is 12 o'clock; bedtime is 8 o'clock at night).

▶ Prerequisite Skills

Use concrete objects or sketches to represent a quantity up through 10.

▶ Common Errors and Misconceptions

- Students might start counting before or after pointing to the first object in a group. Or they might stop counting before or after they point to the last object. Students should point to each object as they count it.
- Students might have difficulty counting only certain items in a group if the items in the group are similar. For example, in a group of green and blue blocks, students might have difficulty counting only the green blocks.
- Students might say more than one number for each object when counting objects in a group. Or they might skip objects. Students should point to each object and say exactly one number. Then they should point to the next object and say exactly one number, and so on.
- Students might use an incorrect counting sequence, such as "one, two, four, six, ten."

▶ Content Background

Students will learn to compare groups of objects using the words *more*, *fewer*, and *equal*.

A set is a group of objects. Set is a mathematical term for group. You may use set or group interchangeably in conversation with students.

Materials to Gather

SUPPLIED

blocks – B (10 red, 10 blue)

Count and Compare activity page

Compare Objects in Groups activity page

Checkpoint (printout)

ALSO NEEDED

crayons

compare – to find the similarities or differences among sizes, values, or amounts

equal – the relationship of expressions, numbers, or amounts that have the same value

fewer – a lesser number than another

fewest – the least number among three or more

more – a greater number or amount than another

most – the greatest number or amount among three or more

GET READY Show the Number

ONLINE
10min

Objectives

- Use concrete objects or sketches to represent a quantity up through 10.

Students will use blocks to represent amounts through 10. Gather the blocks. Students can use either the red or blue blocks for this activity.

1. Read aloud the directions on the first card.

2. **Say:** Place the correct number of blocks in a group.

3. Have students click the icon on the upper right of the card to see if they have placed the correct number of blocks.

4. If necessary, help students correct their answer. Point to the blocks on-screen as they place one block for each.

5. Click the Next Card arrow. Follow the on-screen directions and repeat Steps 2–4 for each card in the deck.

LEARN Count and Compare

OFFLINE
15min

Objectives

- Given two or more sets that have 10 or fewer objects, identify which set has more or fewer objects than another set, or which sets have an equal number of objects.

Students will use the words *more*, *fewer*, and *equal* to compare groups of objects. Gather the blocks, crayons, and Count and Compare activity page. Lay out 4 red blocks in a row. Below the red blocks, lay out 3 blue blocks in a row. The first 3 red blocks should each align vertically with exactly 1 blue block.

1. Point to each pair of blue blocks and red blocks.

   Say: Each blue block matches with 1 red block.

   Point to the last red block.

   Say: There is no blue block to match with this red block. There are *more* red blocks.

2. Clear the work area. Lay out 5 red blocks in a row. Below the red blocks, lay out 7 blue blocks in a row.

   Ask: Which group has more blocks?
   ANSWER: blue

   Explain that because some blue blocks do not have matching red blocks, there are more blue blocks.

Tips

If students have difficulty determining which group has more or fewer objects, have them match objects from one group to the other group. If objects remain in the first group but not in the second, then the first group has more objects. If objects remain in the second group but not in the first, then the first group has fewer objects. If the objects in the two groups are matched one-to-one with no remaining objects, then the groups have an equal number of objects.

3. Clear the work area. Lay out 2 red blocks in a row. Below the red blocks, lay out 4 blue blocks in a row.

   Point to each pair of blue blocks and red blocks.

   Say: Each red block matches with 1 blue block.

   Point to the last 2 blue blocks.

   Say: There are some blue blocks that do not have matching red blocks. There are *fewer* red blocks.

4. Clear the work area. Lay out 8 red blocks and 3 blue blocks.

   Ask: Which group has fewer blocks?
   ANSWER: blue

   Explain that because some red blocks do not have matching blue blocks, there are fewer blue blocks.

5. Clear the work area. Lay out 4 red blocks in a row. Below the red blocks, lay out 4 blue blocks in a row.

   Point to each pair of red blocks and blue blocks.

   Say: Each red block matches with 1 blue block. The number of red blocks and blue blocks is the same, or *equal*.

Give students the crayons and the Count and Compare activity page from their Activity Book. Read the directions with them. Work together to complete the problems. Problems 3–6 compare 3 groups. If students have difficulty, explain that they should approach these problems in the same way as they did Problems 1 and 2. For example, in Problem 4, students should choose the group for which every bee has a match when compared to either of the other groups.

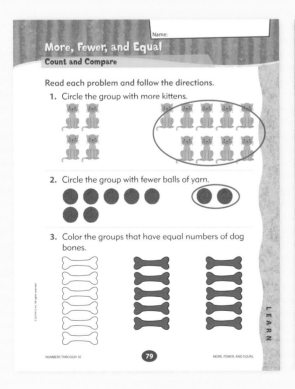

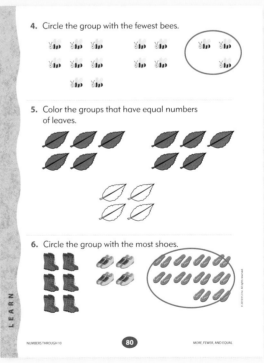

Objectives

Students will practice comparing groups of objects. Then they will answer story problems that ask them to compare groups. Give students the Compare Objects in Groups activity page from their Activity Book and read the directions with them.

- Given two or more sets that have 10 or fewer objects, identify which set has more or fewer objects than another set, or which sets have an equal number of objects.

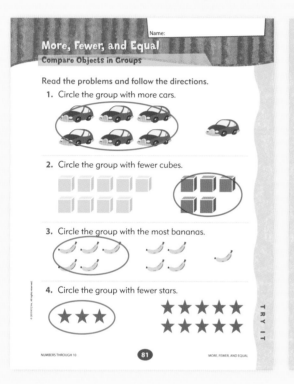

CHECKPOINT

Objectives

Print the Checkpoint and have students complete it on their own. Read the directions, problems, and answer choices to students if necessary. Use the answer key to score the Checkpoint, and then enter the results online.

- Given two or more sets that have 10 or fewer objects, identify which set has more or fewer objects than another set, or which sets have an equal number of objects.

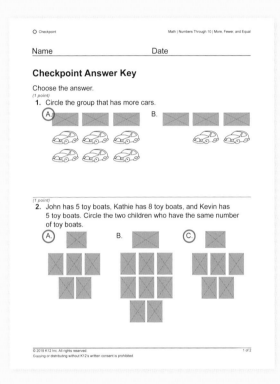

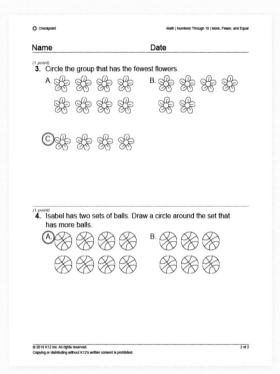

Compare and Order Groups

Lesson Overview

TIME Winnie's Favorite Things to Do	5 minutes	ONLINE
GET READY Compare Rain Gear	5 minutes	ONLINE
LEARN Compare Groups	15 minutes	ONLINE
LEARN Order Groups	10 minutes	ONLINE
TRY IT More, Fewer, Most, and Least	5 minutes	OFFLINE

▶ Lesson Objectives

- Recognize that numbers with greater values describe sets with more objects in them than numbers with lesser values (for sets of 10 or fewer objects).
- Order a group of no more than 10 objects, such as number tiles or stacks of counting chips.
- Identify the time to the nearest hour of everyday events (for example, lunchtime is 12 o'clock; bedtime is 8 o'clock at night).

▶ Prerequisite Skills

- Given two or more sets that have 10 or fewer objects, identify which set has more or fewer objects than another set, or which sets have an equal number of objects.
- Use concrete objects or sketches to represent a quantity up through 10.

▶ Common Errors and Misconceptions

- Students might start counting before or after pointing to the first object in a group. Or they might stop counting before or after they point to the last object. Students should point to each object as they count it.
- Students might say more than one number for each object when counting objects in a group. Or they might skip objects. Students should point to each object and say exactly one number. Then they should point to the next object and say exactly one number, and so on.
- Students might have difficulty counting only certain items in a group if the items in the group are similar. For example, in a group of green and blue blocks, students might have difficulty counting only the green blocks.
- Students might use an incorrect counting sequence, such as "one, two, four, six, ten."

▶ Content Background

Students will learn that numbers with greater values describe groups with more objects than do numbers with lesser values. For example, 3 represents more objects than 2. Students will also order groups of up through 10 objects.

A set is a group of objects. *Set* is a mathematical term for *group*. You may use *set* or *group* interchangeably in conversation with students.

Materials to Gather

SUPPLIED

More, Fewer, Most, and Least activity page

greater – larger in number or amount than another
greatest – the largest in value of three or more numbers or amounts
least – the smallest in value of three or more numbers or amounts
lesser – smaller in number or amount than another

GET READY Compare Rain Gear

ONLINE 5 min

Students will practice comparing groups of objects using the words *more*, *fewer*, and *equal*.

Objectives

- Given two or more sets that have 10 or fewer objects, identify which set has more or fewer objects than another set, or which sets have an equal number of objects.
- Use concrete objects or sketches to represent a quantity up through 10.

LEARN Compare Groups

ONLINE 15 min

Students will compare two or more groups of school supplies. For each group, students will see a picture of the objects as well as a numeral. Students will learn that greater numerals represent groups with more objects.

Objectives

- Recognize that numbers with greater values describe sets with more objects in them than numbers with lesser values (for sets of 10 or fewer objects).

Tips

Have students use counting objects to represent the groups online.

LEARN Order Groups

ONLINE 10 min

Students will order groups of shapes from *least* to *most* and *most* to *least*. Students will learn that groups can be ordered from left to right, right to left, and up and down.

Objectives

- Order a group of no more than 10 objects, such as number tiles or stacks of counting chips.

TRY IT More, Fewer, Most, and Least

Objectives

Students will practice comparing and ordering groups of objects. Give students the More, Fewer, Most, and Least activity page from their Activity Book and read the directions with them.

- Recognize that numbers with greater values describe sets with more objects in them than numbers with lesser values (for sets of 10 or fewer objects).

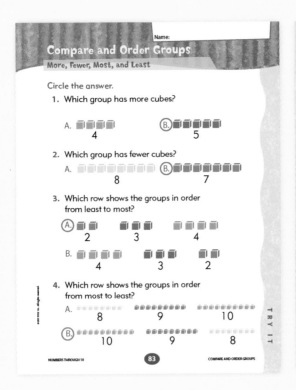

Compare and Order Groups

More, Fewer, Most, and Least

Circle the answer.

1. Which group has more cubes?

   A. ▢▢▢▢ 4   B. ▢▢▢▢▢ 5

2. Which group has fewer cubes?

   A. ▢▢▢▢▢▢▢▢ 8   B. ▢▢▢▢▢▢▢ 7

3. Which row shows the groups in order from least to most?

   A. ▢▢ 2   ▢▢▢ 3   ▢▢▢ 4

   B. ▢▢▢ 4   ▢▢▢ 3   ▢▢ 2

4. Which row shows the groups in order from most to least?

   A. ▢▢▢▢▢▢▢▢ 8   ▢▢▢▢▢▢▢▢▢ 9   ▢▢▢▢▢▢▢▢▢▢ 10

   B. ▢▢▢▢▢▢▢▢▢▢ 10   ▢▢▢▢▢▢▢▢▢ 9   ▢▢▢▢▢▢▢▢ 8

NUMBERS THROUGH 10   83   COMPARE AND ORDER GROUPS

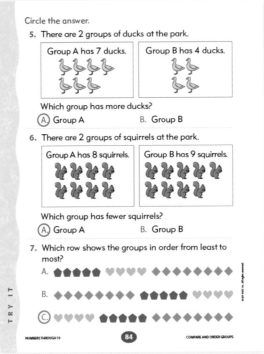

Circle the answer.

5. There are 2 groups of ducks at the park.

   | Group A has 7 ducks. | Group B has 4 ducks. |

   Which group has more ducks?

   A. Group A   B. Group B

6. There are 2 groups of squirrels at the park.

   | Group A has 8 squirrels. | Group B has 9 squirrels. |

   Which group has fewer squirrels?

   A. Group A   B. Group B

7. Which row shows the groups in order from least to most?

   A. ⬠⬠⬠ ♥♥♥♥ ◆◆◆◆◆◆

   B. ◆◆◆◆◆◆ ⬠⬠⬠ ♥♥♥♥

   C. ♥♥♥♥ ⬠⬠⬠ ◆◆◆◆◆◆

NUMBERS THROUGH 10   84   COMPARE AND ORDER GROUPS

Describe and Order Groups by Number

Lesson Overview

TIME Alexander's Day	5 minutes	ONLINE
GET READY Compare Groups of Animals	5 minutes	ONLINE
LEARN Describe Groups with Numbers	10 minutes	OFFLINE
LEARN Order Groups of 10 or Fewer	10 minutes	OFFLINE
TRY IT Describe and Order Groups	5 minutes	OFFLINE
CHECKPOINT	5 minutes	OFFLINE

▶ Lesson Objectives

- Recognize that numbers with greater values describe sets with more objects in them than numbers with lesser values do (for sets of 10 or fewer objects).
- Order a group of no more than 10 objects, such as index cards or stacks of counting chips.
- Identify the time to the nearest hour of everyday events (for example, lunchtime is 12 o'clock; bedtime is 8 o'clock at night).

▶ Prerequisite Skills

- Given two or more sets that have 10 or fewer objects, identify which set has more or fewer objects than another set, or which sets have an equal number of objects.
- Use concrete objects or sketches to represent a quantify up through 10.

▶ Common Errors and Misconceptions

- Students might start counting before or after pointing to the first object in a group. Or they might stop counting before or after they point to the last object. Students should point to each object as they count it.
- Students might say more than one number for each object when counting objects in a group. Or they might skip objects. Students should point to each object and say exactly one number. Then they should point to the next object and say exactly one number, and so on.
- Students might use an incorrect counting sequence, such as "one, two, four, six, ten."

▶ Advance Preparation

Number index cards 1 through 10. Label two other index cards with the following words: **fewest** and **most**.

Materials to Gather

SUPPLIED

blocks – B (10 of each color)

blocks – O (2 red, 6 blue, 4 yellow)

Describe and Order Groups activity page

Checkpoint (printout)

ALSO NEEDED

index cards – numbered 1 through 10

index cards – labeled **most** and **fewest**

▶ Content Background

Students will use blocks to practice comparing and ordering groups of objects. They will continue to learn that numbers with greater values describe groups with more objects than do numbers with lesser values. For example, 3 represents more objects than 2.

A set is a group of objects. *Set* is a mathematical term for group. You may use set or group interchangeably in conversation with students.

Keywords   **order numbers** – to place numbers in a sequence from least to greatest or greatest to least

---

GET READY Compare Groups of Animals

ONLINE 5 min

Students will practice using the words *more*, *fewer*, and *equal* by comparing groups of animals.

Objectives

- Given two or more sets that have 10 or fewer objects, identify which set has more or fewer objects than another set, or which sets have an equal number of objects.

Tips

Provide students with counting objects to model the groups of animals on the screen.

LEARN Describe Groups with Numbers

OFFLINE 10 min

Students will use index cards to describe groups of blocks. Then they will compare the groups to learn that greater numbers describe groups with more objects.
   Gather the circle blocks and index cards numbered 1 through 10.

1. Have students arrange the index cards in order from 1 through 10.

   Say: Point to each number and count from 1 to 10.

   | 1 | 2 | 3 | 4 | 5 | 6 | 7 | 8 | 9 | 10 |

Objectives

- Recognize that numbers with greater values describe sets with more objects in them than numbers with lesser values (for sets of 10 or fewer objects).

Tips

If students have difficulty choosing the group with more circles, align the circles in each group so that they match one-to-one. Explain that the group with unmatched circles has more objects in it.

2. Show one group of 4 circles and one group of 7 circles under the index cards. Use a different color for each group.

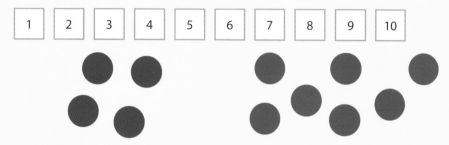

3. Point to the group of 7 circles. Have students count the circles.

Ask: How many circles are in this group?
ANSWER: 7

Say: Move that index card next to the group.

4. Point to the group of 4 circles. Have students count the circles.

Ask: How many circles are in this group?
ANSWER: 4

Say: Move that index card next to the group.

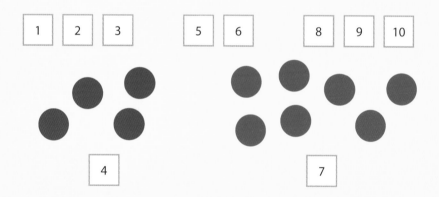

5. **Ask:** Which group has more?
ANSWER: the group with 7 circles

6. **Ask:** How do you know that the group of 7 circles has more objects than the group of 4 circles?
ANSWER: 7 is a greater number than 4.

7. Have students return the index cards to their positions in the row.

8. Clear the groups of circles from the work area. Using a different color for each group, display a group of 8 circles and a group of 3 circles. Label each group with the appropriate index card.

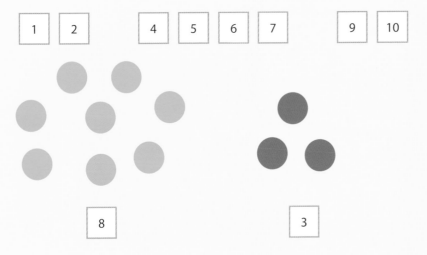

9. Point to the index cards under the groups.
   Ask: This group has 8 circles and this group has 3 circles. Without counting the circles, which group has more?
   ANSWER: the group of 8 circles

10. **Ask:** How do you know the group of 8 circles has more than the group of 3 circles?
    ANSWER: I know that 8 is a greater number than 3.

11. Repeat Steps 8–10 with groups of 6 and 5 circles.

LEARN Order Groups of 10 or Fewer	Objectives

Students will order groups of cubes. Before ordering, they will first identify which group has the fewest cubes and which group has the most cubes.
   Gather the cubes and index cards labeled **most** and **fewest**.

- Order a group of no more than 10 objects, such as index cards or stacks of counting chips.

1. Display a group of 2 red cubes, a group of 6 blue cubes, and a group of 4 yellow cubes.

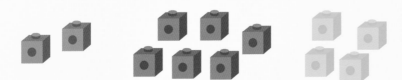

2. **Ask:** How many cubes are in each group?
   ANSWER: 2, 6, 4

3. Have students put the cubes in rows as shown. Align the rows at the left so that the group with the most cubes extends beyond the other groups.

4. **Ask:** Which group has the most cubes?
   ANSWER: blue
   Say: The group that is the longest has the most cubes.

5. Place the **most** card in the work area to the left of students.
   Say: Place the group with the most cubes near the word **most**.

6. **Ask:** Which group has the fewest cubes?
   ANSWER: red
   Say: The group that is the shortest has the fewest cubes.

7. Place the **fewest** card in the work area to the right of students.
   Say: Place the group with the fewest cubes near the word **fewest**.

8. Point to the group with 4 cubes.
   Ask: How many cubes are in this group?
   ANSWER: 4
   Say: This group has fewer cubes than the group with 6. This group has more cubes than the group with 2. So move this group in between the other groups.

9. **Say:** The groups are in order from most to fewest—6 is the greatest number and 2 is the least number.

10. Switch the index cards so the **fewest** card is at the left and the **most** card is at the right.

11. Have students order the groups of cubes from fewest to most.

12. **Say:** The groups are in order from fewest to most—2 is the least number and 6 is the greatest number.

TRY IT Describe and Order Groups

OFFLINE 5 min

Students will practice comparing the number of objects in groups. They will also practice ordering from most to fewest and from fewest to most. Give students the Describe and Order Groups activity page from their Activity Book and read the directions with them.

Objectives

- Order a group of no more than 10 objects, such as index cards or stacks of counting chips.

Tips

If students have difficulty deciding which group has more objects, have them draw lines matching each object in one group to exactly one object in the other group. The group with un-matched objects has more.

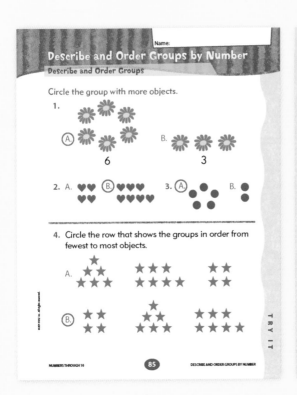

Describe and Order Groups by Number
Describe and Order Groups

Circle the group with more objects.

1.

   (A)   B.

     6   3

2. A.   (B)   3. (A)   B.

4. Circle the row that shows the groups in order from fewest to most objects.

A.

(B)

T R Y   I T

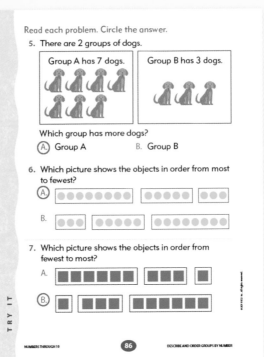

Read each problem. Circle the answer.

5. There are 2 groups of dogs.

Group A has 7 dogs.	Group B has 3 dogs.

Which group has more dogs?

(A) Group A   B. Group B

6. Which picture shows the objects in order from most to fewest?

(A)

B.

7. Which picture shows the objects in order from fewest to most?

A.

(B)

T R Y   I T

CHECKPOINT

OFFLINE
5min

Print the Checkpoint and have students complete it on their own. Read the directions, problems, and answer choices to students if necessary. Use the answer key to score the Checkpoint, and then enter the results online.

Objectives

- Order a group of no more than 10 objects, such as index cards or stacks of counting chips.

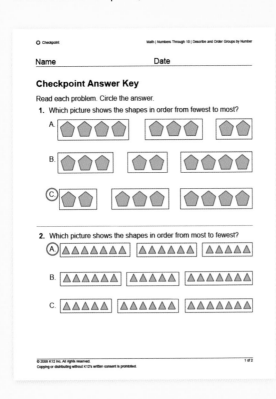

Name   **Date**

Checkpoint Answer Key

Read each problem. Circle the answer.

1. Which picture shows the shapes in order from fewest to most?

A.

B.

(C.)

2. Which picture shows the shapes in order from most to fewest?

(A)

B.

C.

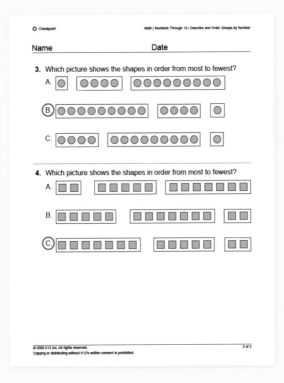

Name   **Date**

3. Which picture shows the shapes in order from most to fewest?

A.

(B)

C.

4. Which picture shows the shapes in order from most to fewest?

A.

B.

(C)

Write Numbers to Describe Groups

Lesson Overview

TIME Your Activities During the Day	5 minutes	ONLINE
GET READY Groups with More	10 minutes	ONLINE
LEARN Write Numbers 1–10	10 minutes	OFFLINE
TRY IT Write How Many	10 minutes	OFFLINE
CHECKPOINT	10 minutes	OFFLINE

▶ Lesson Objectives

- Write numerals from 1 through 10.
- Recognize that numbers with greater values describe sets with more objects in them than numbers with lesser values (for sets of 10 or fewer objects).
- Identify the time to the nearest hour of everyday events (for example, lunchtime is 12 o'clock; bedtime is 8 o'clock at night).

▶ Prerequisite Skills

- Write numerals from 1 through 5.
- Given two or more sets that have 10 or fewer objects, identify which set has more or fewer objects than another set, or which sets have an equal number of objects.

▶ Content Background

Students will write numbers to describe groups. They will recognize that numbers with greater values describe groups with more objects than do numbers with lesser values. For example, 3 represents more objects than 2.

A *set* is a group of objects. *Set* is a mathematical term for *group*. You may use *set* or *group* interchangeably in conversation with students.

Materials to Gather

SUPPLIED

blocks – B (10 of any color)

Write Numbers 1–10 activity page

Write How Many: Part 1 activity page

Write How Many: Part 2 activity page

Checkpoint (printout)

GET READY Groups with More

ONLINE 10 min

Objectives

Students will practice using numbers to compare groups of objects. They will count the shapes in groups. Then they will use the numbers to decide which group has more objects. Students will learn that the group with the greater number is the group with more objects.

- Recognize that numbers with greater values describe sets with more objects in them than numbers with lesser values (for sets of 10 or fewer objects).

Tips

To prevent students from skipping an object or counting an object twice, have students touch each object online as they count it.

LEARN Write Numbers 1-10

OFFLINE 10 min

Objectives

Students will count the objects in a group. Then they will write the number that tells how many. Give students the blocks and the Write Numbers 1–10 activity page from their Activity Book. Read the directions with them.

- Write numerals from 1 through 10.

Tips

To prevent students from counting the same object twice in Problems 5–8, have them cross out each object as they count it.

TRY IT Write How Many

Students will practice writing the number that tells how many objects are in a group. Then they will use numbers to help them compare groups of objects. Give students the Write How Many activity pages from their Activity Book and read the directions with them.

Objectives

- Write numerals from 1 through 10.
- Recognize that numbers with greater values describe sets with more objects in them than numbers with lesser values (for sets of 10 or fewer objects).

Tips

If students have difficulty deciding which group has more objects, have them draw lines matching each object in one group to exactly one object in the other group. The group with un-matched objects has more.

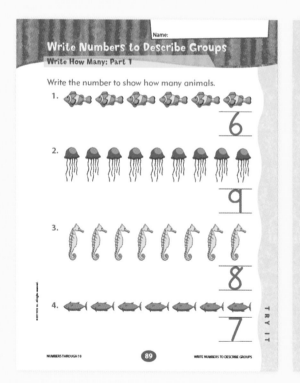

Name:

Write Numbers to Describe Groups
Write How Many: Part 1

Write the number to show how many animals.

1. 6

2. 9

3. 8

4. 7

NUMBERS THROUGH 10   89   WRITE NUMBERS TO DESCRIBE GROUPS

TRY IT

5. Write the number nine.

9

6. Write the number two.

2

7. Write the number ten.

10

8. Write the number four.

4

NUMBERS THROUGH 10   90   WRITE NUMBERS TO DESCRIBE GROUPS

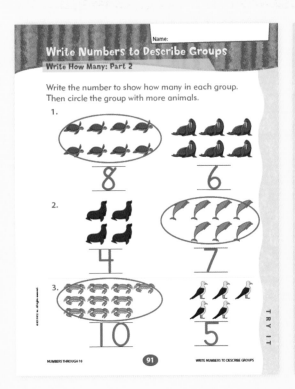

Write Numbers to Describe Groups

Write How Many: Part 2

Write the number to show how many in each group.
Then circle the group with more animals.

1.

8 6

2.

4 7

3.

10 5

TRY IT

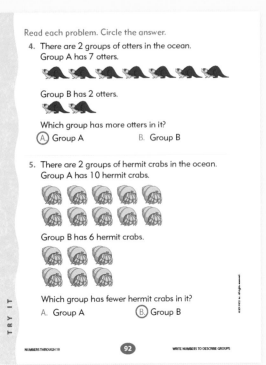

Read each problem. Circle the answer.

4. There are 2 groups of otters in the ocean.
Group A has 7 otters.

Group B has 2 otters.

Which group has more otters in it?

  (A.) Group A   B. Group B

5. There are 2 groups of hermit crabs in the ocean.
Group A has 10 hermit crabs.

Group B has 6 hermit crabs.

Which group has fewer hermit crabs in it?

  A. Group A   (B.) Group B

TRY IT

OFFLINE

10 min

CHECKPOINT

Objectives

Print the Checkpoint and have students complete it on their own. Read the directions, problems, and answer choices to students if necessary. Use the answer key to score the Checkpoint, and then enter the results online.

- Write numerals from 1 through 10.
- Recognize that numbers with greater values describe sets with more objects in them than numbers with lesser values (for sets of 10 or fewer objects).

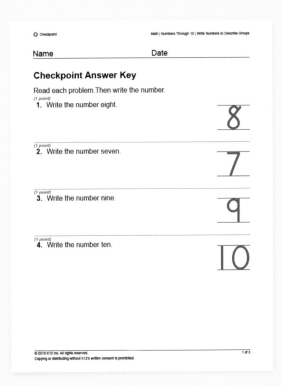

Checkpoint   Math | Numbers Through 10 | Write Numbers to Describe Groups

Name   Date

Checkpoint Answer Key

Read each problem. Then write the number.
(1 point)
1. Write the number eight. 8

(1 point)
2. Write the number seven. 7

(1 point)
3. Write the number nine. 9

(1 point)
4. Write the number ten. 10

   1 of 3

Name _____ Date _____

Read each problem. Circle the answer.

(1 point)

5. Paul has 5 rabbits.

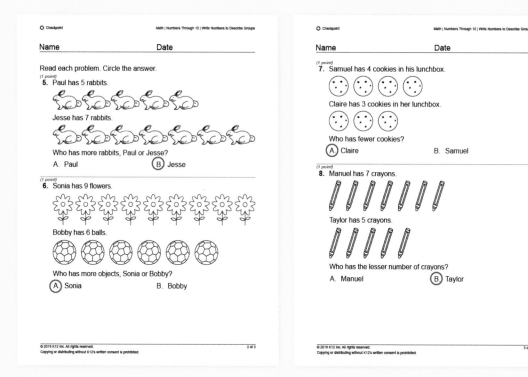

Jesse has 7 rabbits.

Who has more rabbits, Paul or Jesse?

A. Paul   (B) Jesse

(1 point)

6. Sonia has 9 flowers.

Bobby has 6 balls.

Who has more objects, Sonia or Bobby?

(A) Sonia   B. Bobby

Name _____ Date _____

(1 point)

7. Samuel has 4 cookies in his lunchbox.

Claire has 3 cookies in her lunchbox.

Who has fewer cookies?

(A) Claire   B. Samuel

(1 point)

8. Manuel has 7 crayons.

Taylor has 5 crayons.

Who has the lesser number of crayons?

A. Manuel   (B) Taylor

Unit Review

Lesson Overview

UNIT REVIEW Look Back	20 minutes	ONLINE
UNIT REVIEW Checkpoint Practice	10 minutes	OFFLINE
UNIT REVIEW Prepare for the Checkpoint		

▶ Unit Objectives

This lesson reviews the following objectives:

- Count aloud a number of objects up through 10.
- Demonstrate that counting 10 or fewer objects can occur from left to right, right to left, or in any order as long as all the items are counted once.
- Use concrete objects or sketches to represent a quantity up through 10.
- Order a group of no more than 10 objects, such as number tiles or stacks of counting chips.
- Write numerals from 1 through 10.
- Given two or more sets that have 10 or fewer objects, identify which set has more or fewer objects than another set, or which sets have an equal number of objects.
- Recognize that numbers with greater values describe sets with more objects in them than numbers with lesser values (for sets of 10 or fewer objects).

Materials to Gather

SUPPLIED

Checkpoint Practice activity page

▶ Advance Preparation

In this lesson, students will have an opportunity to review previous activities in the Numbers Through 10 unit. Look at the suggested activities in Unit Review: Prepare for the Checkpoint online and gather any needed materials.

Keywords		
	compare	lesser
	count	more
	equal	most
	fewer	number
	fewest	numeral
	greater	order numbers
	greatest	represent
	least	

UNIT REVIEW Look Back

ONLINE 20min

Objectives

- Review unit objectives.

Students learned about numbers through 10. They counted through 10 and made groups of 0 through 10 objects. Students learned that they can count objects in any order as long as they count each object exactly one time. They also learned to read and write the numerals through 10.

Students learned to compare and order groups of up through 10 objects. They learned that greater numbers describe groups with more objects. Students will review these concepts to prepare for the Unit Checkpoint.

UNIT REVIEW Checkpoint Practice

OFFLINE 10min

Objectives

- Review unit objectives.

Students will complete a Checkpoint Practice activity page to prepare for the Unit Checkpoint. If necessary, read the directions, questions, and answer choices to students. Have students answer the problems on their own. Carefully review the answers with students.

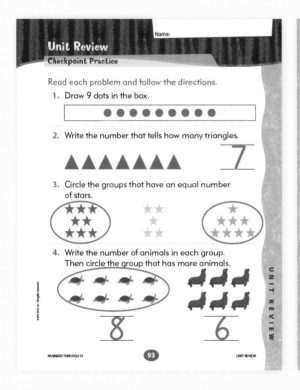

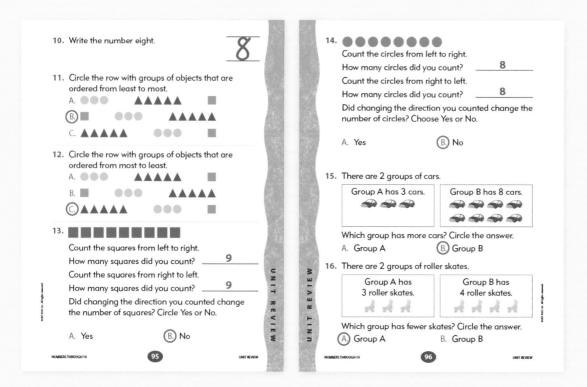

10. Write the number eight. 8

11. Circle the row with groups of objects that are ordered from least to most.
    A. ●●● ▲▲▲▲▲ ■
    (B.) ■ ●●● ▲▲▲▲▲
    C. ▲▲▲▲▲ ●●● ■

12. Circle the row with groups of objects that are ordered from most to least.
    A. ●●● ▲▲▲▲▲ ■
    B. ■ ●●● ▲▲▲▲▲
    (C.) ▲▲▲▲▲ ●●● ■

13. ■■■■■■■■■
    Count the squares from left to right.
    How many squares did you count? ___9___
    Count the squares from right to left.
    How many squares did you count? ___9___
    Did changing the direction you counted change the number of squares? Circle Yes or No.

    A. Yes   (B.) No

14. ●●●●●●●●
    Count the circles from left to right.
    How many circles did you count? ___8___
    Count the circles from right to left.
    How many circles did you count? ___8___
    Did changing the direction you counted change the number of circles? Choose Yes or No.

    A. Yes   (B.) No

15. There are 2 groups of cars.

    | Group A has 3 cars. | Group B has 8 cars. |

    Which group has more cars? Circle the answer.
    A. Group A   (B.) Group B

16. There are 2 groups of roller skates.

    | Group A has 3 roller skates. | Group B has 4 roller skates. |

    Which group has fewer skates? Circle the answer.
    (A) Group A   B. Group B

⇥ UNIT REVIEW Prepare for the Checkpoint

What you do next depends on how students performed in the previous activity, Unit Review: Checkpoint Practice. If students had difficulty with any of the problems, complete the appropriate review activity listed in the table online.

Unit Checkpoint

▶ Unit Objectives

This Unit Checkpoint assesses the following objectives:

- Count aloud a number of objects up through 10.
- Demonstrate that counting 10 or fewer objects can occur from left to right, right to left, or in any order as long as all the items are counted once.
- Use concrete objects or sketches to represent a quantity up through 10.
- Order a group of no more than 10 objects, such as number tiles or stacks of counting chips.
- Write numerals from 1 through 10.
- Given two or more sets, that have 10 or fewer objects, identify which set has more or fewer objects than another set, or which sets have an equal number of objects.
- Recognize that numbers with greater values describe sets with more objects in them than numbers with lesser values do (for sets of 10 or fewer objects).

Materials to Gather

SUPPLIED

Unit Checkpoint (printout)

blocks – O (10 of any color)

UNIT CHECKPOINT Online

ONLINE 15 min

Students will complete this part of the Unit Checkpoint online. Read the directions, problems, and answer choices to students. If necessary, help students with keyboard or mouse operations.

Objectives

- Assess unit objectives.

UNIT CHECKPOINT Offline

Objectives

- Assess unit objectives.

Students will complete this part of the Unit Checkpoint offline. Print the Checkpoint and have students complete it on their own. Read the directions, problems, and answer choices to students, if necessary. Use the answer key to score the Checkpoint, and then enter the results online.

Gather the blocks. For Problem 9, lay out the blocks in a random arrangement.

Name _____ Date _____

Unit Checkpoint Answer Key

Part 1
Read each problem and follow the directions.

Use the pictures below for Problems 1–3

(0.5 point)
1. Count aloud starting with the first bunny. Write the number of bunnies in the group.

8

(0.5 point)
2. Count aloud starting with the last bunny. Write the number of bunnies in the group.

8

(0.5 point)
3. Did changing the counting direction change the number of bunnies? Circle the answer.

A. Yes   **B.** No

Name _____ Date _____

Use the pictures below for Problems 4–6
0.5 point
4. Count aloud starting with the first bunny. Write the number of bunnies in the group.

10

0.5 point
5. Count aloud starting with the last bunny. Write the number of bunnies in the group.

10

0.5 point
6. Did changing the counting direction change the number of bunnies? Circle the answer.

A. Yes   **B.** No

Name _____ Date _____

(1 point)
7. Look at the two groups of teddy bears. Which group has more teddy bears?

Group A   Group B

A. Group A   B. Group B

(1 point)
8. Draw 4 dots in the box.

(1 point)
9. Place 2 cubes in the box.

(1 point)
10. Write the number eight.

8

(1 point)
11. Write the number seven.

7

Calendar and Time

▶ Unit Objectives

- Name the days of the week.
- Demonstrate an understanding of the concepts of today, yesterday, and tomorrow.
- Identify tools that measure time of at least a day, such as a calendar, and describe what those tools measure (for example, a calendar measures days and weeks).
- Demonstrate an understanding of the concepts of day, week, and year.

- Identify tools that measure time within a day, such as a clock, and describe what those tools measure (for example, a clock measures minutes and hours).
- Demonstrate an understanding of the concepts of morning, afternoon, and evening.
- Identify the time to the nearest hour of everyday events (for example, lunch-time is 12 o'clock; bedtime is 8 o'clock at night).

▶ Unit Introduction

Students have completed either a Calendar or Time online activity at the start of each lesson in the previous units. In the Calendar activities, students have named and ordered the days of the week and the months of the year; identified *yesterday*, *today*, and *tomorrow* on the calendar; and found specific dates on a calendar.

In the Time activities, students learned about the clock and what it measures. They learned about clock faces and hands; identified the hour, minute, and second hands; and watched time pass on a clock to see how the movement of the minute hand affects the movement of the hour hand. They also learned about morning, afternoon, and evening. They learned the typical times in a day when certain activities occur (for example, students eat lunch around 12:00 noon). In this unit, students will review calendar and time concepts to prepare for the Unit Checkpoint.

Unit Review

▶ Unit Objectives

This lesson reviews the following objectives:

- Name the days of the week.
- Demonstrate an understanding of the concepts of today, yesterday, and tomorrow.
- Identify tools that measure time of at least a day, such as a calendar, and describe what those tools measure (for example, a calendar measures days and weeks).
- Demonstrate an understanding of the concepts of day, week, and year.
- Identify tools that measure time within a day, such as a clock, and describe what those tools measure (for example, a clock measures minutes and hours).
- Demonstrate an understanding of the concepts of morning, afternoon, and evening.
- Identify the time to the nearest hour of everyday events (for example, lunchtime is 12 o'clock; bedtime is 8 o'clock at night).

Materials to Gather

SUPPLIED

Checkpoint Practice activity page

ALSO NEEDED

crayons

▶ Advance Preparation

In this lesson, students will have an opportunity to review previous Calendar and Time activities. Look at the suggested activities in Unit Review: Prepare for the Checkpoint online and gather any needed materials.

Keywords

afternoon	night
calendar	nighttime
clock	noon
date	number
day	order times
days of the week	part of the day
daytime	second
evening	second hand
face of a clock	shorter
hand of a clock	tick marks
hour	time
hour hand	today
longer	tomorrow
minute	week
minute hand	year
month	yesterday
morning	

UNIT REVIEW **Look Back**

Students have completed either a Calendar or Time online activity at the start of each lesson in the previous units. In the Calendar activities, students have named and ordered the days of the week and the months of the year; identified *yesterday*, *today*, and *tomorrow* on the calendar; and found specific dates on a calendar.

In the Time activities, students learned about the clock and what it measures. They learned about clock faces and hands; identified the hour, minute, and second hands; and watched time pass on a clock to see how the movement of the minute hand affects the movement of the hour hand. They also learned about morning, afternoon, and evening. They learned the typical times in a day when certain activities occur (for example, students eat lunch around 12:00 noon). Students will review these concepts to prepare for the Unit Checkpoint.

UNIT REVIEW **Checkpoint Practice**

Students will complete a Checkpoint Practice activity page to prepare for the Unit Checkpoint. Have students answer the problems on their own. Carefully review the answers with students.

Gather the crayons. Have students use the crayons to complete Problems 1–4.

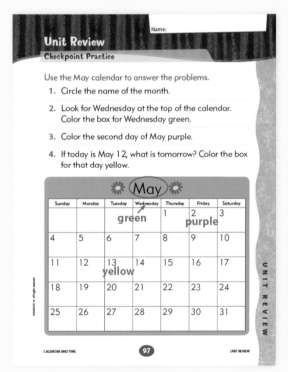

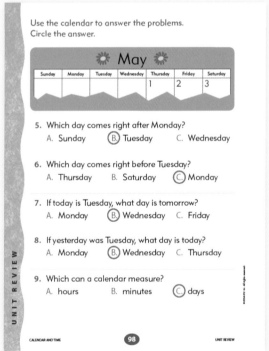

Read each problem and circle the answer.

10. Which tool can measure days?

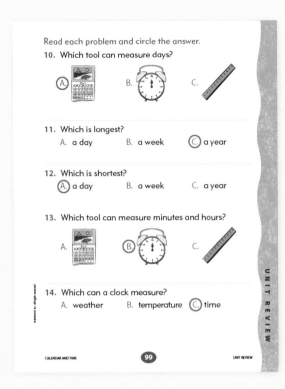

A. (circled - calendar)   B. (clock)   C. (ruler)

11. Which is longest?
   A. a day   B. a week   C. a year (circled)

12. Which is shortest?
   A. a day (circled)   B. a week   C. a year

13. Which tool can measure minutes and hours?

A. (calendar)   B. (circled - clock)   C. (ruler)

14. Which can a clock measure?
   A. weather   B. temperature   C. time (circled)

15. At what time of day do you wake up?

A. morning (circled)   B. afternoon   C. evening

16. About what time do you eat lunch?

A. 12:00 noon (circled)
B. 9:00 in the morning
C. 6:00 in the evening

→ UNIT REVIEW Prepare for the Checkpoint

What you do next depends on how students performed in the previous activity, Unit Review: Checkpoint Practice. If students had difficulty with any of the problems, complete the appropriate review activity listed in the table online.

Unit Checkpoint

Lesson Overview

UNIT CHECKPOINT Online	25 minutes	**ONLINE**
UNIT CHECKPOINT Offline	15 minutes	**OFFLINE**

▶ Unit Objectives

This lesson assesses the following objectives:

- Name the days of the week.
- Demonstrate an understanding of the concepts of today, yesterday, and tomorrow.
- Identify tools that measure time of at least a day, such as a calendar, and describe what those tools measure (for example, a calendar measures days and weeks).
- Demonstrate an understanding of the concepts of day, week, and year.
- Identify tools that measure time within a day, such as a clock, and describe what those tools measure (for example, a clock measures minutes and hours).
- Demonstrate an understanding of the concepts of morning, afternoon, and evening.
- Identify the time to the nearest hour of everyday events (for example, lunchtime is 12 o'clock; bedtime is 8 o'clock at night).

Materials to Gather

SUPPLIED
Unit Checkpoint (printout)

ALSO NEEDED
crayons

UNIT CHECKPOINT Online

ONLINE
25min

Objectives

- Assess unit objectives.

Students will complete this part of the Unit Checkpoint online. Read the directions, problems, and answer choices to students. If necessary, help students with keyboard or mouse operations.

UNIT CHECKPOINT Offline

OFFLINE
15min

Objectives

- Assess unit objectives.

Students will complete this part of the Unit Checkpoint offline. Print the Checkpoint and have students complete it on their own. Read the directions, problems, and answer choices to students, if necessary. Use the answer key to score the Checkpoint, and then enter the results online.

Gather the crayons. Have students use the crayons to complete Problems 1–5.

Name   Date

Unit Checkpoint Answer Key

Use the October calendar to answer Problems 1–5.

(1 point)
1. Circle the name of the month.

(1 point)
2. Look for Friday at the top of the calendar.
Color the box for Friday green.

(1 point)
3. Color the box for the 8th day of October purple.

(1 point)
4. If today is October 5, what is tomorrow?
Color the box for that day yellow.

(1 point)
5. If tomorrow is October 2, what is today?
Color the box for that day red.

					green ↓	
SUNDAY	**MONDAY**	**TUESDAY**	**WEDNESDAY**	**THURSDAY**	**FRIDAY**	**SATURDAY**
			1 red	2	3	4
5 yellow	6	7	8 purple	9	10	11
12	13	14	15	16	17	18
19	20	21	22	23	24	25
26	27	28	29	30	31	

(October is circled)

Name   Date

(2 points)
6. Name all the days of the week.

Award 1 point for naming 1–6 days, 2 points for all 7 days.

Read each problem and circle the answer.

(1 point)
7. Which day comes right before Friday?
    (A.) Thursday   B. Saturday   C. Monday

(1 point)
8. If yesterday was Wednesday, what day is today?
    A. Monday   B. Wednesday   **(C.)** Thursday

(1 point)
9. Which can a calendar measure?
    (A.) months   B. weather   C. hours

(1 point)
10. Which is shortest?
    (A.) a day   B. a week   C. a year

(1 point)
11. Which can a clock measure?
    A. weather   B. temperature   **(C.)** time

Name   Date

(1 point)
12. At what time of day do you eat breakfast?

    (A) morning
    B. afternoon
    C. evening

(1 point)
13. About what time do you go to sleep at night?

    A. 12:00 noon
    (B) 8:00 in the evening
    C. 6:00 in the morning

Data and Graphs

Favorite Colors

🌸	🌸	🌸	🌸	🌸	🌸					
🍌	🍌	🍌	🍌							
▮	▮	▮	▮	▮	▮	▮				

Each picture in the boxes equals 1.

▶ Unit Objectives

- Use objects, pictures, and picture graphs to record the results of data collection from a sample size up through 10.

- Answer "most, fewest, same" questions about data shown in a picture graph that has up through 10 objects in each category.

- Answer "how many" questions about data shown in a picture graph that has up through 10 objects in each category.

- Collect data from a sample size up through 10.

- Pose information questions from a sample size up through 10.

▶ Big Ideas

Graphs and charts are useful ways to represent and compare numerical data.

▶ Unit Introduction

In this unit, students will learn how to pose questions and collect data. They will learn to represent the data with objects, pictures, and finally picture graphs. They will compare and answer questions about their data. Students will also compare and answer questions about data in graphs that they have not prepared themselves.

Collect Data and Pose Questions

Lesson Overview

Skills Update	5 minutes	ONLINE
GET READY Groups of Crayons	5 minutes	ONLINE
LEARN Data for Blocks	10 minutes	OFFLINE
LEARN Pose Questions	10 minutes	OFFLINE
TRY IT Kitchen Data	5 minutes	OFFLINE
CHECKPOINT	10 minutes	OFFLINE

▶ Lesson Objectives

- Collect data from a sample size up through 10.
- Pose information questions from a sample size up through 10.

▶ Prerequisite Skills

- Use concrete objects or sketches to represent a quantity up through 10.
- Recognize that numbers with greater values describe sets with more objects in them than numbers with lesser values do (for sets of 10 or fewer objects).

▶ Advance Preparation

- Using the appropriate color crayon for each word, write the following on the front of one index card: ____**red**, ____**blue**, and ____**green.**
- Place 4 green blocks, 4 red blocks, and 2 blue blocks into a paper bag.
- For each of the last three activities, students will need to survey 5 friends or family members.
- Keep the data about pets that students collect and record in the Learn: Pose Questions activity; you will use this data in a future lesson.

```
_____ red

_____ blue

_____ green
```

▶ Safety

Caution students to handle utensils carefully. Show them how to hold the utensils so pointed ends face away from them.

▶ Content Background

In this lesson, students will learn how to pose questions and collect data.

The term *data* is the plural of *datum*. Data are pieces of information that can be gathered. For example, the ages of each member of your family are data. There are several ways to record data. Usually data is recorded in tables. You can use numbers, tallies, pictures, or graphs to represent data.

Materials to Gather

SUPPLIED

blocks – B (10 green, 7 red, 6 blue)
Kitchen Data activity page
Checkpoint (printout)

ALSO NEEDED

index card – 1
index card – labeled ____**red**, ____**blue**, ____**green**
crayons
paper bag
plastic utensils – 4 spoons, 3 forks

GET READY Groups of Crayons

ONLINE
5min

Students will practice comparing by choosing the numbered groups of crayons that has more or fewer crayons.

Objectives

- Recognize that numbers with greater values describe sets with more objects in them than numbers with lesser values do (for sets of 10 or fewer objects).

Tips

Explain to students that greater numbers describe groups with *more* objects, and lesser numbers describe groups with *fewer* objects.

LEARN Data for Blocks

OFFLINE
10min

Students will collect data about blocks and record the results.

Gather the crayons, index card that you have labeled, blank index card, paper bag that you have filled with blocks, and 13 loose blocks. Lay out the 13 blocks in a random arrangement.

1. Show students the index card you labeled. Point to the word *red*.

   Say: We will count the red circles and write the number next to the word *red*. We will do the same for the blue and green circles.

   Say: The numbers of the circles are called *data*. Data are information that we collect. We can record the data by writing the numbers.

2. **Ask:** How many red circles are there?
   ANSWER: 3

3. Have students write the number on the line next to *red* on the card.

4. **Ask:** What other data can we collect about the circles?
   ANSWER: the number of blue circles and green circles

5. Guide students in collecting and recording the number of blue and green circles.

6. **Say:** You wrote numbers to record data. You can also draw pictures to record data.

   Show students the paper bag.

   Say: There are circles in this bag. Let's collect data about the circles in this bag. Then let's draw pictures to record this data.

Objectives

- Collect data from a sample size up through 10.
- Pose information questions from a sample size up through 10.

Tips

If students have difficulty counting the blocks in Step 5, have them first sort the blocks by color and then count each sorted group.

_____ red

_____ blue

_____ green

7. Give students the crayons and blank index card.

   Say: Pull a circle from the bag. On the card, draw a circle to match the color of the circle you pulled.

8. Have students pull each circle from the bag and draw a matching circle on their card. After students have pulled all circles from the bag, have them count their drawings to determine how many circles of each color they pulled. (4 green, 4 red, 2 blue)

LEARN Pose Questions

OFFLINE
10 min

Students will pose questions, collect data, and record the results. There are no materials to gather for this activity.

1. **Say:** You can collect data on many things. You could collect data on the number of shapes in a bag, number of letters in your name, favorite foods of friends, and favorite seasons of friends.

2. **Ask:** You want to collect data about the number of pets your friends have. What question should you ask?
   ANSWER: How many pets do you have?

3. **Ask:** How would you record the answer to your question?
   ANSWER: I would draw a picture of the friend and write a number next to it.

4. **Say:** You will ask 5 people how many pets they have. Pick 5 friends or family members. Draw a picture of each person on paper. When you find out how many pets they have, you can write the number next to the picture.

   Write each person's initials next to students' drawing of that person.

5. **Ask:** What will you write if a person has no pets?
   ANSWER: 0

6. Have students collect the data and record the results. Check students' work.

   As data collection may be time consuming, you may complete the next steps at a later time.

7. **Ask:** What other questions would you like to ask family and friends, so that you could collect data?
   ANSWER: Students should say the specific questions they would ask.

8. **Ask:** How could you record the results to your question?
   ANSWER: with numbers or pictures

9. Have students collect the data and record the results. Check students' work.

Objectives

- Collect data from a sample size up through 10.
- Pose information questions from a sample size up through 10.

CP **2**

BH **2**

TS **3**

CV **0**

LM **2**

Tips

If students have difficulty thinking of questions in Step 7, they can use the examples in Step 1.

TRY IT Kitchen Data

OFFLINE 5min

Students will practice gathering and recording data. Give students the Kitchen Data activity page from their Activity Book and read the directions with them.

Gather the plastic utensils. Lay out the utensils in a random arrangement. Read Problem 1 to students, and ask them to use the displayed utensils.

Objectives

• Collect data from a sample size up through 10.

• Pose information questions from a sample size up through 10.

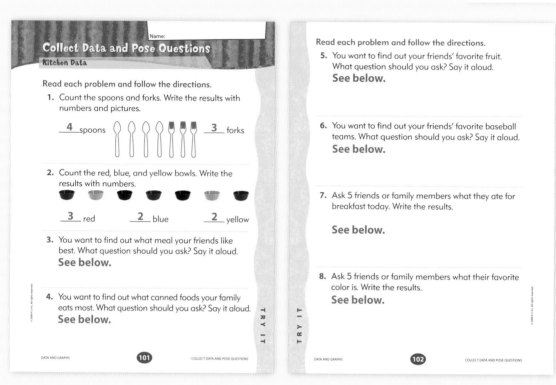

Additional Answers

3. Example: Is your favorite meal breakfast, lunch, or dinner?
4. Example: How many cans of soup do we have? How many cans of tuna do we have?
5. Example: What is your favorite fruit?
6. Example: Which baseball team do you like best?
7. Students should record the results of their data collection.
8. Students should record the results of their data collection.

CHECKPOINT

Print the Checkpoint and have students complete it on their own. Read the directions, problems, and answer choices to students if necessary. Use the answer key to score the Checkpoint, and then enter the results online.

- Collect data from a sample size up through 10.
- Pose information questions from a sample size up through 10.

Name _____   Date _____

Checkpoint Answer Key

Read each problem and follow the directions.

1. You want to find out your friends' favorite cartoons. What question should you ask? Say it aloud.
   (1 point)

   Example: What is your favorite cartoon?

2. You want to find out your friends' favorite kinds of ice cream. What question should you ask? Say it aloud.
   (1 point)

   Example: What is your favorite kind of ice cream?

3. Ask 5 friends or family members what their favorite kind of animal is. Write the results.
   (1 point)

   Students should record the results of their data collection.

Name _____   Date _____

Use the pairs of shoes to answer Problems 4–6.
(1 point)

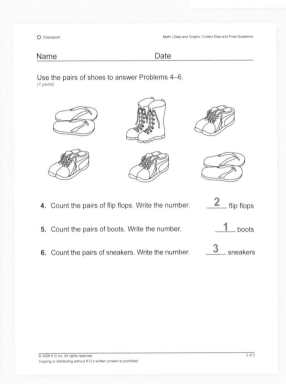

4. Count the pairs of flip flops. Write the number.   __2__ flip flops

5. Count the pairs of boots. Write the number.   __1__ boots

6. Count the pairs of sneakers. Write the number.   __3__ sneakers

Ways to Show Data

Lesson Overview

Skills Update	5 minutes	ONLINE
GET READY Count the Blocks	5 minutes	OFFLINE
LEARN Color Tile Picture Graph	15 minutes	OFFLINE
LEARN Make a Picture Graph	5 minutes	OFFLINE
TRY IT Show Data	5 minutes	OFFLINE
CHECKPOINT	5 minutes	OFFLINE

▶ Lesson Objectives

Use objects, pictures, and picture graphs to record the results of data collection from a sample size up through 10.

▶ Prerequisite Skills

- Count aloud a number of objects up through 10.
- Recognize that numbers with greater values describe sets with more objects in them than numbers with lesser values do (for sets of 10 or fewer objects).

▶ Advance Preparation

- Print the Picture Graph.
- Gather the data about pets students collected and recorded in the Collect Data and Pose Questions lesson. If you do not have the data, have students pose a question of their choice to five people, collect data, and record the results.
- Keep the Color Tile Picture Graph activity page and Picture Graph printout after students complete them; you will use these graphs in future lessons.

▶ Content Background

In this lesson, students will learn to use objects, pictures, and picture graphs to show their data.

A picture graph is a graph that uses pictures to represent data. A key is provided to describe how many each picture represents.

Materials to Gather

SUPPLIED

blocks – O (10 of any color)
blocks – E (4 red, 2 blue, 5 yellow)
Color Tile Picture Graph activity page
Picture Graph (printout)
Show Data activity page
Checkpoint (printout)

ALSO NEEDED

crayons

Keywords

data point – one piece of data in a graph
picture graph – a graph that uses pictures to represent data

GET READY Count the Blocks

Students will practice counting objects by counting aloud groups of blocks.
Gather the cubes. Lay out 9 cubes in a random arrangement.

1. **Say:** Count the cubes.

   Ask: How many cubes are there?
   ANSWER: 9

2. **Ask:** How do you know there are 9 cubes?
   ANSWER: I counted each cube once and there were 9.

3. Gather all the cubes into one group.
   Say: Take a handful of cubes and count them.

   Ask: How many cubes did you count?
   ANSWER: Answers will vary.

4. Repeat Step 3 twice.

5. Gather all the cubes into one group. Take a handful of cubes and ask students to count them.

   Ask: How many cubes did you count?
   ANSWER: Answers will vary.

6. Repeat Step 5 twice.

Objectives

- Count aloud a number of objects up through 10.

Tips

To prevent students from skipping a cube or counting the same cube twice, have them move each cube away from the group as they count it.

LEARN Color Tile Picture Graph

Students will collect data about tiles and record the results. Then they will represent data using pictures, objects, and picture graphs.
Gather the Color Tile Picture Graph activity page, crayons, and tiles. Lay out the tiles in a random arrangement.

1. **Say:** Sort the tiles by color. Beginning with red, make a row of each color. Start each row at the same place so that the tiles are lined up.

   Check that students have correctly sorted by color.

2. **Say:** You organized your tiles to make it easy to see which colors there are more or fewer of. Organizing your data makes it easier to see.

3. **Ask:** How many red tiles are there?
   ANSWER: 4

4. Repeat Step 3, asking about the blue and yellow tiles.

5. **Say:** We can use pictures to stand for, or represent, the tiles. We can organize the pictures in rows as we did with the tiles. These rows of pictures are called picture graphs.

6. Give students the crayons and Color Tile Picture Graph activity page.

7. Point to the title of the graph, "Color Tiles," on the activity page.

   Say: All graphs have a title. The title can be found at the top of the graph. The title of the picture graph we are going to make is Color Tiles.

Objectives

- Use objects, pictures, and picture graphs to record the results of data collection from a sample size up through 10.

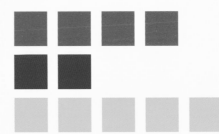

Tips

If students have difficulty correctly filling in the rows of data on the picture graph, have them cover up any rows they are not using so that only the row they are outlining is visible.

8. Point to the key.

   Say: The key tells us what each picture represents. In this picture graph, each picture in the boxes represents one color tile.

9. Point to the tiles.
   Ask: What color is the first row of your tiles?
   ANSWER: red

   Ask: How many red tiles are there?
   ANSWER: 4

10. Point to the red tile on the top row of the picture graph.
    Say: Outline each of the first four squares with a red crayon. Color these squares red.

11. **Ask:** What do these 4 squares represent?
    ANSWER: the number of red tiles

12. Repeat the Steps 9–11 with the blue and yellow tiles. Make sure students outline only one row for each color.

13. Have students compare their picture graphs to the rows of tiles. Have them count the tiles and the pictures to make sure the numbers match.

14. **Say:** The graph and the rows of tiles show the same data. A picture graph is another way to show data.

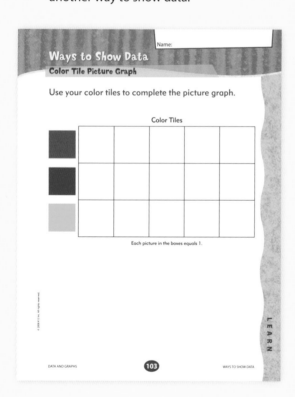

LEARN Make a Picture Graph

Students will represent data in a picture graph.

Gather the Picture Graph printout, crayons, and the data about pets students collected and recorded in the Collect Data and Pose Questions lesson.

1. **Say:** You have asked friends and family members a question and collected data. Now you can organize the data into a picture graph.

2. **Ask:** What is a picture graph?
   ANSWER: a graph that uses pictures to represent data

3. Ask students to think back to the data they collected. Remind them how many people they spoke to, what question they asked, and why they asked that question.

4. Give students the crayons and Picture Graph printout.

   Ask: Before you get started, your picture graph needs a title. What would be a good title for your graph?

   Help students write an appropriate title in the rectangular box above the picture graph.

5. **Ask:** There are 5 rows on your graph. Each row is for one person. How can you name each row?
   ANSWER: draw a picture of each person; write person's initials

   Guide students in drawing pictures or writing initials to label each row.

6. **Ask:** What pictures will you draw to represent each answer—or in other words, each piece of data?
   ANSWER: Answers may include: dog; cat; fish

   Make sure students understand that one type of picture will represent each pet. For example, if students choose a dog's face to represent the data, the dog's face will represent all types of pets.

7. **Say:** The key for the picture graph says, "Each picture in the boxes equals 1."

8. Point to the answers that students have collected.

   Ask: Look at the data you collected. How many pictures will you draw to represent the data for the person in the first row?

9. Draw the first picture for students.
   Say: Now finish the row. Draw a picture for each piece of data. Remember that there should only be one picture in each box.

10. Continue until students have recorded all the data that they collected.

11. **Say:** Now tell about your graph.
    ANSWER: Students should describe their graph, explaining what each picture represents, and so forth.

Objectives

- Use objects, pictures, and picture graphs to record the results of data collection from a sample size up through 10.

Tips

Help students understand that the graph is a clear way to show the information they have collected.

Objectives

Students will practice representing data in picture graphs. Give students the crayons and Show Data activity page from their Activity Book. Read the directions with them.

- Use objects, pictures, and picture graphs to record the results of data collection from a sample size up through 10.

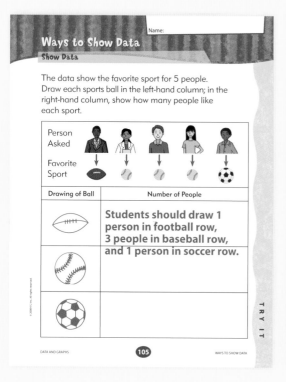

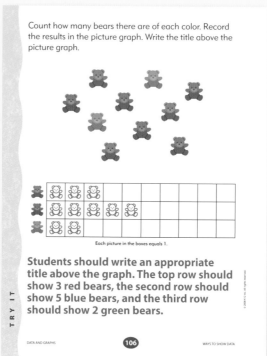

CHECKPOINT

Objectives

Print the Checkpoint and have students complete it on their own. Read the directions, problems, and answer choices to students if necessary. Use the answer key to score the Checkpoint, and then enter the results online.

- Use objects, pictures, and picture graphs to record the results of data collection from a sample size up through 10.

Checkpoint   Math | Data and Graphs | Ways to Show Data

Name _____ Date _____

Checkpoint Answer Key

Read each problem and follow the directions.
(1 point)
1. Count how many of each shape. Record your results in the picture graph. Write the title above the picture graph.

How Many Shapes							

Each picture in the boxes equals 1.

Students should record 5 squares, 3 triangles, and 1 circle.

1 of 3

Checkpoint   Math | Data and Graphs | Ways to Show Data

Name _____ Date _____

(1 point)
2. Count how many crayons of each color. Record your results in the picture graph. Write the title above the picture graph.

red red red   green green green   blue blue

Colors of Crayons					

Each picture in the boxes equals 1.

Students should record 3 red, 3 green, and 2 blue crayons.

2 of 3

Checkpoint   Math | Data and Graphs | Ways to Show Data

Name _____ Date _____

(1 point)
3. Rosa made a graph of her friends' favorite animals. Circle Rosa's graph.

A.

Favorite Shape							

Each picture in the boxes equals 1.

B.

Favorite Fruit							

Each picture in the boxes equals 1.

C.

Favorite Animal							

Each picture in the boxes equals 1.

3 of 3

Compare Data in a Picture Graph

Lesson Overview

Skills Update	5 minutes	ONLINE
GET READY Count the Animals	5 minutes	ONLINE
LEARN Use Picture Graphs to Compare	20 minutes	ONLINE
TRY IT Compare Data	15 minutes	OFFLINE

▶ Lesson Objectives

- Answer "most, fewest, same" questions about data shown in a picture graph that has up through 10 objects in each category.
- Use objects, pictures, and picture graphs to record the results of data collection from a sample size up through 10.

▶ Prerequisite Skills

Given two or more sets that have 10 or fewer objects, identify which set has more or fewer objects than another set, or which sets have an equal number of objects.

▶ Content Background

In this lesson, students will learn how to use picture graphs to compare data.

A picture graph is a graph that uses pictures to represent data. A key is provided to describe how many each picture represents.

Materials to Gather

SUPPLIED

Compare Data activity page

GET READY Count the Animals

ONLINE 5 min

Students will compare groups of animals to identify the group with more, fewer, or the same number of animals.

Objectives

- Given two or more sets that have 10 or fewer objects, identify which set has more or fewer objects than another set, or which sets have an equal number of objects.

Tips

Explain to students that greater numbers describe groups with *more* objects, and lesser numbers describe groups with *fewer* objects.

LEARN Use Picture Graphs to Compare

Students will learn how to compare data in picture graphs. They will answer questions about the data using the words *more*, *fewer*, and *equal*.

In the picture graphs online, make sure students realize the picture on the far left is a label that describes the data in that row—it should not be counted as a piece of data. Show students the vertical line to the right of each label. Explain that the pictures to the right of the line show the data and should be counted.

- Answer "most, fewest, same" questions about data shown in a picture graph that has up through 10 objects in each category.

TRY IT Compare Data

Students will answer questions about picture graphs. Give students the Compare Data activity page from their Activity Book and read the directions with them.

- Use objects, pictures, and picture graphs to record the results of data collection from a sample size up through 10.

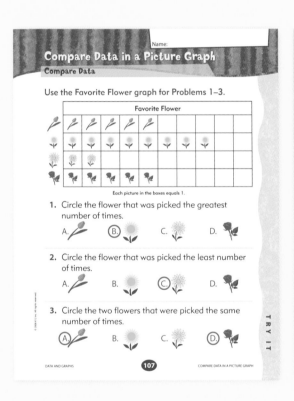

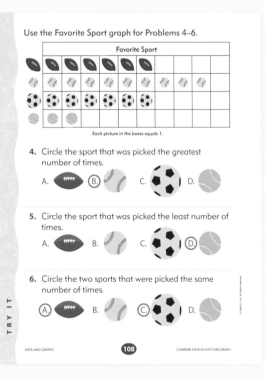

Read each problem and circle the answer.

7. Look at the picture graph. Which animals are there the most of in the zoo?

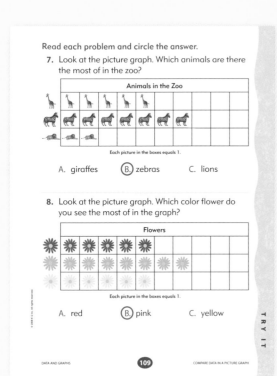

Each picture in the boxes equals 1.

A. giraffes   (B.) zebras   C. lions

8. Look at the picture graph. Which color flower do you see the most of in the graph?

Flowers

Each picture in the boxes equals 1.

A. red   (B.) pink   C. yellow

9. Look at the picture graph. Which drink was picked the most?

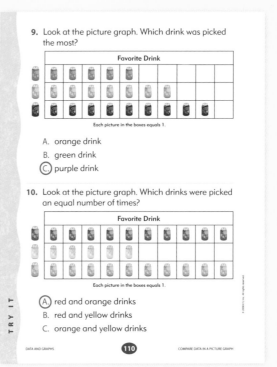

Each picture in the boxes equals 1.

A. orange drink
B. green drink
(C) purple drink

10. Look at the picture graph. Which drinks were picked an equal number of times?

Favorite Drink

Each picture in the boxes equals 1.

(A) red and orange drinks
B. red and yellow drinks
C. orange and yellow drinks

TRY IT

Interpret Picture Graphs

Lesson Overview

Skills Update	5 minutes	**ONLINE**
GET READY Compare Groups	5 minutes	**OFFLINE**
LEARN Compare Data in a Picture Graph	15 minutes	**OFFLINE**
LEARN Picture Graph Questions	5 minutes	**OFFLINE**
TRY IT Picture Graph Data	10 minutes	**OFFLINE**

▶ Lesson Objectives

Answer "most, fewest, same" questions about data shown in a picture graph that has up through 10 objects in each category.

▶ Prerequisite Skills

Given two or more sets that have 10 or fewer objects, identify which set has more or fewer objects than another set, or which sets have an equal number of objects.

▶ Advance Preparation

- Gather the completed Color Tile Picture Graph activity page from the Ways to Show Data lesson. If you do not have the activity page, refer to the Ways to Show Data lesson in the Lesson Guide for instructions on how to create the picture graph.

- Keep the Compare Data in a Picture Graph activity page after students complete it; you will use this graph in a future lesson.

▶ Content Background

In this lesson, students will read and interpret data in picture graphs.

A picture graph is a graph that uses pictures to represent data. A key is provided to describe how many each picture represents.

Keywords

symbol – a figure that is used to represent something else, such as + represents *plus* or *addition*, or = represents *equals*

Materials to Gather

SUPPLIED

blocks – O (6 red, 9 blue, 8 green)

Compare Data in a Picture Graph activity page

Picture Graph Data activity page

ALSO NEEDED

completed Color Tile Picture Graph activity page from Ways to Show Data lesson

GET READY Compare Groups

Students will compare blocks using the words *more*, *most*, *fewer*, *fewest*, and *equal*.
Gather the blocks. Display 4 red cubes in a one pile. Display 6 blue cubes in another pile.

1. **Ask:** How can you find the group that has more cubes?
   ANSWER: count the cubes and choose the group with the greater number; line up the groups and choose the group with unmatched cubes

2. **Ask:** Which group has more cubes?
   ANSWER: the blue group

3. **Ask:** Which group has fewer cubes?
   ANSWER: the red group

4. Clear the work area. Make 3 groups of cubes: 5 red, 9 blue, and 1 green.

5. **Ask:** Which group has the most cubes?
   ANSWER: the blue group

6. **Ask:** Which group has the fewest cubes?
   ANSWER: the green group

7. **Ask:** Do any of the groups have an equal number of cubes?
   ANSWER: No

8. Clear the work area. Make 3 groups of cubes: 6 red, 3 blue, and 6 green.

9. **Ask:** Which group has the fewest cubes?
   ANSWER: the blue group

10. **Ask:** Which groups have an equal number of cubes?
    ANSWER: the red and green groups

11. Clear the work area. Make 3 groups of cubes: 2 red, 2 blue, and 8 green.

12. **Ask:** Which group has the most cubes?
    ANSWER: the green group

13. **Ask:** Do any of the groups have an equal number of cubes?
    ANSWER: Yes; the red and blue groups

- Given two or more sets that have 10 or fewer objects, identify which set has more or fewer objects than another set, or which sets have an equal number of objects.

Tips

If students have difficulty determining which group has more by counting, have them put the groups in lines beginning at the same place. Explain that the group with the longest line is the group with *more* objects.

Explain that *more* and *fewer* are used when comparing 2 groups and that *most* and *fewest* are used when comparing 3 or more groups.

Explain to students that greater numbers describe groups with *more* objects, and lesser numbers describe groups with *fewer* objects.

LEARN Compare Data in a Picture Graph

Students will analyze data about favorite seasons. They will determine which seasons were picked the most times, the fewest times, and the same number of times in the survey.
Gather the Compare Data in a Picture Graph activity page.

1. Point to the Data table.

   Say: Some people were asked about their favorite season. The table shows their answers. Use this data to make a picture graph. The title, labels, and key have already been done for you.

2. Have students complete the picture graph.

3. **Ask:** Look at your picture graph and at the data. Do the numbers match? If the numbers do not match, guide students in correcting their graph.

- Answer "most, fewest, same" questions about data shown in a picture graph that has up through 10 objects in each category.

4. Explain to students that because their graph shows 1 picture for each piece of data, their graph shows the data.

Say: We can ask questions about the graph to learn about the data.

5. Ask: Which season was picked the most?
ANSWER: summer

Ask: How many times was summer picked?
ANSWER: 7

6. Ask: Which season was picked the least?
ANSWER: fall

Ask: How do you know?
ANSWER: It has only 3 pictures. It is the shortest row.

7. Ask: Which two seasons were picked the same number of times?
ANSWER: winter and spring

8. Ask: How many times were winter and spring picked?
ANSWER: 4 times each

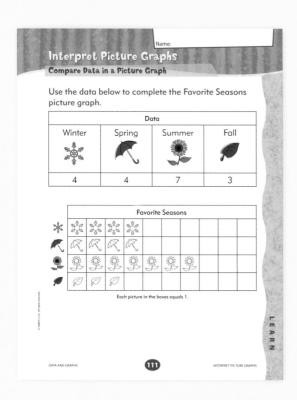

OFFLINE 5 min

Students will analyze the data in the Color Tile Picture Graph.

Gather the completed Color Tile Picture Graph activity page from the Ways to Show Data lesson.

1. **Say:** Look at the picture graph. Tell me about the parts of the graph.
   ANSWER: Students should tell about the title, labels, and key.

2. **Say:** Let's answer some questions about this graph.

   Ask: Which color had the most tiles?
   ANSWER: yellow

   Explain that the longest row has the most tiles. This row also has the greatest number of tiles.

3. **Ask:** Which color had the fewest tiles?
   ANSWER: blue

   Explain that the shortest row has the fewest tiles. This row also has the least number of tiles.

4. **Ask:** Did any of the colors have an equal number of tiles?
   ANSWER: No

Explain that rows with an equal number of tiles would be the same length.

- Answer "most, fewest, same" questions about data shown in a picture graph that has up through 10 objects in each category.

OFFLINE 10 min

Students will answer questions about picture graphs. Give students the Picture Graph Data activity page from their Activity Book and read the directions with them.

- Answer "most, fewest, same" questions about data shown in a picture graph that has up through 10 objects in each category.

Interpret Picture Graphs
Picture Graph Data

Use the Favorite Toys picture graph for Problems 1–3.

Favorite Toys

Each picture in the boxes equals 1.

1. Circle the toy that was picked the greatest number of times.
   A.   B.   C.   (D.)

2. Circle the toy that was picked the least number of times.
   A.   B.   (C.)   D.

3. Circle the two toys that were picked the same number of times.
   (A.)   (B.)   C.   D.

DATA AND GRAPHS 113 INTERPRET PICTURE GRAPHS

Use the Favorite Pizza Toppings picture graph for Problems 4–6.

Favorite Pizza Toppings

Each picture in the boxes equals 1.

4. Circle the topping that was picked the greatest number of times.
   A.   (B.)   C.   D.

5. Circle the topping that was picked the least number of times.
   A.   B.   (C.)   D.

6. Circle the two toppings that were picked the same number of times.
   (A.)   B.   C.   (D.)

DATA AND GRAPHS 114 INTERPRET PICTURE GRAPHS

TRY IT

Circle the answer.

7. Look at the Favorite Fruit picture graph. Which two fruits were picked the same number of times?

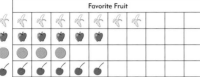

Each picture in the boxes equals 1.

A. banana and orange

B. apple and cherry

C. cherry and orange

8. Look at the Number of Pet Treats Eaten picture graph. Which pet ate the most treats?

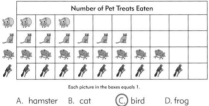

Each picture in the boxes equals 1.

A. hamster   B. cat   C. bird   D. frog

Circle the answer.

9. Look at the Favorite Ice Cream picture graph below. Which ice cream flavor was picked the least number of times?

Each picture in the boxes equals 1.

A. mint ice cream

B. chocolate ice cream

C. strawberry ice cream

10. Look at the Favorite Ice Cream picture graph below. Which ice cream flavor was picked the greatest number of times?

Each picture in the boxes equals 1.

A. vanilla ice cream

B. chocolate ice cream

C. blueberry ice cream

T R Y I T

Answer Data Questions

Lesson Overview

Skills Update	5 minutes	ONLINE
GET READY Counting Fun	5 minutes	ONLINE
LEARN Picture Graph Questions	20 minutes	ONLINE
TRY IT Favorite Snacks	10 minutes	OFFLINE

▶ Lesson Objectives

Answer "how many" questions about data shown in a picture graph that has up through 10 objects in each category.

▶ Prerequisite Skills

- Count aloud a number of objects up through 10.
- Use concrete objects or sketches to represent a quantity up through 10.

▶ Content Background

In this lesson, students will answer questions about data shown in picture graphs.

A picture graph is a graph that uses pictures to represent data. A key is provided to describe how many each picture represents.

Materials to Gather

SUPPLIED

Favorite Snacks activity page

GET READY Counting Fun

ONLINE
5 min

Students will count aloud objects along with audio.

Objectives

- Count aloud a number of objects up through 10.
- Use concrete objects or sketches to represent a quantity up through 10.

LEARN Picture Graph Questions

Students will be guided to answer questions about data in a picture graphs. Students will learn to count the total pictures in a graph, count the pictures in each row, and compare the number of pictures in two rows.

Objectives

- Answer "how many" questions about data shown in a picture graph that has up through 10 objects in each category.

Tips

To help students decide which row has more pictures, have them use their finger to match objects in the rows until there are no more matches. The longer row has more pictures.

TRY IT Favorite Snacks

Students will answer questions about picture graphs. Give students the Favorite Snacks activity page from the Activity Book and read the directions with them.

Objectives

- Answer "how many" questions about data shown in a picture graph that has up through 10 objects in each category.

Tips

To prevent students from counting the same picture twice, have them cross out each picture as they count it.

Name:

Answer Data Questions
Favorite Snacks

Use the picture graph to answer Problems 1–4.
Write the answer on the line.

Students' Favorite Snacks

Each picture in the boxes equals 1.

1. How many students like raisins best? **6**

2. How many students like pretzels best? **3**

3. How many more students chose raisins than crackers? **5**

4. How many students answered the question "What is your favorite snack?" **10**

5. Look at the picture graph. How many snails are in the aquarium? Circle the answer.

Sea Animals in the Aquarium

Each picture in the boxes equals 1.

A. 2   B. 6   C. 7

TRY IT

TRY IT

Use the picture graph to answer Problems 6 and 7.

Animals in the Pet Shop

Each picture in the boxes equals 1.

6. How many cats are in the pet shop? Circle the answer.
A. 2   B. 5   C. 7

7. How many parrots are in the pet shop? Circle the answer.
A. 2   B. 5   C. 7

8. Look at the picture graph. How many children like french fries? Circle the answer.

Foods Children Like

Each picture in the boxes equals 1.

A. 3   B. 4   C. 6

Analyze Data in Picture Graphs

Lesson Overview

Skills Update	5 minutes	ONLINE
GET READY Amounts Through 10	5 minutes	OFFLINE
LEARN Analyze Favorite Seasons Graph	10 minutes	OFFLINE
LEARN Analyze Number of Pets Graph	5 minutes	OFFLINE
TRY IT Analyze Data	5 minutes	OFFLINE
CHECKPOINT	5 minutes	OFFLINE

▶ Lesson Objectives

Answer "how many" questions about data shown in a picture graph that has up through 10 objects in each category.

▶ Prerequisite Skills

- Count aloud a number of objects up through 10.
- Use concrete objects or sketches to represent a quantity up through 10.

▶ Advance Preparation

- Fold a sheet of paper into 6 equal sections. Write one of the following numbers in each section: 5, 3, 9, 1, 6, and 10.
- Gather the completed Compare Data in a Picture Graph activity page from the Interpret Picture Graphs lesson. If you do not have the activity page, refer to the Interpret Picture Graphs lesson in the Lesson Guide for instructions on how to create the picture graph.
- Gather the completed Picture Graph printout from the Ways to Show Data lesson. If you do not have the printout, refer to the Ways to Show Data lesson in the Lesson Guide for instructions on how to create the picture graph.

▶ Content Background

In this lesson, students will answer questions about data shown in a picture graph.
   A picture graph is a graph that uses pictures to represent data. A key is provided to describe how many each picture represents.

Materials to Gather

SUPPLIED

blocks – B (10 of any mix of colors)

Analyze Data activity page

Checkpoint (printout)

ALSO NEEDED

crayons

completed Compare Data in a Picture Graph activity page from Interpret Picture Graphs lesson

completed Picture Graph printout from Ways to Show Data lesson

OFFLINE
5min

- Use concrete objects or sketches to represent a quantity up through 10.
- Count aloud a number of objects up through 10.

Students will use blocks and drawings to show amounts through 10.

Gather the blocks, crayons, and the paper you folded. Lay out the circles in a random arrangement.

1. **Say:** Show 7 circles in a row.

   Have students count aloud each circle as they move it into the row. Students should say exactly one number for each circle.

2. Combine all circles back into one group.

3. Repeat Steps 1 and 2 with the numbers 8, 4, 2, and 0. When students show 0, you may need to remind them that showing 0 means showing no objects.

4. **Say:** You have shown different numbers of circles. Now you will draw pictures to show numbers.

5. Give students the paper and crayons.

   Say: Draw 5 circles in the section of your paper labeled "5." You can use any colors to draw the circles.

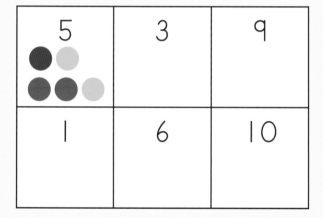

6. Have students check their work by counting aloud each drawing as they touch it. Students should say exactly one number for each drawing.

7. Repeat Steps 5 and 6 with the numbers 3, 9, 1, 6, and 10.

8. **Ask:** How do objects or drawings help you show a number?
   ANSWER: They help me see and count the number.

Tips

You may wish to store the blocks in a box, bag, or cup. Have students remove the blocks from the container to show each amount and then return them to the container before showing another amount.

OFFLINE
10min

- Answer "how many" questions about data shown in a picture graph that has up through 10 objects in each category.

Students will look at a picture graph and answer questions involving counting and comparing.

Gather the completed Compare Data in a Picture Graph activity page from the Interpret Picture Graphs lesson.

Tips

If students have difficulty comparing the pictures in two rows, have them use cubes to build each row of the graph, aligning rows at the left to model the graph. Then have them match the cubes in the two rows, moving the rows next to each other if needed. When they cannot match any more cubes, they should count the cubes that are left.

1. Display the Favorite Seasons picture graph. Have students point out the title and key, and explain what the graph shows. For example, ask, "What does the row with the flower show? What does each snowflake show?"

2. **Ask:** How many students like winter best?
   ANSWER: 4

   Ask: How did you find that answer?
   ANSWER: I counted the pictures in the winter row.

   Have students count aloud each snowflake in sequence as they point to it. Count aloud with students if necessary.

3. **Ask:** How many students like summer best?
   ANSWER: 7

4. **Say:** Let's figure out how many more students chose summer than winter.

   Point to the rows for winter and summer.

   Say: Match the pictures in the two rows. When you cannot match any more pictures, count the pictures that are left. That number is the answer.

5. **Ask:** How many more students chose summer than winter?
   ANSWER: 3

6. **Ask:** How many more students chose spring than fall?
   ANSWER: 1

7. **Say:** Here's a new kind of question. How many students chose fall and winter? To find the answer, count the pictures in both rows.

   Have students count aloud each snowflake in sequence as they point to it. Then guide their finger to the first leaf.

8. **Say:** You counted 4 snowflakes. Count on the number of leaves.

   If necessary, count aloud "5, 6, 7," with students.

9. **Ask:** How many students chose fall and winter?
   ANSWER: 7

OFFLINE
5min

Objectives

- Answer "how many" questions about data shown in a picture graph that has up through 10 objects in each category.

Tips

Remind students that the picture on the far left of the graph is a label that describes the data in that row—it should not be counted as a piece of data. Show students the vertical line to the right of each label. Explain that the pictures to the right of the line show the data and should be counted.

Students will continue to answer questions about picture graphs.
Gather the completed Picture Graph printout from the Ways to Show Data lesson.

1. Display the picture graph. Have students point out the title and key, and explain what the graph shows.

2. **Ask:** How many people answered your question about how many pets they have?
   ANSWER: 5

   Ask: How did you find your answer?
   ANSWER: I counted the rows.

   Explain to students that in this graph, each row represents 1 person. The pictures in each row show the number of pets each person has. Explain that graphs can be set up in different ways.

3. Point to the first row, and ask students how many pets that person has.

4. Repeat Step 3 with each row.

5. Choose two rows of different lengths. Ask students which person has more pets and how many more pets this person has.

6. Repeat Step 5 using two other rows.

7. Point to two rows. Ask students to find the total number of pets the people in these two rows have. Ask students how they found the answer. (I counted the pictures in both rows.)

TRY IT Analyze Data

Students will practice answering questions about picture graphs. Give students the Analyze Data activity page from their Activity Book and read the directions with them.

Objectives

- Answer "how many" questions about data shown in a picture graph that has up through 10 objects in each category.

Tips

To prevent students from counting the same picture twice, have them cross out each picture as they count it.

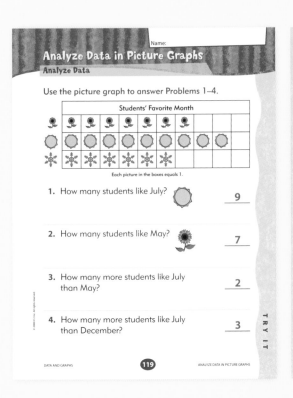

Analyze Data in Picture Graphs

Analyze Data

Name: _____

Use the picture graph to answer Problems 1–4.

Students' Favorite Month

Each picture in the boxes equals 1.

1. How many students like July? ___9___

2. How many students like May? ___7___

3. How many more students like July than May? ___2___

4. How many more students like July than December? ___3___

DATA AND GRAPHS　　119　　ANALYZE DATA IN PICTURE GRAPHS

5. Look at the picture graph. How many fish live in the pond?

Animals in the Pond

Each picture in the boxes equals 1.

　A. 10　　B. 9　　C. 7

Use the picture graph to answer Problems 6 and 7.

Animals in the Zoo

Each picture in the boxes equals 1.

6. How many zebras are there in the zoo?
　A. 2　　B. 5　　C. 7

7. How many lions are there in the zoo?
　A. 7　　B. 5　　C. 2

DATA AND GRAPHS　　120　　ANALYZE DATA IN PICTURE GRAPHS

TRY IT

CHECKPOINT

Objectives

Print the Checkpoint and have students complete it on their own. Read the directions, problems, and answer choices to students if necessary. Use the answer key to score the Checkpoint, and then enter the results online.

- Answer "how many" questions about data shown in a picture graph that has up through 10 objects in each category.

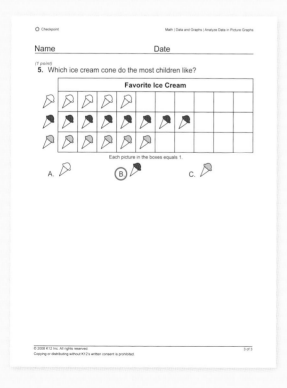

Unit Review

UNIT REVIEW Look Back	20 minutes	**ONLINE**
UNIT REVIEW Checkpoint Practice	10 minutes	**OFFLINE**
UNIT REVIEW Prepare for the Checkpoint		

▶ Unit Objectives

This lesson reviews the following objectives:

- Use objects, pictures, and picture graphs to record the results of data collection from a sample size up through 10.
- Answer "most, fewest, same" questions about data shown in a picture graph that has up through 10 objects in each category.
- Answer "how many" questions about data shown in a picture graph that has up through 10 objects in each category.
- Collect data from a sample size up through 10.
- Pose information questions from a sample size up through 10.

▶ Advance Preparation

In this lesson, students will have an opportunity to review previous activities in the Data and Graphs unit. Look at the suggested activities in Unit Review: Prepare for the Checkpoint online and gather any needed materials.

Materials to Gather

SUPPLIED

Checkpoint Practice activity page

Keywords

data	picture graph
data point	symbol

UNIT REVIEW Look Back

ONLINE 20 min

In this unit, students have learned how to pose questions and collect data. They have learned how to represent the data with objects, pictures, and finally picture graphs. They have compared and answered questions about their data. Students have also compared and answered questions about data in graphs that they have not prepared themselves. Students will review these concepts to prepare for the Unit Checkpoint.

Objectives

- Review unit objectives.

UNIT REVIEW Checkpoint Practice

Students will complete a Checkpoint Practice activity page to prepare for the Unit Checkpoint. If necessary, read the directions, questions, and answer choices to students. Have students answer the problems on their own. Carefully review the answers with students.

Objectives

- Review unit objectives.

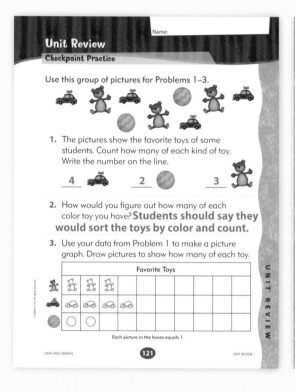

Unit Review

Checkpoint Practice

Name:

Use this group of pictures for Problems 1–3.

1. The pictures show the favorite toys of some students. Count how many of each kind of toy. Write the number on the line.

    <u>4</u> 🚗   <u>2</u> ⚪   <u>3</u> 🧸

2. How would you figure out how many of each color toy you have? **Students should say they would sort the toys by color and count.**

3. Use your data from Problem 1 to make a picture graph. Draw pictures to show how many of each toy.

   Favorite Toys

   Each picture in the boxes equals 1.

   DATA AND GRAPHS   **121**   UNIT REVIEW

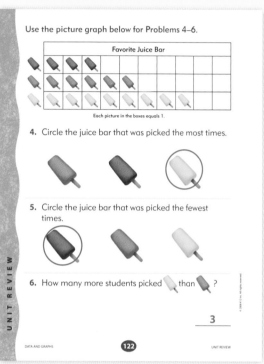

Use the picture graph below for Problems 4–6.

Favorite Juice Bar

Each picture in the boxes equals 1.

4. Circle the juice bar that was picked the most times.

5. Circle the juice bar that was picked the fewest times.

6. How many more students picked 🍦 than 🍡 ?

    <u>3</u>

DATA AND GRAPHS   **122**   UNIT REVIEW

UNIT REVIEW **177**

Read each problem and follow the directions.

7. How would you figure out which eye color is most common in your family? **Students should suggest ways to answer the question by collecting data from their family members.**

8. How would you figure out how many different colors of shoes you have? **Students should suggest ways they could gather information to answer the question.**

9. Look at the group of shapes below. Count how many of each shape. Write the number on the line.

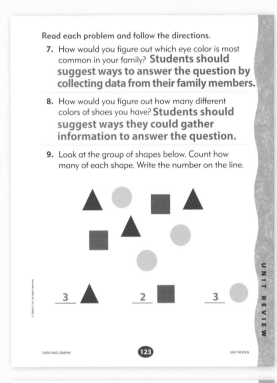

3 ▲   2 ■   3 ●

Read each problem and follow the directions.

10. Which group has the same data as the data shown? Circle the answer.

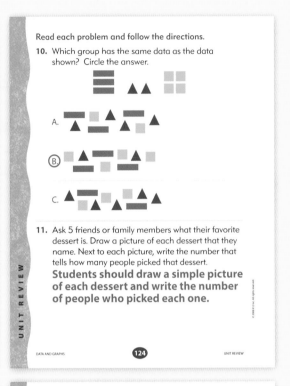

A.

(B.)

C.

11. Ask 5 friends or family members what their favorite dessert is. Draw a picture of each dessert that they name. Next to each picture, write the number that tells how many people picked that dessert. **Students should draw a simple picture of each dessert and write the number of people who picked each one.**

12. Which picture graph best shows the data for favorite foods? Circle the answer.

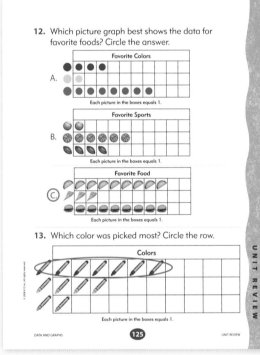

A.

Favorite Colors

Each picture in the boxes equals 1.

B.

Favorite Sports

Each picture in the boxes equals 1.

(C.)

Favorite Food

Each picture in the boxes equals 1.

13. Which color was picked most? Circle the row.

Colors

Each picture in the boxes equals 1.

14. Look at the picture graph. How many more people liked bananas best than liked oranges best? Circle the answer.

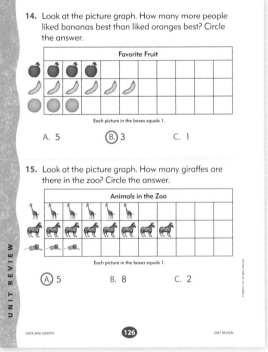

Favorite Fruit

Each picture in the boxes equals 1.

A. 5   (B.) 3   C. 1

15. Look at the picture graph. How many giraffes are there in the zoo? Circle the answer.

Animals in the Zoo

Each picture in the boxes equals 1.

(A.) 5   B. 8   C. 2

➔ UNIT REVIEW Prepare for the Checkpoint

What you do next depends on how students performed in the previous activity, Unit Review: Checkpoint Practice. If students had difficulty with any of the problems, complete the appropriate review activity listed in the table online.

Unit Checkpoint

Lesson Overview

UNIT CHECKPOINT Offline   40 minutes | **OFFLINE**

▶ Unit Objectives

This Unit Checkpoint assesses the following objectives:

- Use objects, pictures, and picture graphs to record the results of data collection from a sample size up through 10.

- Answer "most, fewest, same" questions about data shown in a picture graph that has up through 10 objects in each category.

- Answer "how many" questions about data shown in a picture graph that has up through 10 objects in each category.

- Collect data from a sample size up through 10.

- Pose information questions from a sample size up through 10

▶ Advance Preparation

Have students ask 5 friends or family members what they ate for breakfast today and record the results. Students will use this data to answer Problem 3 of the Unit Checkpoint.

Materials to Gather

SUPPLIED

Unit Checkpoint (printout)

blocks – O (5 blue, 2 red, 3 yellow)

ALSO NEEDED

crayons

UNIT CHECKPOINT Offline   40 min

Objectives

- Assess unit objectives.

Students will complete the Unit Checkpoint offline. Print the Checkpoint and have students complete it on their own. Read the directions, problems, and answer choices to students, if necessary. Use the answer key to score the Checkpoint, and then enter the results online.

Gather the blocks, crayons, and the data students collected about what their friends and family members ate for breakfast. Students will use the data to answer Problem 3 and the cubes and crayons to answer Problem 5. For Problem 5, lay out the cubes in a random arrangement. Do not group colors together.

Name _____ Date _____

Unit Checkpoint Answer Key

Read each problem and follow the directions.

(1 point)
1. You want to find out how many different pets your friends have. Which question should you ask? Circle the best answer.
   - (A.) How many different pets do you have?
   - B. What is your favorite kind of animal?
   - C. What color is your pet?

(1 point)
2. You want to find out your friends' favorite sports. Which question should you ask? Circle the best answer.
   - A. What is your favorite ice cream flavor?
   - (B.) What is your favorite sport?
   - C. What is your favorite color?

(1 point)
3. Ask 5 friends or family members what they ate for breakfast today. Draw a picture of each breakfast food in the space below.

   Students should ask 5 people what they had for breakfast and then draw a picture of each breakfast food.

Name _____ Date _____

(1 point)
4. Look at the group of shapes. Which answer tells how many of each shape? Circle the answer.

   □ ○ △ □ □ ○ ○ □ ○ △

   A. □ ○ △
      2 4 3

   (B.) □ ○ △
      3 4 2

   C. □ ○ △
      4 3 2

(1 point)
5. Look at the red, yellow, and blue cubes. Count how many cubes of each color. Then record the results in the picture graph.

Color Cubes

blue   **Students should count 5 blue, 2 red, and 3 yellow cubes. They should color in boxes to show the number of each color cube.**

red

yellow

Each picture in the boxes equals 1.

Name _____ Date _____

(1 point)
6. Which picture graph shows students' favorite sports? Circle the answer.

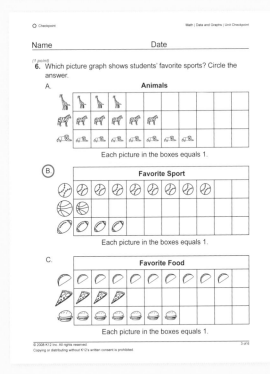

A.
Animals

Each picture in the boxes equals 1.

(B.)
Favorite Sport

Each picture in the boxes equals 1.

C.
Favorite Food

Each picture in the boxes equals 1.

Name _____ Date _____

Read each problem and circle the answer.

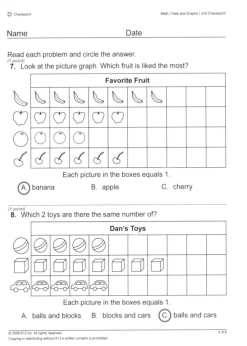

(1 point)
7. Look at the picture graph. Which fruit is liked the most?

Favorite Fruit

Each picture in the boxes equals 1.
   - (A.) banana
   - B. apple
   - C. cherry

(1 point)
8. Which 2 toys are there the same number of?

Dan's Toys

Each picture in the boxes equals 1.
   - A. balls and blocks
   - B. blocks and cars
   - (C.) balls and cars

Name _____ Date _____

(1 point)
9. Look at the picture graph. Which kind of ball is there the fewest of?

	Sports Balls								

Each picture in the boxes equals 1.

A. basketball   B. football   **C.** baseball

(1 point)
10. Look at the picture graph. How many students liked bananas best?

	Favorite Fruit								

Each picture in the boxes equals 1.

A. 5   B. 3   C. 10

(1 point)
11. Look at the picture graph. There is vanilla ice cream, chocolate ice cream, and strawberry ice cream. How many students like chocolate ice cream best?

	Favorite Ice Cream								

Each picture in the boxes equals 1.

A. 4   B. 5   **C.** 7

(1 point)
12. Look at the picture graph. How many trees are in the park?

	Things to See in the Park								

Each picture in the boxes equals 1.

A. 3   B. 4   C. 6

Numbers Through 20

▶ Unit Objectives

- Count aloud a number of objects up through 20.

- Demonstrate that counting 20 or fewer objects can occur from left to right, right to left, or in any order as long as all the items are counted once.

- Use concrete objects or sketches to represent a quantity up through 20.

- Given two or more sets of 20 or fewer objects, identify which set has more or fewer objects than another set, or which sets have an equal number of objects.

- Write numerals from 1 through 20.

- Recognize that numbers with greater values describe sets with more objects in them than numbers with lesser values (for sets of 20 or fewer objects).

▶ Big Ideas

Numbers can represent basic counting results.

▶ Unit Introduction

Students will count groups of up through 20 objects, learning that they can count in any order as long as they count each item exactly one time. They will use models, drawings, and finally numerals to represent groups of up through 20 objects.

Students will then compare groups of 20 or fewer objects to determine which has more, fewer, the most, or the fewest objects. They will compare numbers from 1 through 20 to determine which is greater and which is lesser.

Students will also learn to write the numerals from 11 through 20.

Count Aloud Through 20

Lesson Overview

Skills Update	5 minutes	ONLINE
GET READY Choose the Greater Number	5 minutes	ONLINE
LEARN Count Aloud Through 20	10 minutes	ONLINE
LEARN Count Groups Through 20	10 minutes	OFFLINE
TRY IT Numbers Through 20	10 minutes	OFFLINE

▶ Lesson Objectives

- Count aloud a number of objects up through 20.
- Demonstrate that counting 20 or fewer objects can occur from left to right, right to left, or in any order as long as all the items are counted once.

▶ Prerequisite Skills

- Count aloud a number of objects up through 10.
- Recognize that numbers with greater values describe sets with more objects in them than numbers with lesser values do (for sets of 10 or fewer objects).

▶ Common Errors and Misconceptions

- Students might start counting before or after pointing to the first object in a group. Or they might stop counting before or after they point to the last object. Students should point to each object as they count it.
- Students might say more than one number for each object when counting objects in a group. Or they might skip objects. Students should point to each object and say exactly one number. Then they should point to the next object and say exactly one number, and so on.
- Students might use an incorrect counting sequence, such as "one, two, four, six, ten."

▶ Advance Preparation

Prepare five plastic bags with the following numbers of cubes: 18, 11, 20,14, and 17. Use a mix of colors in each bag.

▶ Content Background

Students will count groups with up through 20 objects. Students will learn that they can count in any order as long as they count each object exactly one time.

A *set* is a group of objects. *Set* is a mathematical term for *group*. You may use *set* and *group* interchangeably in conversation with students.

In mathematics, the word *number* represents the quantity, and the word *numeral* represents the written symbol. So numerals, such as 0, 1, 2, and 3, symbolically represent numbers, or quantities. In everyday language, we say *number* to describe both the symbol and the quantity. As you speak with students, you may use number only.

Materials to Gather

SUPPLIED

Numbers Through 20 activity page

blocks – O (all colors)

blocks – B (1 red, 10 green, 8 blue)

ALSO NEEDED

resealable plastic bags, medium – 5

count – to say each number according to a defined sequence, such as consecutively, by 2s, or backward
fewer– a lesser number than another
fewest – the least number among three or more
more – a greater number or amount than another
most – the greatest number or amount among three or more
number – a quantity or value
set – a collection of items

ONLINE 5 min

GET READY Choose the Greater Number

Students will count aloud groups of up through 10 animals, people, or objects at the zoo and choose the group that represents the greater or greatest number. Students should recognize that greater numbers describe groups with *more* objects, and lesser numbers describe groups with *fewer* objects.

Objectives

- Count aloud a number of objects up through 10.
- Recognize that numbers with greater values describe sets with more objects in them than numbers with lesser values do (for sets of 10 or fewer objects).

Tips

To prevent students from skipping an object or counting an object twice, have students touch each object online as they count it.

ONLINE 10 min

LEARN Count Aloud Through 20

Students will learn to count aloud a group of up through 20 objects by counting aloud animals at the zoo along with the audio. It is important students understand that the order in which they count objects in a group does not change the number of objects as long as they count each object exactly once.

Objectives

- Count aloud a number of objects up through 20.
- Demonstrate that counting 20 or fewer objects can occur from left to right, right to left, or in any order as long as all the items are counted once.

LEARN Count Groups Through 20

Students will practice counting through 20 by counting groups of cubes. It is important students understand that the order in which they count objects in a group does not change the number of objects as long as they count each object exactly once.

Gather the five bags that you have filled with cubes.

1. Give students the bag with 18 cubes. Have them pour out the cubes in the work area.

2. **Say:** Count the cubes to find how many there are.

   Have students touch and move each cube as they count it to ensure they count it only once.

3. **Ask:** How many cubes are there?
   ANSWER: 18

4. **Ask:** If you count the cubes in a different order, will it change the number of cubes?
   ANSWER: Accept students' predictions.

5. **Say:** Lay out the cubes in a different way, and count again.
   If necessary, help students rearrange the cubes in a different way
   (e.g., vertical line, circle, tower).

6. **Ask:** Did you count the same number of cubes or a different number of cubes?
   If students say they counted a different number of cubes, have them count the cubes again.

7. Repeat Steps 1–6 with each bag of cubes.

Objectives

- Count aloud a number of objects up through 20.
- Demonstrate that counting 20 or fewer objects can occur from left to right, right to left, or in any order as long as all the items are counted once.

TRY IT **Numbers Through 20**

Objectives

- Count aloud a number of objects up through 20.
- Demonstrate that counting 20 or fewer objects can occur from left to right, right to left, or in any order as long as all the items are counted once.

This Try It activity has two parts.

Part 1

Students will count groups of up through 20 blocks, counting the groups in different orders.

Gather the circle blocks.

1. Make a row of 16 circles. Have students count the circles starting from the far left.

2. **Ask:** How many circles did you count?
   ANSWER: 16

3. Now have students count again, starting from the far right.

   Ask: How many circles did you count?
   ANSWER: 16

4. **Ask:** Does the number of circles change if you count in a different direction?
   ANSWER: No

5. Make a row of 19 circles. Place a red circle in the middle (the tenth circle). Have students count the circles starting with the red circle.

6. **Ask:** How many circles did you count?
   ANSWER: 19

7. Now have students count again, starting from the far left.

   Ask: How many circles did you count?
   ANSWER: 19

8. **Ask:** Does the number of circles change if you start counting from a different place?
   ANSWER: No

Part 2

Students will count groups of up through 20 animals. Give students the Numbers Through 20 activity page from the Activity Book and read the directions with them.

Count Aloud Through 20
Numbers Through 20

Read each problem and follow the directions.

1. Count. How many giraffes are there?
   Circle the answer.

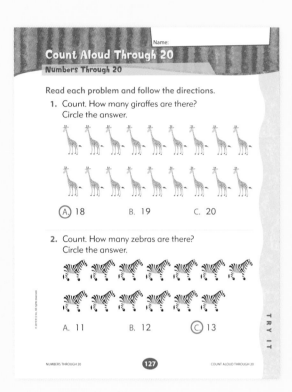

   (A) 18   B. 19   C. 20

2. Count. How many zebras are there?
   Circle the answer.

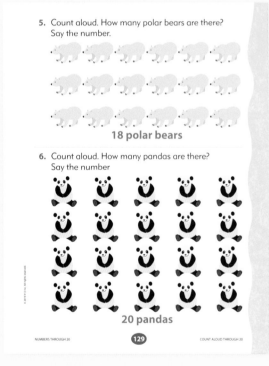

   A. 11   B. 12   (C) 13

3. Count the cubes. Point to each cube as you count it.

   How many cubes did you count? Circle the answer.
   A. 12   B. 13   (C) 14

   Count the cubes in a different order.
   Did counting in a different order change the
   number of cubes?
   A. Yes   (B) No

4. Count the cubes. Point to each cube as you count it.

   How many cubes did you count? Circle the answer.
   A. 15   B. 16   (C) 17

   The cubes are in a different order.
   Count the cubes again.

   How many cubes did you count? Circle the answer.
   A. 15   B. 16   (C) 17

   Did counting in a different order change the
   number of cubes?
   A. Yes   (B) No

5. Count aloud. How many polar bears are there?
   Say the number.

   18 polar bears

6. Count aloud. How many pandas are there?
   Say the number

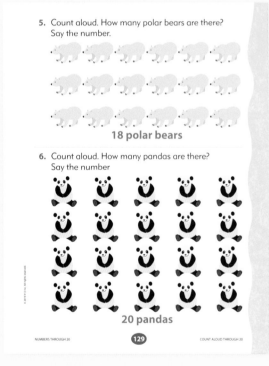

   20 pandas

7. The pandas eat bamboo. Count aloud the bamboo
   sticks. Circle the number that tells how many.

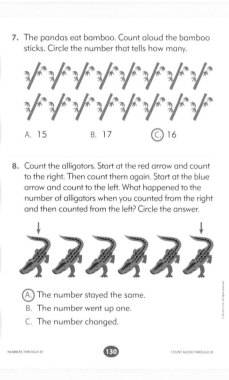

   A. 15   B. 17   (C) 16

8. Count the alligators. Start at the red arrow and count
   to the right. Then count them again. Start at the blue
   arrow and count to the left. What happened to the
   number of alligators when you counted from the right
   and then counted from the left? Circle the answer.

   (A) The number stayed the same.
   B. The number went up one.
   C. The number changed.

Represent an Amount Through 20

Lesson Overview

Skills Update	5 minutes	**ONLINE**
GET READY Show Amounts	5 minutes	**OFFLINE**
LEARN Show and Sketch Amounts	20 minutes	**OFFLINE**
TRY IT Amounts Through 20	10 minutes	**OFFLINE**

▶ Lesson Objectives

Use concrete objects or sketches to represent a quantity up through 20.

▶ Prerequisite Skills

Use concrete objects or sketches to represent a quantity up through 10.

▶ Common Errors and Misconceptions

- Students might start counting before or after pointing to the first object in a group. Or they might stop counting before or after they point to the last object. Students should point to each object as they count it.
- Students might say more than one number for each object when counting objects in a group. Or they might skip objects. Students should point to each object and say exactly one number. Then they should point to the next object and say exactly one number, and so on.
- Students might use an incorrect counting sequence, such as "one, two, four, six, ten."

▶ Advance Preparation

- Prepare a bag of 20 cubes. Prepare a bag of 20 counting objects (for example, dry macaroni).
- Divide a sheet of paper into 4 sections by drawing lines or folding.

▶ Content Background

Students will use objects and drawings to represent amounts through 20.

Keywords

represent – to symbolize or stand for something else

Materials to Gather

SUPPLIED

blocks – B (10 of any color)
blocks – O (20 of any color)
Amounts Through 20 activity page

ALSO NEEDED

counting objects – 20
resealable plastic bags, medium – 2
crayons

GET READY Show Amounts

Objectives

- Use concrete objects or sketches to represent a quantity up through 10.

Students will use blocks to represent numbers.
Gather the circles. Lay out circles in a pile.

1. **Say:** Show 3 with the circles.

   Students should count 3 circles, moving each from the pile as they count it.

2. **Ask:** How do you know that you showed 3?
   ANSWER: I counted. When I reached 3, I stopped counting.

   Return the 3 circles to the pile.

3. Repeat Steps 1 and 2 with the numbers 5, 2, 8, 7, 9 and 10.

Tips

Reinforce the idea that different objects can represent the same number.

LEARN Show and Sketch Amounts

Objectives

- Use concrete objects or sketches to represent a quantity up through 20.

Students will represent amounts through 20 using objects and drawings.
Gather the crayons, paper you divided into 4 sections, and bags you prepared with cubes and counting objects. Give students the bag of counting objects.

1. **Say:** We are going to show amounts with counting objects, cubes, and pictures.

2. **Say:** Use your counting objects to show 13.
   Students should take 13 counting objects from the bag. As they remove each object, they should count aloud exactly one number.

3. **Ask:** How do you know that you showed 13?
   ANSWER: The last number I said when I counted was 13.

   Return the counting objects to the bag.

4. Repeat Steps 2 and 3 with the numbers 16, 10, and 18.

5. Remove 11 cubes from the bag, counting each cube as you remove it.

   Say: I can show 11 with cubes. Use the counting objects to show 11.

6. Have them count aloud their group of counting objects to check that they showed the correct amount.

7. **Ask:** What other ways can we show 11?
   ANSWER: We can draw a picture of 11 objects.

8. Have students draw 11 circles in one section of the paper. As students draw each circle, they should count aloud exactly one number.

9. **Ask:** How is your group of counting objects like your pictures?
   ANSWER: They show the same amount. Both show 11.

   Return the cubes and counting objects to the bags.

10. Repeat Steps 5–9 with the numbers 12, 20, and 15.

11. **Ask:** How did the objects and pictures help you show an amount?
    ANSWER: They helped me show the amount using things I can count.

Tips

For counting objects, use small, durable household items (for example, dry macaroni, shells, or twists).

OFFLINE

10 min

Objectives

- Use concrete objects or sketches to represent a quantity up through 20.

Students will use blocks and drawings to show amounts. Give students the crayons, cubes, and Amounts Through 20 activity page from their Activity Book. Read the directions with them.

Name:

Represent an Amount Through 20
Amounts Through 20

Read each problem and follow the directions.

1. Draw 13 circles.

2. Draw 19 squares.

3. Show 14 cubes.

4. Show 16 cubes.

T R Y I T

---

5. Show 10 cubes.

6. Show 12 cubes.

7. Madison has 11 bananas. Draw shapes on the fruit plate to show all of her bananas.

8. Troy has 18 golf balls. Draw shapes on the putting green to show the golf balls.

T R Y I T

Count Through 20

Lesson Overview

Skills Update	5 minutes	ONLINE
GET READY Shape Count	5 minutes	ONLINE
LEARN Sort and Count	15 minutes	OFFLINE
TRY IT Count in Nature	10 minutes	OFFLINE
CHECKPOINT	10 minutes	OFFLINE

▶ Lesson Objectives

- Count aloud a number of objects up through 20.
- Demonstrate that counting 20 or fewer objects can occur from left to right, right to left, or in any order as long as all the items are counted once.

▶ Prerequisite Skills

- Count aloud a number of objects up through 10.
- Demonstrate that counting 10 or fewer objects can occur from left to right, right to left, or in any order as long as all the items are counted once.

▶ Common Errors and Misconceptions

- Students might start counting before or after pointing to the first object in a group. Or they might stop counting before or after they point to the last object. Students should point to each object as they count it.
- Students might say more than one number for each object when counting objects in a group. Or they might skip objects. Students should point to each object and say exactly one number. Then they should point to the next object and say exactly one number, and so on.
- Students might use an incorrect counting sequence, such as "one, two, four, six, ten."

▶ Advance Preparation

Prepare six bags with the following numbers of counting objects (for example, dry macaroni and dry beans): 12, 14, 15, 16, 18, and 20. Be sure to include some of each type of counting object in each bag.

▶ Content Background

Students will count groups with up through 20 objects. Students will learn that they can count in any order as long as they count each object exactly one time.

Materials to Gather

SUPPLIED

Numbers Through 20 activity page
Checkpoint (printout)

ALSO NEEDED

counting objects – 50 of one type, 45 of another type
resealable plastic bags, medium – 7
crayons

GET READY Shape Count

Students will use the Counting Learning Tool to practice counting groups of up through 10 objects.

DIRECTIONS FOR USING THE COUNTING LEARNING TOOL

1. Click Practice Mode.
   - Click the cube.
   - Click No when asked if you'd like to use ten-frames.
   - Click Start.

2. Have students move 8 cubes into the grid. Students should count aloud as they place each cube. Students may arrange the cubes as they choose.

   After students have placed 8 cubes, have them click the broom to clear the grid.

3. Have students move and count 8 cubes again. This time, however, have them arrange the cubes in a different way.

   Ask: Does placing the cubes in a different way change the number of cubes?
   ANSWER: No

4. Click Menu, and then click Restart.

5. Repeat Steps 1–7 with the following numbers and shapes: 7 stars, 3 butterflies, 10 flowers, and 4 frogs.

Objectives

- Count aloud a number of objects up through 10.
- Demonstrate that counting 10 or fewer objects can occur from left to right, right to left, or in any order as long as all the items are counted once.

LEARN Sort and Count

Students will organize and count different groups of counting objects. It is important students understand that the order in which they count objects in a group does not change the number of objects as long as they count each object exactly once.

Gather the six bags you have filled with counting objects.

1. Give students the bag with 12 counting objects. Have them pour out the objects in the work area.

2. Explain that there are two types of counting objects.
   Ask: How could you arrange the objects to make them easier to count?
   ANSWER: Accept students' responses.

3. Point to one type of counting object, such as a macaroni noodle.
   Say: Let's start with the noodles. Count the noodles first. Then count on the number of beans.

   Have students count the objects. Then ask how many they counted. (12)

4. **Say:** Count the objects again. This time start with the beans.

   Have students count the objects. Then ask how many they counted. (12)

5. **Ask:** Did the number of objects change whether you counted the noodles first or beans first?
   ANSWER: No

6. **Ask:** Why did the number stay the same?
   ANSWER: The order that I count does not change the number of objects as long as I count each object one time.

7. Repeat Steps 1–6 with each bag of counting objects.

Objectives

- Count aloud a number of objects up through 20.
- Demonstrate that counting 20 or fewer objects can occur from left to right, right to left, or in any order as long as all the items are counted once.

Tips

For counting objects, use two types of small, durable household items (for example, dry macaroni and dry beans).

TRY IT Count in Nature

Students will practice counting groups of up through 20 objects. Give students the Count in Nature activity page from their Activity Book and read the directions with them.

Objectives

- Count aloud a number of objects up through 20.
- Demonstrate that counting 20 or fewer objects can occur from left to right, right to left, or in any order as long as all the items are counted once.

CHECKPOINT

OFFLINE 10min

Objectives

Print the Checkpoint and have students complete it on their own. Read the directions, problems, and answer choices to students if necessary. Use the answer key to score the Checkpoint, and then enter the results online.

Gather the crayons. Students will use the crayons for Problem 6.

- Count aloud a number of objects up through 20.
- Demonstrate that counting 20 or fewer objects can occur from left to right, right to left, or in any order as long as all the items are counted once.

⚙ Checkpoint   Math | Numbers Through 20 | Count Through 20

Name _____ Date _____

Checkpoint Answer Key

Read each problem and follow the directions.

(1 point)
1. Count aloud the stars. Write the total.

☆ ☆ ☆ ☆ ☆
☆ ☆   **7** stars

(1 point)
2. Count aloud each group of circles. Which group has 13 circles? Circle the answer.

A. ○○○○○○
   ○○○○○○

B. ○○○○○○
   ○○○○○○○

Ⓒ ○○○○○○○
   ○○○○○○○

(1 point)
3. Count aloud. How many cherries are there? Circle the answer.

🍒🍒🍒🍒🍒🍒🍒🍒🍒🍒🍒🍒🍒🍒🍒

A. 14   Ⓑ 15   C. 16

⚙ Checkpoint   Math | Numbers Through 20 | Count Through 20

Name _____ Date _____

(1 point)
4. Look at the fish tank.

Count the fish in the tank. Circle each fish as you count it.

How many fish did you count?

A. 18   Ⓑ 19   C. 20

Count the fish in a different order.
This time, cross out each fish as you count it.

How many fish did you count?

A. 17   B. 18   Ⓒ 19

⚙ Checkpoint   Math | Numbers Through 20 | Count Through 20

Name _____ Date _____

(1 point)
5. Look at the row of squares.

☆ □□□□□□□□□□□ ☾

Start at the square with the star on it. Count all the squares.

If your friend also counted all the squares, starting at the square with the moon, how many would your friend count? Circle the answer.

A. 12 – The answer is one less.
Ⓑ 13 – The answer doesn't change when you start at a different place.
C. 14 – The answer is one more.

(1 point)
6. Count aloud the circles. Color each circle as you count it.

○○○○○○○○○
○○○○○○○○

Ⓐ 17   B. 18   C. 19

(1 point)
7. Count the circles in a different order. This time, cross out each circle as you count it. How many circles did you count each time? Circle the answer.

A. 17 the first time, and 16 the second time
B. 17 the first time, and 15 the second time
Ⓒ 17 the first time, and 17 the second time

---

196   NUMBERS THROUGH 20

Show Amounts Through 20

Lesson Overview

Skills Update	5 minutes	ONLINE
GET READY Count the Balls	5 minutes	ONLINE
LEARN Represent with Drawings	15 minutes	OFFLINE
TRY IT Show Numbers Through 20	10 minutes	OFFLINE
CHECKPOINT	5 minutes	OFFLINE

▶ Lesson Objectives

- Use concrete objects or sketches to represent a quantity up through 20.
- Count aloud a number of objects up through 20.
- Demonstrate that counting 20 or fewer objects can occur from left to right, right to left, or in any order as long as all the items are counted once.

▶ Prerequisite Skills

Use concrete objects or sketches to represent a quantity up through 10.

▶ Common Errors and Misconceptions

- Students might start counting before or after pointing to the first object in a group. Or they might stop counting before or after they point to the last object. Students should point to each object as they count it.
- Students might say more than one number for each object when counting objects in a group. Or they might skip objects. Students should point to each object and say exactly one number. Then they should point to the next object and say exactly one number, and so on.
- Students might use an incorrect counting sequence, such as "one, two, four, six, ten."

▶ Content Background

Students will represent amounts through 20. They will learn that an amount can be shown in more than one way.

Materials to Gather

SUPPLIED

Represent with Drawings activity page

Show Numbers Through 20 activity page

blocks – O (20 of any color)

blocks – B (10 each of two colors)

Checkpoint (printout)

GET READY Count the Balls

ONLINE
5 min

Students will count groups of sports balls. Then they will use cubes to represent the same amount. Gather the cubes, and follow the instructions online.

Objectives

- Use concrete objects or sketches to represent a quantity up through 10.

LEARN Represent with Drawings

OFFLINE
15min

Objectives

- Use concrete objects or sketches to represent a quantity up through 20.

Students will use drawings to represent amounts through 20. Give students the Represent with Drawings activity page from their Activity Book and read the directions with them.

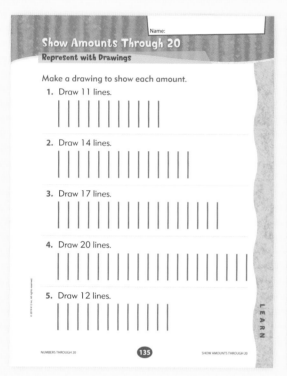

TRY IT Show Numbers Through 20

OFFLINE
10min

Objectives

- Count aloud a number of objects up through 20.
- Demonstrate that counting 20 or fewer objects can occur from left to right, right to left, or in any order as long as all the items are counted once.

Students will practice using drawings and objects to show amounts through 20. Give students the circle blocks, cubes, and the Show Numbers Through 20 activity page from their Activity Book. Read the directions with them.

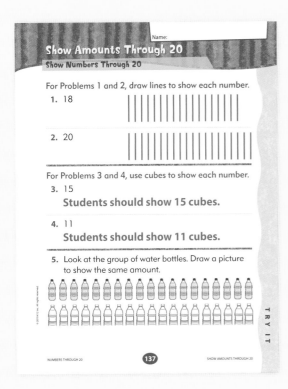

Show Amounts Through 20

Show Numbers Through 20

For Problems 1 and 2, draw lines to show each number.

1. 18

2. 20

For Problems 3 and 4, use cubes to show each number.

3. 15

   Students should show 15 cubes.

4. 11

   Students should show 11 cubes.

5. Look at the group of water bottles. Draw a picture to show the same amount.

NUMBERS THROUGH 20   **137**   SHOW AMOUNTS THROUGH 20

TRY IT

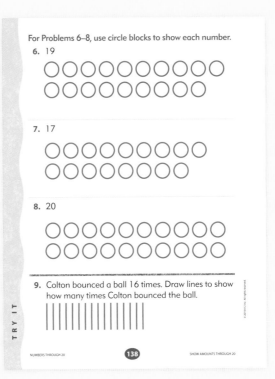

For Problems 6–8, use circle blocks to show each number.

6. 19

7. 17

8. 20

9. Colton bounced a ball 16 times. Draw lines to show how many times Colton bounced the ball.

TRY IT

NUMBERS THROUGH 20   **138**   SHOW AMOUNTS THROUGH 20

CHECKPOINT

OFFLINE

5 min

Print the Checkpoint and have students complete it on their own. Read the directions, problems, and answer choices to students if necessary. Use the answer key to score the Checkpoint, and then enter the results online.

Objectives

- Use concrete objects or sketches to represent a quantity up through 20.

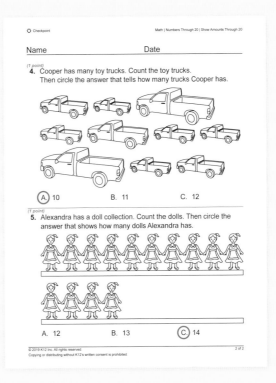

Checkpoint   Math | Numbers Through 20 | Show Amounts Through 20

Name   Date

Checkpoint Answer Key

Read each problem and follow the directions.

(1 point)
1. Draw 14 lines.

(1 point)
2. Mary has 10 square blocks. Draw shapes to show Mary's blocks on the table.

(1 point)
3. Which group of ducks shows the number 9? Circle the answer.

   A.

   B.

   Ⓒ

© 2019 K12 Inc. All rights reserved.
Copying or distributing without K12's written consent is prohibited   1 of 2

Checkpoint   Math | Numbers Through 20 | Show Amounts Through 20

Name   Date

(1 point)
4. Cooper has many toy trucks. Count the toy trucks. Then circle the answer that tells how many trucks Cooper has.

   Ⓐ 10   B. 11   C. 12

(1 point)
5. Alexandra has a doll collection. Count the dolls. Then circle the answer that shows how many dolls Alexandra has.

   A. 12   B. 13   Ⓒ 14

© 2019 K12 Inc. All rights reserved.
Copying or distributing without K12's written consent is prohibited   2 of 2

Compare Sets Through 20

Lesson Overview

Skills Update	5 minutes	**ONLINE**
GET READY Compare Sets Through 10	5 minutes	**ONLINE**
LEARN Compare Two or More Sets	10 minutes	**OFFLINE**
LEARN Make Sets	10 minutes	**OFFLINE**
TRY IT Compare Sets	10 minutes	**OFFLINE**
CHECKPOINT	5 minutes	**OFFLINE**

▶ Lesson Objectives

Given two or more sets of 20 or fewer objects, identify which set has more or fewer objects than another set, or which sets have an equal number of objects.

▶ Prerequisite Skills

Given two or more sets that have 10 or fewer objects, identify which set has more or fewer objects than another set, or which sets have an equal number of objects.

▶ Common Errors and Misconceptions

- Students might start counting before or after pointing to the first object in a group. Or they might stop counting before or after they point to the last object. Students should point to each object as they count it.

- Students might say more than one number for each object when counting objects in a group. Or they might skip objects. Students should point to each object and say exactly one number. Then they should point to the next object and say exactly one number, and so on.

- Students might use an incorrect counting sequence, such as "one, two, four, six, ten."

▶ Advance Preparation

Cut out each card from the Make Sets activity page.

▶ Content Background

In this lesson, students will count and compare groups of up through 20 objects.

A *set* is a group of objects. *Set* is a mathematical term for *group*. You may use *set* and *group* interchangeably in conversation with students.

Materials to Gather

SUPPLIED

blocks – E (all colors)

blocks – O (all colors)

Compare Two or More Sets activity page

Make Sets activity page

Compare Sets activity page

Checkpoint (printout)

ALSO NEEDED

scissors, adult

GET READY Compare Sets Through 10

Students will practice identifying groups with more, fewer, or the same number of objects by comparing baskets of fruit and vegetables.

Objectives

- Given two or more sets that have 10 or fewer objects, identify which set has more or fewer objects than another set, or which sets have an equal number of objects.

Tips

If students have difficulty, have them use a different color group of cubes to represent the objects in each basket. Have them put the groups of cubes in lines beginning at the same place. Explain that the group with the longer line is the group with more fruit or vegetables.

LEARN Compare Two or More Sets

Students will compare groups of objects using the terms *more, most, fewer, fewest*, and *equal*. Review these terms with students. Explain that *more* and *fewer* are used when comparing 2 groups and that *most* and *fewest* are used when comparing 3 or more groups. Explain to students that greater numbers describe groups with *more* objects, and lesser numbers describe groups with *fewer* objects.

Give students the Compare Two or More Sets activity page and read the directions with them.

Objectives

- Given two or more sets of 20 or fewer objects, identify which set has more or fewer objects than another set, or which sets have an equal number of objects.

Tips

Have students use blocks to represent the objects on the activity page. Have students match the blocks to help determine the answers.

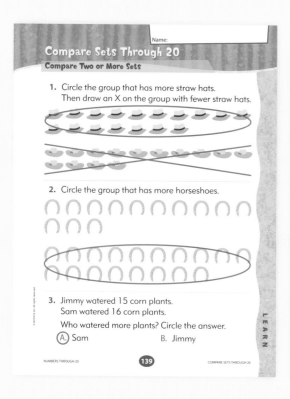

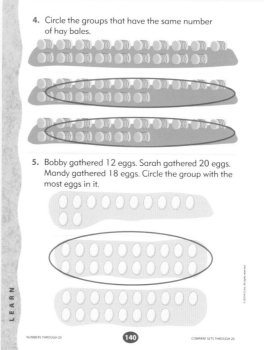

Compare Sets Through 20
Compare Two or More Sets

Name: _____

1. Circle the group that has more straw hats.
   Then draw an X on the group with fewer straw hats.

2. Circle the group that has more horseshoes.

3. Jimmy watered 15 corn plants.
   Sam watered 16 corn plants.
   Who watered more plants? Circle the answer.
   (A.) Sam   B. Jimmy

4. Circle the groups that have the same number of hay bales.

5. Bobby gathered 12 eggs. Sarah gathered 20 eggs. Mandy gathered 18 eggs. Circle the group with the most eggs in it.

LEARN Make Sets

OFFLINE
10 min

Students will make groups with an equal number of tiles as dots on each card. They will also make groups with fewer or more tiles than dots on each card. Finally, they will compare the cards to determine those with the same number of dots, the fewest dots, and the most dots.

Gather the tiles and the cut-out cards from the Make Sets activity page.

1. Display the card with 15 green dots.

   Say: Make a group of tiles that shows the same number as the number of dots.

   Students may take one of several approaches to making the group of tiles:

   - Counting the total number of dots and then counting out that many tiles
   - Copying the arrangement of the dots with the tiles, by counting each row
   - Placing one tile on top of each dot

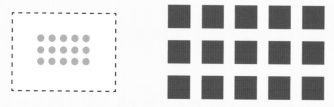

2. **Ask:** How many dots are on the card?
   ANSWER: 15

   Ask: How many tiles did you show?
   ANSWER: 15

   Say: Each group shows the same number—15.

Objectives

- Given two or more sets of 20 or fewer objects, identify which set has more or fewer objects than another set, or which sets have an equal number of objects.

Tips

Place the tiles in a container. Have students take out only what they need for each step.

3. **Say:** Now make a group of tiles that has *fewer* tiles than green dots.

Students may take away tiles from their existing group.

4. **Ask:** How many tiles did you show?
Say: There are fewer tiles than dots. There are more dots than tiles.

5. **Say:** Now make a group of tiles that has *more* tiles than green dots.

Students may add tiles to their existing group.

6. **Ask:** How many tiles did you show?
Say: There are more tiles than dots. There are fewer dots than tiles.

7. Repeat Steps 1–6 with each card.

8. Clear the work area. Display the four cards. Point to the card with 15 green dots.

Say: Point to another card that has the same number of dots.

Students should point to the card with 15 red dots. To check that the cards show the same number, have students count aloud the dots of each card, touching each dot as they count it.

Say: Both cards show 15 dots. They have an equal number of dots.

  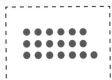 

9. **Ask:** Which card has the fewest dots?
ANSWER: the card with 13 yellow dots

  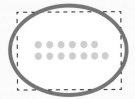 

10. **Ask:** Which card has the most dots?
ANSWER: the card with 19 blue dots

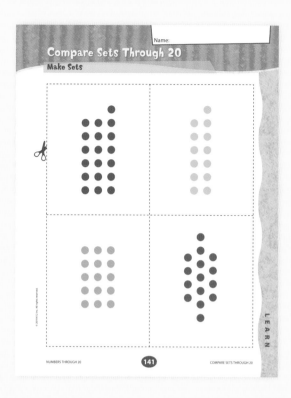

TRY IT Compare Sets

OFFLINE 10 min

This Try It activity has two parts.

Part 1

Students will compare three groups of cubes. Gather the cubes.

1. Make three groups of the following numbers of cubes as shown: 12, 12, and 17.

   Ask: Which groups have the same number of cubes?
   ANSWER: the two groups with 12 cubes

2. Make three groups of the following numbers of cubes as shown: 14, 12, and 15.

   Ask: Which group has the most cubes?
   ANSWER: the group with 15 cubes

Part 2

Students will compare sets of up through 20 objects. Give students the Compare Sets activity page from their Activity Book and read the directions with them.

Objectives

- Given two or more sets of 20 or fewer objects, identify which set has more or fewer objects than another set, or which sets have an equal number of objects.

Tips

If students have difficulty choosing the group with more objects, have them match the objects in the groups. Explain that the group with unmatched objects has more objects in it.

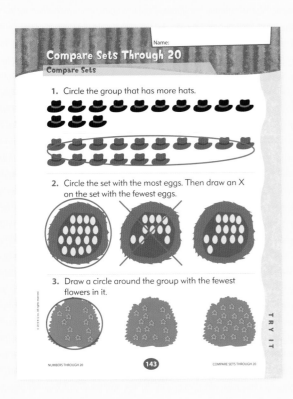

Compare Sets Through 20

Compare Sets

1. Circle the group that has more hats.

2. Circle the set with the most eggs. Then draw an X on the set with the fewest eggs.

3. Draw a circle around the group with the fewest flowers in it.

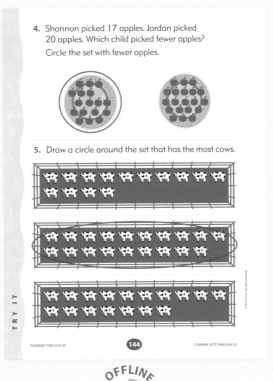

4. Shannon picked 17 apples. Jordan picked 20 apples. Which child picked fewer apples? Circle the set with fewer apples.

5. Draw a circle around the set that has the most cows.

OFFLINE 5 min

CHECKPOINT

Objectives

Print the Checkpoint. In Part 1, students will take a performance-based assessment. In Part 2, students will complete the problems on their own. Read the directions, problems, and answer choices to students if necessary. Use the answer key to score the Checkpoint, and then enter the results online.

Gather the cubes. Students will use the cubes for Problems 1 and 2.

- Given two or more sets of 20 or fewer objects, identify which set has more or fewer objects than another set, or which sets have an equal number of objects.

○ Checkpoint   Math | Numbers Through 20 | Compare Sets Through 20

Name _____ Date _____

Checkpoint Answer Key

Part 1
Perform the task and circle the answer.
(1 point)
1. Place 15 cubes in one group and 17 in another group. Which group has fewer cubes?

(A) 15   B. 17

(1 point)
2. Place 11 cubes in one group and 12 in another group. Which group has more cubes?

A. 11   (B) 12

Give students Part 2 of the assessment.

○ Checkpoint   Math | Numbers Through 20 | Compare Sets Through 20

Name _____ Date _____

Checkpoint Answer Key

Part 2
Read each problem and circle the answer.
(1 point)
3. Avi has two groups of balls. Which group has more balls?

A. [barrels]   (B) [soccer balls]

(1 point)
4. Marc has three groups of cars. Which group has the fewest cars?

(A) [cars]

B. [cars]

C. [cars]

Write Numerals Through 20

Lesson Overview

Skills Update	5 minutes	ONLINE
GET READY Write Numbers Through 10	10 minutes	ONLINE
LEARN Paint Numbers 1–20	10 minutes	OFFLINE
LEARN See, Feel, and Write 1–20	10 minutes	OFFLINE
TRY IT Count and Write 1–20	5 minutes	OFFLINE

▶ **Lesson Objectives**

Write numerals from 1 through 20.

▶ **Prerequisite Skills**

Write numerals from 1 through 10.

▶ **Common Errors and Misconceptions**

- Students might say more than one number for each object when counting objects in a group. Or they might skip objects. Students should point to each object and say exactly one number. Then they should point to the next object and say exactly one number, and so on.

- Students might use an incorrect counting sequence, such as "one, two, four, six, ten."

▶ **Advance Preparation**

- The Paint Numbers 1–20 activity calls for finger-paint paper, which is available in art supply stores. You also may use a brown paper bag or the blank side of wrapping paper.

- Print the Numeral Writing Guide.

▶ **Content Background**

Students will learn to write the numerals 11 through 20.

In mathematics, the word *number* represents the quantity, and the word *numeral* represents the written symbol. So numerals, such as 0, 1, 2, and 3, symbolically represent numbers, or quantities. In everyday language, we say *number* to describe both the symbol and the quantity. As you speak with students, you may use *number* only. This lesson is titled "Write Numerals Through 20" to convey correct mathematical terminology.

Materials to Gather

SUPPLIED
Numeral Writing Guide (printout)
See, Feel, and Write 1–20 activity page
Count and Write 1–20 activity page

ALSO NEEDED
paper, wide-line handwriting
paper, finger-paint
finger paint

Keywords

numeral – a symbol that stands for a number

GET READY Write Numbers Through 10

ONLINE 10 min

Objectives

- Write numerals from 1 through 10.

Students will review how to write the numbers 1 though 10 by watching a virtual pencil write each number. Gather the wide-line handwriting paper.

Follow the directions on each screen. Have students write each number in the air after they see it written online. Give students the wide-line handwriting paper when they reach the last screen, and have them practice writing the numbers on the paper.

LEARN Paint Numbers 1–20

OFFLINE 10 min

Objectives

- Write numerals from 1 through 20.

Students will trace the numbers 1 through 20 on the Numeral Writing Guide. Then they will finger paint the numbers 1 through 20.

Gather the Numeral Writing Guide, finger paint, and finger-paint paper.

Tips

Place the Numeral Writing Guide in a clear plastic bag so that students can refer to it if needed while finger painting.

If finger paints are not available, students may use crayons to write each number.

1. Display the Numeral Writing Guide.

   Say: Let's trace some numbers.

2. Have students point to each number in sequence, say the number, and trace it with their index finger. To trace, have students place their finger at the top of each number and then move it down along the line. They should pick up and reposition their finger when tracing the numbers 4 and 5.

   When you feel that students are comfortable forming each number, prepare the work area for finger painting.

3. **Say:** You practiced writing the numbers 1 through 10. You can use these numbers to write the numbers 11 through 20.

4. Put some paint in the center of the paper.

5. **Say:** Use your finger to paint the number 11.

   Ask: What numbers did you use to write the number 11?
   ANSWER: 1

6. Have students smooth out the finger paint.

7. Repeat Steps 5 and 6 for each number 1 through 20, calling the numbers in a random order.

8. Check that students paint each number correctly, forming the numbers from left to right and from top to bottom.

9. You may wish to have students choose a favorite number to show on the paper and allow the paper to dry with that number.

LEARN See, Feel, and Write 1–20

Objectives

- Write numerals from 1 through 20.

Students will write the number that describes a group of 1 through 20 objects. Then students will identify numbers traced on their hand.

Give students the See, Feel, and Write 1–20 activity page and read the directions with them.

1. Have students complete the activity page.

2. **Say:** Look at your activity page. I am going to use my finger to trace one of these numbers on your hand. Tell me which number you feel, and show me the number on your activity page.

   Trace the number 12 on students' palm. Form the numbers from left to right and from top to bottom.

   Students should point to the group of 12 spools on the activity page.

3. Repeat Step 2 with each number on the activity page, calling the numbers in a random order.

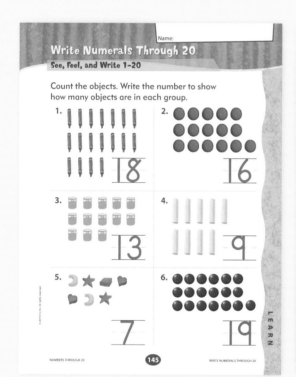

TRY IT Count and Write 1-20

Students will write the number that describes a group of 1 through 20 objects. Give students the Count and Write 1–20 activity page from their Activity Book and read the directions with them.

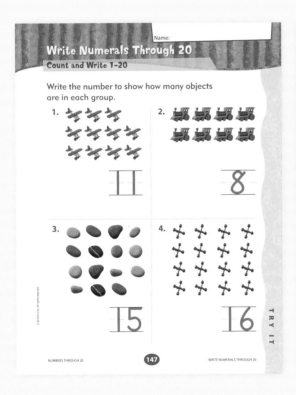

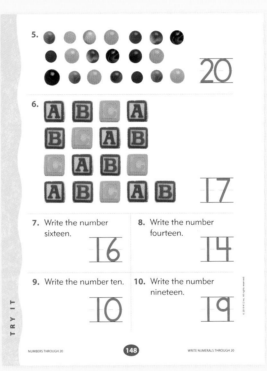

Compare Numbers and Sets Through 20

Lesson Overview

Skills Update	5 minutes	ONLINE
GET READY Compare Numbers Through 10	5 minutes	ONLINE
LEARN Label the Set	15 minutes	OFFLINE
LEARN Greater and Lesser Values	10 minutes	OFFLINE
TRY IT Compare Numbers Through 20	5 minutes	OFFLINE
CHECKPOINT	5 minutes	OFFLINE

▶ Lesson Objectives

Recognize that numbers with greater values describe sets with more objects in them than numbers with lesser values (for sets of 20 or fewer objects).

▶ Prerequisite Skills

Recognize that numbers with greater values describe sets with more objects in them than numbers with lesser values do (for sets of 10 or fewer objects).

▶ Advance Preparation

- Prepare five bags with the following numbers of blocks: 12, 18, 20, 14, and 6.
- Number index cards 0 through 20. Label two other index cards as follows: **more** on one side and **greater** on the other side; **fewer** on one side and **lesser** on the other side. Save cards for use in future lessons.

▶ Content Background

Students will label and compare sets of objects, including blocks and pictures of bugs. Students will learn to connect the word *more* with *greater* and *fewer* with *lesser*.

A *set* is a group of objects. *Set* is a mathematical term for *group*. You may use *set* and *group* interchangeably in conversation with students.

Keywords	**greater** – larger in number or amount than another
	lesser – smaller in number or amount than another

Materials to Gather

SUPPLIED

blocks – B (all colors)

Greater and Lesser Values activity page

Compare Numbers Through 20 activity page

Checkpoint (printout)

ALSO NEEDED

resealable plastic bags, medium – 5

index cards – numbered 0 through 20

index cards – labeled **more/greater** and **fewer/lesser**

GET READY Compare Numbers Through 10

Students will practice comparing numbers through 10. They will compare two numbered groups of bugs and choose the group with the greater or lesser number. Explain to students that greater numbers describe groups with *more* objects, and lesser numbers describe groups with *fewer* objects.

- Recognize that numbers with greater values describe sets with more objects in them than numbers with lesser values do (for sets of 10 or fewer objects).

OFFLINE
15 min

LEARN Label the Set

Objectives

Students will use number cards to describe sets of circles. Then they will compare sets using the terms *more* and *fewer*. Students will connect the term *greater* with *more* and *lesser* with *fewer*.

Gather the index cards you have numbered and labeled, and the bags you have filled with circle blocks.

- Recognize that numbers with greater values describe sets with more objects in them than numbers with lesser values (for sets of 20 or fewer objects).

1. Display the group 12 circles and the group of 18 circles.

   Ask students to place the **more** card next to the group with more circles.

2. **Ask:** If that group has *more*, what word tells about the other group?
   ANSWER: fewer

   If students say *lesser*, explain that *fewer* refers to objects and *lesser* refers to numbers.

   Ask students to place the **fewer** card next to the group with fewer circles.

3. Have students count the circles in each pile and label each pile with the number card that tells how many.

4. Point to the number cards and the **more** and **fewer** cards. Ask students if the correct cards are placed.

5. **Say:** A greater number describes a set with more. Turn over the **more** card to show **greater**.

6. **Say:** A lesser number describes a set with fewer. Turn over the **fewer** card to show **lesser**.

7. Repeat Steps 1–6 with the following groups: 14 and 20, 6 and 12, 14 and 18, 20 and 18.

LEARN Greater and Lesser Values

OFFLINE 10 min

Students will learn that numbers with greater values describe sets with more objects, or larger sets, and that numbers with lesser values describe sets with fewer objects, or smaller sets.

Give students the Greater and Lesser Values activity page from their Activity Book and read the directions with them.

Objectives

- Recognize that numbers with greater values describe sets with more objects in them than numbers with lesser values (for sets of 20 or fewer objects).

Tips

Emphasize the words *more, fewer, greater, lesser, larger,* and *smaller* when reading the problems.

If students have difficulty comparing the numbers, have them use counting objects to represent each number.

TRY IT Compare Numbers Through 20

OFFLINE 5 min

Students will practice comparing numbers and groups of objects through 20. Give students the Compare Numbers Through 20 activity page from their Activity Book and read the directions with them.

Objectives

- Recognize that numbers with greater values describe sets with more objects in them than numbers with lesser values (for sets of 20 or fewer objects).

Compare Numbers and Sets Through 20

Compare Numbers Through 20

1. Circle the jar with more butterflies.

5   15

2. Circle the number with the greater value.

20   13

3. Circle the number with the lesser value.

10   16

Say the name that answers each question.

4. Cody saw 12 caterpillars.
   Max saw 5 caterpillars.
   Who saw more caterpillars? **Cody**

TRY IT

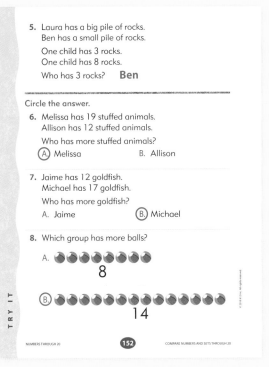

5. Laura has a big pile of rocks.
   Ben has a small pile of rocks.

   One child has 3 rocks.
   One child has 8 rocks.

   Who has 3 rocks? **Ben**

Circle the answer.

6. Melissa has 19 stuffed animals.
   Allison has 12 stuffed animals.

   Who has more stuffed animals?
   (A) Melissa   B. Allison

7. Jaime has 12 goldfish.
   Michael has 17 goldfish.

   Who has more goldfish?
   A. Jaime   (B.) Michael

8. Which group has more balls?

   A.
      8

   (B.)
      14

TRY IT

OFFLINE
5min

CHECKPOINT

Print the Checkpoint and have students complete it on their own. Read the directions, problems, and answer choices to students if necessary. Use the answer key to score the Checkpoint, and then enter the results online.

Objectives

- Recognize that numbers with greater values describe sets with more objects in them than numbers with lesser values (for sets of 20 or fewer objects).

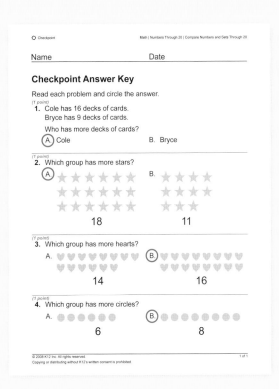

☼ Checkpoint   Math | Numbers Through 20 | Compare Numbers and Sets Through 20

Name _____   Date _____

Checkpoint Answer Key

Read each problem and circle the answer.
(1 point)
1. Cole has 16 decks of cards.
   Bryce has 9 decks of cards.

   Who has more decks of cards?
   (A) Cole   B. Bryce

(1 point)
2. Which group has more stars?
   (A) ★ ★ ★ ★ ★ ★   B. ★ ★ ★ ★
       ★ ★ ★ ★ ★ ★   ★ ★ ★ ★
       ★ ★ ★ ★ ★ ★   ★ ★ ★
          18   11

(1 point)
3. Which group has more hearts?
   A. ♥ ♥ ♥ ♥ ♥ ♥ ♥   (B.) ♥ ♥ ♥ ♥ ♥ ♥ ♥ ♥
      ♥ ♥ ♥ ♥ ♥ ♥ ♥   ♥ ♥ ♥ ♥ ♥ ♥ ♥ ♥
            14   16

(1 point)
4. Which group has more circles?
   A. ●●●●●●   (B.) ●●●●●●●●
         6   8

Write Numerals from 1 Through 20

Lesson Overview

Skills Update	5 minutes	**ONLINE**
GET READY Practice Writing Numbers 1–10	15 minutes	**OFFLINE**
LEARN Trace and Write Through 20	15 minutes	**OFFLINE**
TRY IT Write Numbers Through 20	10 minutes	**OFFLINE**
CHECKPOINT	5 minutes	**OFFLINE**

▶ Lesson Objectives

Write numerals from 1 through 20.

▶ Prerequisite Skills

Write numerals from 1 through 10.

▶ Advance Preparation

Fold each sheet of construction paper into 6 equal sections.

▶ Safety

Supervise students to make sure they use their scissors safely and stay seated.

▶ Content Background

Students will say the numbers 1 through 20 in preparation for writing numerals 1 through 20.

In mathematics, the word *number* represents the quantity, and the word *numeral* represents the written symbol. So numerals, such as 0, 1, 2, and 3, symbolically represent numbers, or quantities. In everyday language, we say *number* to describe both the symbol and the quantity. As you speak with students, you may use *number* only. This lesson is titled "Write Numerals from 1 Through 20" to convey correct mathematical terminology.

Materials to Gather

SUPPLIED

Trace and Write Through 20 activity page

Write Numbers Through 20 activity page

Checkpoint (printout)

ALSO NEEDED

paper, construction – 2 light-colored sheets

crayons

yarn – 1 ball

paper, wide-line handwriting

scissors, round-end safety

glue stick

GET READY Write Numbers 1–10

OFFLINE 15 min

Objectives

- Write numerals from 1 through 10.

Students will practice writing the numbers 1 through 10.
   Gather the crayons and the construction paper you have folded.

1. **Say:** Count aloud from 1 through 10. Raise a finger each time you say a number.

   Have students first raise the thumb on their right hand, followed by their index finger, and so on. When they say "6," they should raise their left thumb and continue with their other fingers in order.

2. Give students the paper and crayons.

   Say: Now you will write the numbers with crayons. Write 1 through 5 on one side of the paper with the red crayon, writing one number in each section. Say each number as you write it.

   There will be one empty section.

3. Have students turn over the paper and write 6 through 10 with the red crayon. They should write each number in one section and say each number as they write it. There will be one empty section.

4. Have students count to 10, pointing to each number on their paper as they count.

5. Repeat Steps 3–5 using the blue crayon and second sheet of paper.

LEARN Trace and Write Through 20

OFFLINE 15 min

Objectives

- Write numerals from 1 through 20.

Students will trace the numbers 11 through 20 with a glue stick, yarn, and their finger. Then they will write the numbers on handwriting paper.
   Gather the Trace and Write Through 20 activity page, glue stick, scissors, yarn, and wide-line handwriting paper.

1. **Say:** Let's write the numbers 11 through 20. The numbers 11 through 20 are each made by writing two numbers from 0 through 9.

2. Point to the activity page.

   Ask: What is the first number in most of the numbers?
   ANSWER: 1

   Say: Each 1 is followed by a second number—1 through 9.

3. **Ask:** Which number does not begin with a 1?
   ANSWER: 20

   Ask: How do you write 20?
   ANSWER: Write a 2 and then a 0.

4. Point to the number 11, and ask students to read the number.

5. Have students trace the number 11 with the glue stick. Show students how to place the glue stick at the top of each 1 and then move it down along the line.

6. Next have students cover the number 11 with yarn.

Tips

The numeral 4 is formed with two strokes, and should be formed with two pieces of yarn. Guide students to start at the top leftmost point when forming this numeral.

Say: Place the end of the yarn at the top of each number. Push the yarn down into the glue. Cut the yarn when you get to the end of the number.

If students have difficulty cutting the yarn, hold the end of the yarn against the paper as they cut to ensure that the yarn does not move.

7. Repeat Steps 4–6 with each number on the activity page. Remind students to start at the top of each number when tracing it with the glue stick and when placing the yarn.

8. Have students count from 11 through 20, tracing each number on the activity page with their finger as they say it.

9. Name several numbers from 11 through 20 in a random order (e.g., 19, 14, 20, 16, 13). As you name each number, students should point to the number on the activity page and trace it with their finger.

10. Give students a sheet of handwriting paper.

    Repeat Step 9, naming numbers from 11 through 20 in a random order. Instead of tracing the number, students should write the number on the handwriting paper. Continue naming numbers until students have written each number twice.

    Students may reference the activity page when writing the numbers.

TRY IT Write Numbers Through 20

Students will practice writing the numbers 11 through 20 out of sequence. Give students the Write Numbers Through 20 activity page from their Activity Book and read the directions with them.

Tips

If students have difficulty forming the numbers, model how to write each number. Have students practice writing the numbers on handwriting paper before beginning the activity page.

Name: _____

Write Numerals from 1 Through 20
Write Numbers Through 20

Write the number of objects shown in each picture.

1.   13

2.   16

3.   17

4.   18

Write the number for each word.

5. eleven   11   6. twelve   12

7. thirteen   13   8. fourteen   14

9. fifteen   15   10. sixteen   16

11. seventeen   17   12. eighteen   18

13. nineteen   19   14. twenty   20

Print the Checkpoint and have students complete it on their own. Read the directions, problems, and answer choices to students if necessary. Use the answer key to score the Checkpoint, and then enter the results online.

- Write numerals from 1 through 20.

☼ Checkpoint   Math | Numbers Through 20 | Write Numerals from 1 Through 20

Name _____ Date _____

Checkpoint Answer Key

Read each problem and write each number on the line.
(1 point)   (1 point)
1. Write the number eleven.   2. Write the number twelve.

11   12

(1 point)   (1 point)
3. Write the number fifteen.   4. Write the number twenty.

15   20

1 of 1

Unit Review

UNIT REVIEW Look Back	20 minutes	ONLINE
UNIT REVIEW Checkpoint Practice	20 minutes	OFFLINE
▶ UNIT REVIEW Prepare for the Checkpoint		

▶ Unit Objectives

This lesson reviews the following objectives:
- Count aloud a number of objects up through 20.
- Demonstrate that counting 20 or fewer objects can occur from left to right, right to left, or in any order as long as all the items are counted once.
- Use concrete objects or sketches to represent a quantity up through 20.
- Given two or more sets of 20 or fewer objects, identify which set has more or fewer objects than another set, or which sets have an equal number of objects.
- Write numerals from 1 through 20.
- Recognize that numbers with greater values describe sets with more objects in them than numbers with lesser values (for sets of 20 or fewer objects).

▶ Advance Preparation

In this lesson, students will have an opportunity to review previous activities in the Numbers Through 20 unit. Look at the suggested activities in Unit Review: Prepare for the Checkpoint online and gather any needed materials.

Materials to Gather

SUPPLIED

Checkpoint Practice activity page

Keywords

count	most
fewer	number
fewest	numeral
greater	represent
lesser	set
more	

UNIT REVIEW Look Back

Objectives

- Review unit objectives.

In this unit, students have counted groups of up through 20 objects, learning that they can count in any order as long as they count each item exactly one time. They have used models, drawings, and finally numerals to represent groups of up through 20 objects.

Students have compared groups of 20 or fewer objects to determine which has more, fewer, the most, or the fewest objects. They have compared numbers from 1 through 20 to determine which is greater and which is lesser.

Students have also learned to write the numerals from 11 through 20. Students will review these concepts to prepare for the Unit Checkpoint.

UNIT REVIEW Checkpoint Practice

Objectives

- Review unit objectives.

Students will complete a Checkpoint Practice activity page to prepare for the Unit Checkpoint. If necessary, read the directions, questions,.and answer choices to students. Have students answer the problems on their own. Carefully review the answers with students

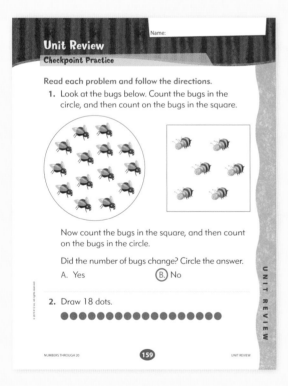

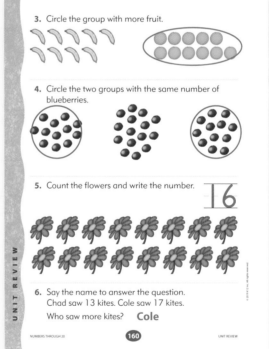

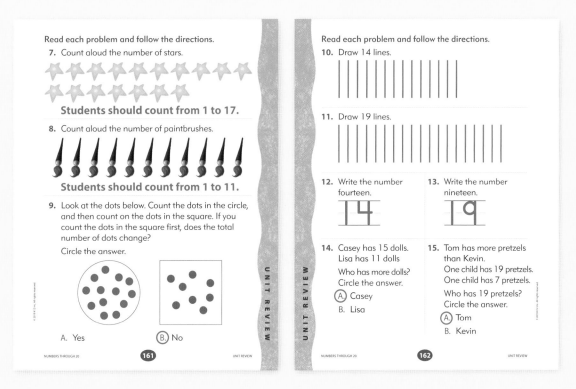

Read each problem and follow the directions.

7. Count aloud the number of stars.

Students should count from 1 to 17.

8. Count aloud the number of paintbrushes.

Students should count from 1 to 11.

9. Look at the dots below. Count the dots in the circle, and then count on the dots in the square. If you count the dots in the square first, does the total number of dots change?

Circle the answer.

A. Yes   (B.) No

Read each problem and follow the directions.

10. Draw 14 lines.

11. Draw 19 lines.

12. Write the number fourteen.

14

13. Write the number nineteen.

19

14. Casey has 15 dolls. Lisa has 11 dolls.

Who has more dolls? Circle the answer.
(A.) Casey
B. Lisa

15. Tom has more pretzels than Kevin.
One child has 19 pretzels.
One child has 7 pretzels.

Who has 19 pretzels? Circle the answer.
(A.) Tom
B. Kevin

➔ UNIT REVIEW Prepare for the Checkpoint

What you do next depends on how students performed in the previous activity, Unit Review: Checkpoint Practice. If students had difficulty with any of the problems, complete the appropriate review activity listed in the table online.

Unit Checkpoint

| **UNIT CHECKPOINT** Offline | 40 minutes | **OFFLINE** |

▶ Unit Objectives

This lesson assesses the following objectives:

- Count aloud a number of objects up through 20.
- Demonstrate that counting 20 or fewer objects can occur from left to right, right to left, or in any order as long as all the items are counted once.
- Use concrete objects or sketches to represent a quantity up through 20.
- Given two or more sets of 20 or fewer objects, identify which set has more or fewer objects than another set, or which sets have an equal number of objects.
- Write numerals from 1 through 20.
- Recognize that numbers with greater values describe sets with more objects in them than numbers with lesser values (for sets of 20 or fewer objects).

▶ Advance Preparation

Prepare 7 bags with the following numbers and types of blocks. Except for the cubes, color does not matter: 20 green cubes, 20 blue cubes, 10 circles, 11 circles, 12 circles, 12 circles, and 15 circles.

Materials to Gather

SUPPLIED

blocks – B (all colors)

blocks – O (20 green, 20 blue)

Unit Checkpoint (printout)

ALSO NEEDED

resealable plastic bags, medium – 7

OFFLINE
40 min

UNIT CHECKPOINT Offline

Objectives

- Assess unit objectives.

Students will complete the Unit Checkpoint offline. In Part 1, students will take a performance-based assessment. In Part 2, students will complete the problems on their own. Print the Unit Checkpoint. Read the directions, problems, and answer choices to students, if necessary. Use the answer key to score the Checkpoint, and then enter the results online.

Gather the bags you have filled with blocks. Give students the following bags for the following problems:

- Problem 1: 20 green cubes
- Problem 2: 20 blue cubes
- Problem 3: 12 circles, 12 circles, 11 circles
- Problem 4: 12 circles, 10 circles, 15 circles

Name _____ Date _____

Unit Checkpoint Answer Key

Part 1

Read each problem and follow the directions.

(1 point)

1. Take 10 green cubes from the bag.

Students should show 10 green cubes.

(1 point)

2. Take 12 blue cubes from the bag.

Students should show 12 blue cubes.

(1 point)

3. Empty the 3 bags of circles in 3 piles. Point to the 2 groups that have the same number of circles.

Students should point to the two groups that have 12 circles.

Name _____ Date _____

(1 point)

4. Empty the 3 bags of circles into 3 piles. Point to the group that has the most circles.

Students should point to the group with 15 circles.

(1 point)

5. Count aloud the squares in each group. Which group has more squares?

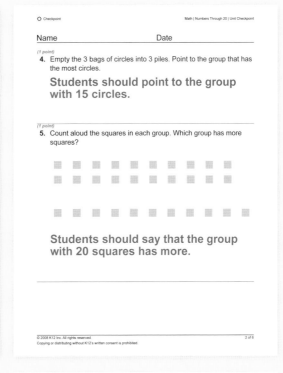

Students should say that the group with 20 squares has more.

Name _____ Date _____

Part 2

Read each problem and follow the directions.

(1 point)

6. Count the stones on the path from the white arrow to the black arrow. Then count them from the black arrow to the white arrow. What happened to the number of stones? Circle the answer.

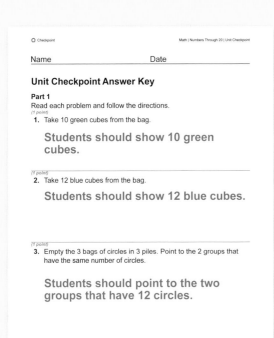

     A. The number changed.

     B. The number went up one.

     (C.) The number stayed the same.

(1 point)

7. Count aloud. How many apples are there? Circle the answer.

     A. 14   (B.) 15   C. 16

(1 point)

8. Count aloud. How many butterflies are there? Circle the answer.

     A. 17   B. 18   (C.) 19

Name _____ Date _____

(1 point)

9. Count the flowers in the circle, and then count on the number of flowers in the square. If you count the flowers in the square first, does the total number of flowers change? Circle the answer.

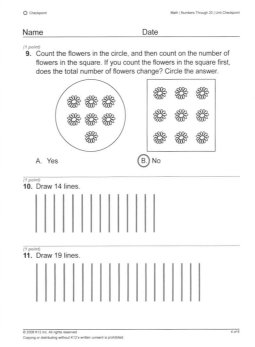

     A. Yes   (B.) No

(1 point)

10. Draw 14 lines.

     | | | | | | | | | | | | | |

(1 point)

11. Draw 19 lines.

     | | | | | | | | | | | | | | | | | | |

Name _____ Date _____

(1 point)
12. Which group has the fewest flowers? Circle the answer.

(A.)   B.   C.

(1 point)
13. Which group has the most bears? Circle the answer.

A.

(B.)

C.

(1 point)
14. Write the number eleven.

| |

(1 point)
15. Write the number twelve.

I2

(1 point)
16. Write the number fifteen.

I5

(1 point)
17. Write the number twenty.

20

Name _____ Date _____

(1 point)
18. Melissa has 19 stuffed animals. Allison has 12 stuffed animals. Who has more stuffed animals? Circle the answer.

(A.) Melissa   B. Allison

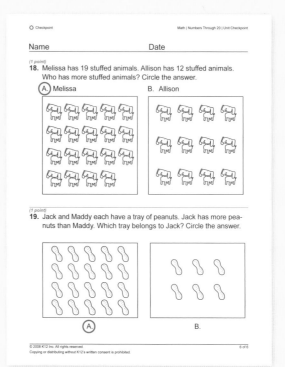

(1 point)
19. Jack and Maddy each have a tray of peanuts. Jack has more peanuts than Maddy. Which tray belongs to Jack? Circle the answer.

(A.)   B.

Introduction
to Addition

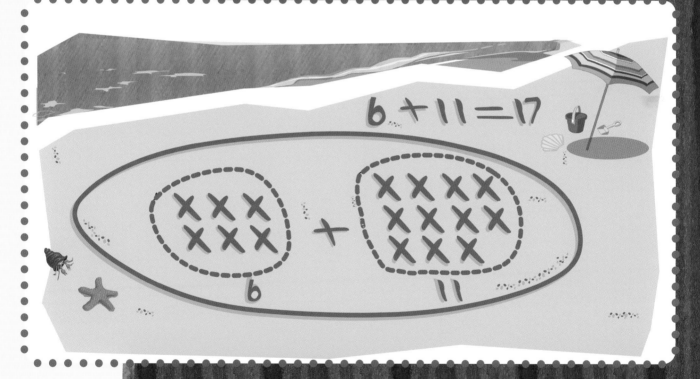

▶ Unit Objectives

- Demonstrate the meaning of addition as the combining of two sets (for sums up through 20).
- Demonstrate with concrete objects representing numbers up to 10 that changing the order in which numbers are added does not affect the sum.
- Use concrete objects or sketches to model and solve addition or subtraction computation problems involving sums or minuends up through 20.

▶ Big Ideas

Addition represents the combining of two sets.

▶ Unit Introduction

Students will learn the meaning of addition by combining two groups of objects to find the total, or sum. By experimenting with groups of objects, they will learn that adding numbers in a different order does not change the sum.

Students will then learn to add numbers with sums through 20 using models, sketches, and number lines. On the number line, they will add by counting on from a number by 1s and by 2s.

Combine to Add

Lesson Overview

Skills Update	5 minutes	ONLINE
GET READY Count Sets	5 minutes	ONLINE
LEARN Model and Add	10 minutes	ONLINE
LEARN Change the Order	10 minutes	ONLINE
LEARN Add Groups	5 minutes	ONLINE
TRY IT Add with Cubes	10 minutes	OFFLINE

▶ Lesson Objectives

- Demonstrate the meaning of addition as the combining of two sets (for sums up through 20).
- Demonstrate with concrete objects representing numbers up to 10 that changing the order in which numbers are added does not affect the sum.

▶ Prerequisite Skills

- Count aloud a number of objects up through 20.
- Use concrete objects or sketches to represent a quantity up through 20.
- Demonstrate that counting 20 or fewer objects can occur from left to right, right to left, or in any order as long as all the items are counted once.

▶ Common Errors and Misconceptions

Students might say more than one number for each object when counting objects in a group. Or they might skip objects. To avoid such problems, draw a line down the center of a sheet of paper. Have students move objects from one side of the paper to the other as they count.

▶ Content Background

Students will combine two groups of objects to show the meaning of addition. Students will use concrete objects to show that adding numbers in a different order does not change the sum.

Addition is combining, or putting together, groups of objects. The total number of objects is the sum.

Materials to Gather

SUPPLIED

blocks – B (red, blue)

blocks – O (red, blue)

Keywords

add – to combine, or put together, groups of objects or numbers

addition – the process of combining, or putting together, groups of objects or numbers; a mathematical operation

sum – the solution to an addition problem

total – all of the objects in a set

GET READY Count Sets

ONLINE 5 min

Students will count aloud two groups of blocks. Then they will watch the blocks are combined. They will count aloud with Bror to find how many blocks in all.

Objectives

- Count aloud a number of objects up through 20.
- Use concrete objects or sketches to represent a quantity up through 20.
- Demonstrate that counting 20 or fewer objects can occur from left to right, right to left, or in any order as long as all the items are counted once.

LEARN Model and Add

ONLINE 10 min

Students will watch Serena combine two groups of objects. They will count aloud with Serena to find the sum.

Objectives

- Demonstrate the meaning of addition as the combining of two sets (for sums up through 20).

LEARN Change the Order

ONLINE 10 min

Students will combine two groups to find the sum. Then they will add the same groups in a different order to learn that adding in a different order does not change the sum.

Tell students about the words *add* and *sum*. To add is to combine two or more groups. When the groups are added, the total number of objects is the sum.

Objectives

- Demonstrate the meaning of addition as the combining of two sets (for sums up through 20).
- Demonstrate with concrete objects representing numbers up to 10 that changing the order in which numbers are added does not affect the sum.

LEARN Add Groups

Students will combine two groups to find the sum. Then they will add the same groups in a different order to learn that adding in a different order does not change the sum.

Gather the circles. On the last screen, have students use red circles to model the 5 bears and blue circles to model the 7 bears. Students may use the circles throughout the activity if they wish.

- Demonstrate the meaning of addition as the combining of two sets (for sums up through 20).

TRY IT Add with Cubes

Students will model addition problems with cubes. Note how students perform, and then enter the results online.

Gather the cubes. Lay out the blue cubes in one pile and the red cubes in a separate pile.

1. Let's use cubes to show addition problems.

2. **Say:** Count and snap 9 blue cubes. Count and snap 3 red cubes. Snap the groups to make a train. Tell the sum.
   ANSWER: 12

3. **Say:** Count and snap 6 red cubes. Count and snap 14 blue cubes. To add the groups of cubes, snap them to make one long train. Tell how many you have in all.
   ANSWER: 20

4. **Say:** Count and snap 3 red cubes. Count and snap 5 blue cubes. Snap the groups to make a train. Tell the sum.
   ANSWER: 8
   Say: Now change the order of the red cubes and blue cubes to show 5 and 3. Tell the sum.
   ANSWER: 8

   Ask: Did changing the order that you added change the sum?
   ANSWER: No

5. **Say:** Snap 7 blue cubes together. Then add 2 red cubes to make one train.

   Ask: This train shows 7 and 2. What happens to the sum if I flip it over to show 2 and 7?
   ANSWER: The sum stays the same.

- Demonstrate the meaning of addition as the combining of two sets (for sums up through 20).

- Demonstrate with concrete objects representing numbers up to 10 that changing the order in which numbers are added does not affect the sum.

Count On to Add

Lesson Overview

Skills Update	5 minutes	**ONLINE**
LEARN Add with Alexander	5 minutes	**ONLINE**
LEARN Add in Any Order	5 minutes	**ONLINE**
LEARN Count on a Number Line	10 minutes	**OFFLINE**
TRY IT Add on a Number Line	10 minutes	**OFFLINE**
CHECKPOINT	10 minutes	**OFFLINE**

▶ Lesson Objectives

- Demonstrate the meaning of addition as the combining of two sets (for sums up through 20).
- Demonstrate with concrete objects representing numbers up to 10 that changing the order in which numbers are added does not affect the sum.

▶ Prerequisite Skills

- Count aloud a number of objects up through 20.
- Use concrete objects or sketches to represent a quantity up through 20.
- Demonstrate that counting 20 or fewer objects can occur from left to right, right to left, or in any order as long as all the items are counted once.

▶ Common Errors and Misconceptions

Students might say more than one number for each object when counting objects in a group. Or they might skip objects. To avoid such problems, draw a line down the center of a sheet of paper. Have students move objects from one side of the paper to the other as they count.

▶ Advance Preparation

- Number index cards 0 through 20, or gather the number cards you created previously. Cut a piece of yarn about 7 feet long.
- Lay out the number cards along the yarn to set up a number line from 0–20. Make sure to space cards evenly along the yarn. Secure the yarn and cards to the floor with tape.   Students will use the number line for the Learn: Count on a Number Line and Try It: Add on a Number Line activities.

▶ Content Background

Students will learn to use a number line to add two numbers.

Addition is combining, or putting together, groups of objects. The total number of objects is the sum.

Materials to Gather

SUPPLIED

Add on a Number Line activity page

blocks – B (red, blue)

blocks – O (green, yellow)

Checkpoint (printout)

ALSO NEEDED

index cards – numbered 0 through 20

scissors, adult

tape, masking

yarn

number line – a line consisting of points equally spaced, each of which corresponds to a unique number

LEARN Add with Alexander

ONLINE
5min

Objectives

- Demonstrate the meaning of addition as the combining of two sets (for sums up through 20).
- Demonstrate with concrete objects representing numbers up to 10 that changing the order in which numbers are added does not affect the sum.

Students will add using a number line.

LEARN Add in Any Order

ONLINE
5min

Objectives

- Demonstrate the meaning of addition as the combining of two sets (for sums up through 20).
- Demonstrate with concrete objects representing numbers up to 10 that changing the order in which numbers are added does not affect the sum.

Students will add two numbers using a number line. Then they will add the same numbers in a different order to learn that adding in a different order does not change the sum.

Explain to students that there is more than one way to move on the number line. For example, to move from 0 to 3 on the number line, students can make three separate jumps. Or they can start at 0 and jump directly to the number 3.

LEARN Count on a Number Line

OFFLINE 10 min

Students will model addition using a number line made of yarn and index cards. Have students stand or sit in front of the number line you created with yarn and number cards.

1. **Say:** Let's practice counting on the number line.

2. Start at 0. Count aloud to 3 using the number line. Touch each number as you say it.

   Students should count and touch 1, then 2, then 3.

3. Repeat Step 2, using the numbers 11 and 15.

4. **Say:** Now let's add numbers on the number line.

   Explain to students that when they add on a number line, they start at 0 and count the first number. Then they stay at the first number and count on the second number.

5. **Ask:** Now let's use the number line to add 4 and 6. Where should you start?
   ANSWER: 0

   Ask: The first number we are adding is 4. How can you show 4 on the number line?
   ANSWER: I can count to 4.

   Have students start at 0 and count to 4, touching each number as they say it. Have students keep their finger on 4.

   Say: You are at 4 on the number line. Now show how to add 6.

   Have students start at 4 and count on six more numbers. They should count and touch 5, 6, 7, 8, 9, 10.

   Ask: What is the sum of 4 and 6?
   ANSWER: 10

6. Repeat Step 5, having students add 9 and 3, then 5 and 2.

7. **Say:** Now show how to add 2 and 5.

   Students should start at 0. They should count and point to 1, 2, and then to 3, 4, 5, 6, 7.

   Ask: What is the sum of 2 and 5?
   ANSWER: 7

   Ask: Is the sum the same as when you added 5 and 2?
   ANSWER: Yes

Objectives

- Demonstrate the meaning of addition as the combining of two sets (for sums up through 20).

- Demonstrate with concrete objects representing numbers up to 10 that changing the order in which numbers are added does not affect the sum.

TRY IT Add on a Number Line

Objectives

Students will practice adding on a number line. Give students the blocks and the Add on a Number Line activity page from their Activity Book. Make sure students are seated near the yarn number line you created. Read the directions with them. Use the answer key to check students' answers, and then enter the results online.

- Demonstrate the meaning of addition as the combining of two sets (for sums up through 20).

- Demonstrate with concrete objects representing numbers up to 10 that changing the order in which numbers are added does not affect the sum.

Name:

Count On to Add

Add on a Number Line

Use your number line to answer the problem. Circle the answer.

1. Add 5 and 6.
   A. 9   B. 10   (C.) 11

2. Add 8 and 1.
   A. 8   (B.) 9   C. 10

Read each problem. Draw jumps on the number line to show how to add. Write numbers over the jumps to show each number you add and the sum.

3. Add 5 and 7.

12
5   7
0 1 2 3 4 5 6 7 8 9 10 11 12 13 14 15 16 17 18 19 20

4. Add 7 and 5.

12
7   5
0 1 2 3 4 5 6 7 8 9 10 11 12 13 14 15 16 17 18 19 20

Did adding the numbers in a different order change the sum? Circle Yes or No.
(A.) No   B. Yes

TRY IT

Read each problem and circle the answer.

5. Ron's teacher told him to add 3 toy cars to 9 toy cars. What did Ron's teacher have him do?
   (A.) Put the two groups together.
   B. Take some away from one of the groups.

6. Use green cubes to show 6 and yellow cubes to show 4. Add 6 and 4.
   Now add the cubes the other way: 4 and 6.
   Did adding the cubes in a different order change the sum?
   (A.) No   B. Yes

Use circle blocks to find the sum.
7. 3 circles and 5 circles
   Show groups of three and five circles.
   5 circles and 3 circles
   Show groups of five and three circles.

   What are the sums? __8__ ; __8__

   Did adding the circles in a different order change the sum?
   Circle the answer. Explain.
   (A.) No   B. Yes

   The sum of two numbers does not change when the numbers are added in a different order.

TRY IT

CHECKPOINT

Objectives

Print the Checkpoint. Students will take a performance-based assessment. Read the directions and problems to students. Use the answer key to score the Checkpoint, and then enter the results online.

Gather the blocks. Students will use circles for Problems 1 and 4. They will use cubes for Problems 2, 3, 5, 6, and 7.

- Demonstrate the meaning of addition as the combining of two sets (for sums up through 20).

- Demonstrate with concrete objects representing numbers up to 10 that changing the order in which numbers are added does not affect the sum.

○ Checkpoint   Math | Introduction to Addition | Count On to Add

Name _____ Date _____

Checkpoint Answer Key

Read each problem and follow the directions.

1. Put 5 red circles in one group and 2 blue circles in another group. What will you be doing if you combine the red and blue circles and count them as one group?
(1 point)

   Students should say they would be adding the two groups together.

2. Use cubes to show how to add 3 and 15. Find the sum.
(1 point)

   Students should combine 3 cubes with 15 cubes to make 18 cubes.

3. Lee has 11 crayons. She finds 9 more. How many crayons does Lee have in all? Use cubes to show the problem and find the sum.
(1 point)

   Students should make a group of 11 cubes and a group of 9 cubes and combine the groups.
(1 point)

   Students should say the sum is 20.

○ Checkpoint   Math | Introduction to Addition | Count On to Add

Name _____ Date _____

4. Put 3 red circles in one group and 4 blue circles in another group. Add the groups starting with the red circles. Then add the groups starting with the blue circles. Did the sum change when you added the circles in a different order?
(1 point)

   Students should say No.

5. Use cubes to add 2 and 8. Then use the cubes to add 8 and 2. Are the sums the same?
(1 point)

   Students should say Yes.

6. Put 3 yellow cubes in one group and 6 green cubes in another group. Add the groups starting with the yellow cubes. Then add the groups starting with the green cubes. How many cubes are there in all?
(0.5 point)

   Students should say 9.

7. Did the sum change when you added the cubes in a different order?
(0.5 point)

   Students should say No.

Count On

Lesson Overview

Skills Update	5 minutes	ONLINE
GET READY Numbers Through 20	5 minutes	ONLINE
LEARN Count On by One	10 minutes	ONLINE
LEARN Count On by Two	10 minutes	ONLINE
TRY IT Count On by One and Two	15 minutes	OFFLINE

▶ Lesson Objectives

Use concrete objects or sketches to model and solve addition or subtraction computation problems involving sums or minuends up through 20.

▶ Prerequisite Skills

Demonstrate the meaning of addition as the combining of two sets (for sums up through 20).

▶ Common Errors and Misconceptions

- Students might have difficulty adding and subtracting with zero.
- Students might say more than one number for each object when counting objects in a group. Or they might skip objects. To avoid such problems, draw a line down the center of a sheet of paper. Have students move objects from one side of the paper to the other as they count.

▶ Content Background

Students will use models to count on by 1 and by 2. They will learn that counting on by 1 and by 2 is the same as adding 1 and 2. Then they will count on to add 1 and 2.

Addition is combining, or putting together, groups of objects. The total number of objects is the sum.

Materials to Gather

SUPPLIED

blocks – B (18 red, 2 blue)

Count On by One and Two activity page

count – to say each number according to a defined sequence, such as consecutively, by 2s, or backward

count on – to add two groups by starting with the number of objects in one group and then counting up, in order, the number of objects in the other group

model (noun) – a physical object, diagram, or picture that represents an amount, an expression, an equation, or a problem situation

model (verb) – to use physical objects, diagrams, or pictures to represent an amount, an expression, an equation, or a problem situation

GET READY Numbers Through 20

Students will make groups of objects to represent numbers through 20. They will also combine two groups to show addition.

Objectives

- Demonstrate the meaning of addition as the combining of two sets (for sums up through 20).

LEARN Count On by One

Students will add 1 to numbers using red and white circles. As students continue to add 1 to numbers in this activity, help them recognize that adding 1 is the same as counting on one number.

Objectives

- Use concrete objects or sketches to model and solve addition or subtraction computation problems involving sums or minuends up through 20.

LEARN Count On by Two

Students will add 2 to numbers using red and white circles. As students continue to add 2 to numbers in this activity, help them recognize that adding 2 is the same as counting on two numbers.

Objectives

- Use concrete objects or sketches to model and solve addition or subtraction computation problems involving sums or minuends up through 20.

TRY IT Count On by One and Two

Objectives

Students will use blocks to model adding 1 and 2. Give students the circles and the Count On by One and Two activity page from their Activity Book. Read the directions with them. Use the answer key to check students' answers, and then enter the results online.

- Use concrete objects or sketches to model and solve addition or subtraction computation problems involving sums or minuends up through 20.

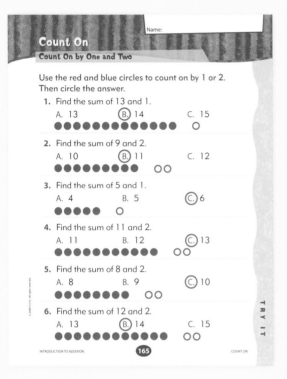

Count On

Count On by One and Two

Name:

Use the red and blue circles to count on by 1 or 2. Then circle the answer.

1. Find the sum of 13 and 1.
   A. 13   (B.) 14   C. 15

2. Find the sum of 9 and 2.
   A. 10   (B.) 11   C. 12

3. Find the sum of 5 and 1.
   A. 4   B. 5   (C.) 6

4. Find the sum of 11 and 2.
   A. 11   B. 12   (C.) 13

5. Find the sum of 8 and 2.
   A. 8   B. 9   (C.) 10

6. Find the sum of 12 and 2.
   A. 13   (B.) 14   C. 15

INTRODUCTION TO ADDITION   165   COUNT ON

TRY IT

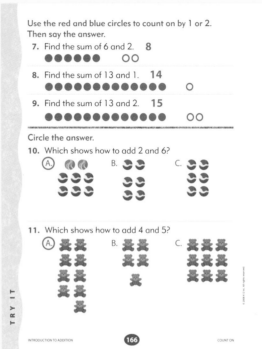

Use the red and blue circles to count on by 1 or 2. Then say the answer.

7. Find the sum of 6 and 2.   **8**

8. Find the sum of 13 and 1.   **14**

9. Find the sum of 13 and 2.   **15**

Circle the answer.

10. Which shows how to add 2 and 6?
    (A.)   B.   C.

11. Which shows how to add 4 and 5?
    (A)   B.   C.

INTRODUCTION TO ADDITION   166   COUNT ON

TRY IT

Add with Models

Skills Update	5 minutes	ONLINE
LEARN Model Sums	10 minutes	ONLINE
LEARN More Ways to Model	10 minutes	OFFLINE
TRY IT Find the Sum	10 minutes	OFFLINE
LEARN Sketch with Models	10 minutes	OFFLINE
TRY IT Sketch to Solve	5 minutes	OFFLINE

▶ Lesson Objectives

Use concrete objects or sketches to model and solve addition or subtraction computation problems involving sums or minuends up through 20.

▶ Prerequisite Skills

Demonstrate the meaning of addition as the combining of two sets (for sums up through 20).

▶ Common Errors and Misconceptions

- Students might have difficulty adding and subtracting with zero.
- Students might say more than one number for each object when counting objects in a group. Or they might skip objects. To avoid such problems, draw a line down the center of a sheet of paper. Have students move objects from one side of the paper to the other as they count.

▶ Advance Preparation

Print the Domino Tiles, and cut out the dominoes. Save the dominoes for use in future lessons.

▶ Content Background

Students will use dominoes and sketches to solve addition problems with sums through 20.

Addition is combining, or putting together, groups of objects. The total number of objects is the sum.

Materials to Gather

SUPPLIED

blocks – B (red, blue)
More Ways to Model activity page
Find the Sum activity page
Sketch with Models activity page
Sketch to Solve activity page
Domino Tiles (printout)

ALSO NEEDED

scissors, adult

LEARN Model Sums

Students will use blocks and number lines to find sums through 20.

- Use concrete objects or sketches to model and solve addition or subtraction computation problems involving sums or minuends up through 20.

LEARN More Ways to Model

Students will use dominoes as models to add two numbers. Students will use circle blocks and number lines to find the sum of the dots on each domino.

Gather the circle blocks, cut-out dominoes from the Domino Tiles printout, and More Ways to Model activity page.

- Use concrete objects or sketches to model and solve addition or subtraction computation problems involving sums or minuends up through 20.

DOMINOES AND CIRCLES

1. Choose a domino. Model for students how to use circles to show the numbers represented by the two parts of the domino, as shown below. Show students how to combine the circles to find the sum.

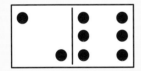

2. Have students choose a domino. Point to one part of the domino.

   Ask: How many dots are on this part of the domino? How many dots are on the other part of the domino?
   Have students use circles to show the numbers represented by the two parts of the domino.

   Ask: What is the sum of the two numbers that the domino shows?

   Students should combine the circles and count them to find the sum.

3. Repeat Step 2 with four more dominoes, making sure one of the dominoes has a blank part.

   Explain to students that a domino part with no dots shows the number 0. Explain that when adding 0 to a number, the number stays the same. When modeling with circles, emphasize that students should use no circles to show 0.

DOMINOES AND NUMBER LINES

4. Show students the example problem on the More Ways to Model activity page. Point to the example domino, asking students to tell you how many dots each part has. (4 and 6)

5. **Say:** I will show you how to add 4 and 6 on a number line.

   Explain that to show 4, we jump four numbers on the number line. Draw an arc on the number line from 0 to 4, and write the number 4 above it.

6. Explain that to show adding 6, we start at 4 and jump six numbers. Draw an arc from 4 to 10, and write the number 6 above it.

7. Point to the large arc from 0 to 10 and write the number 10 above it. Explain that the large arc shows the sum, or total number of jumps.

8. Have students choose five dominoes and follow the process in Steps 4–7 to model the addition problems represented by the dominoes on the number lines. Guide students as needed.

   Explain to students that when modeling 0 on the number line, students should not draw an arc. Tell students that 0 represents no jumps forward.

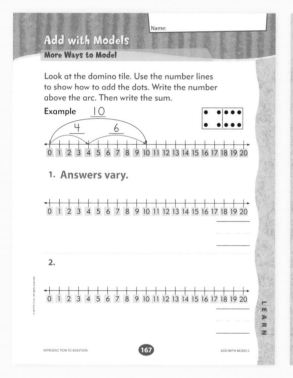

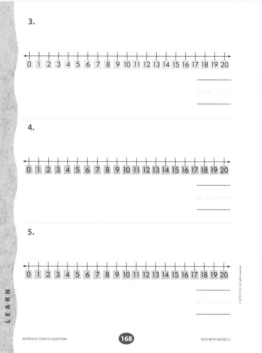

TRY IT Find the Sum

- Use concrete objects or sketches to model and solve addition or subtraction computation problems involving sums or minuends up through 20.

This Try It activity has two parts.

Part 1
Students will use blocks to add. Gather the circle blocks.

1. **Say:** Use circles to show how to add 3 and 5. What is the sum?
   ANSWER: 8

   Students should model 3 circles of one color and 5 circles of a different color. To add, they should combine the groups.

2. **Say:** Use circles to show how to add 13 and 4. What is the sum?
   ANSWER: 17

   Students should model 13 circles of one color and 4 circles of a different color. To add, they should combine the groups.

Part 2
Students will use number lines to find sums. Then they will add the dots on dominoes. Give students the Find the Sum activity page from their Activity Book and read the directions with them. Use the answer key to check students' answers, and then enter the results online.

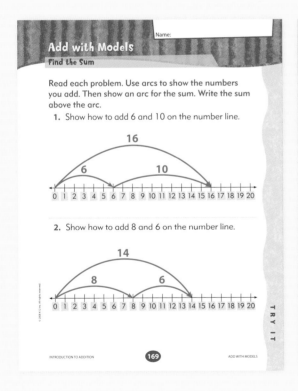

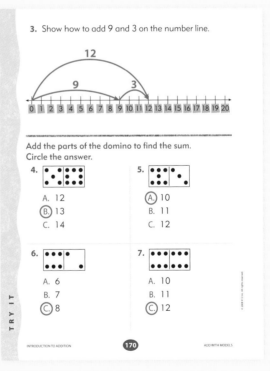

OFFLINE
10 min

Objectives

- Use concrete objects or sketches to model and solve addition or subtraction computation problems involving sums or minuends up through 20.

Students will use dominoes as models to add two numbers. Students will make drawings based on the dots on each domino and use their drawings to help find the sum.

Gather the cut-out dominoes from the Domino Tiles printout and the Sketch with Models activity page.

1. Complete Problem 1 with students. Choose a domino. Have students count the dots in each part. Have students make simple drawings (dots, X's, etc.) to represent each dot. Tell students they can count their drawings to find the sum. Have them find the sum and write it on the line.

2. Have students complete Problems 2–4. Check that their drawings show the same number as the dominoes.

3. Have students complete Problems 5–8.

Tips

Drawings do not have to show the dots arranged the same way as on the domino.

Add with Models
Sketch with Models

Name: _____

Choose a domino. Make a drawing to show the numbers on the domino. Use dots, lines, or X's to make your drawing. Find the sum, and write it on the line.

Answers will vary.

1. ⬜⬜ _____

2. ⬜⬜ _____

3. ⬜⬜ _____

4. ⬜⬜ _____

Make a drawing to add. Write the sum on the line.

5. Draw circles to find the sum of 2 and 9.

○ ○○○
○ ○○○
    ○○○

11

6. Draw squares to find the sum of 8 and 4.

⬜⬜⬜⬜
⬜⬜⬜⬜
⬜⬜⬜⬜

12

7. Draw dots to find the sum of 5 and 5.

●●●●●
●●●●●

10

8. Draw lines to find the sum of 7 and 9.

|||||||
|||||||||

16

Objectives

- Use concrete objects or sketches to model and solve addition or subtraction computation problems involving sums or minuends up through 20.

Students will use blocks to model addition and find the sum. Give students the circle blocks and the Sketch to Solve activity page from their Activity Book. Read the directions with them. Use the answer key to check students' answers, and then enter the results online.

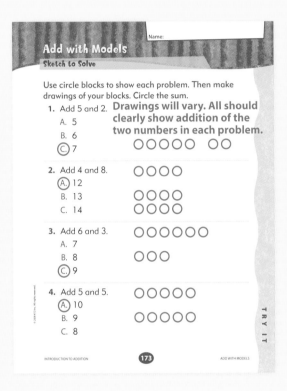

Add with Models
Sketch to Solve

Use circle blocks to show each problem. Then make drawings of your blocks. Circle the sum.

1. Add 5 and 2. **Drawings will vary. All should clearly show addition of the two numbers in each problem.**
   A. 5
   B. 6
   C. 7

2. Add 4 and 8.
   A. 12
   B. 13
   C. 14

3. Add 6 and 3.
   A. 7
   B. 8
   C. 9

4. Add 5 and 5.
   A. 10
   B. 9
   C. 8

INTRODUCTION TO ADDITION   **173**   ADD WITH MODELS

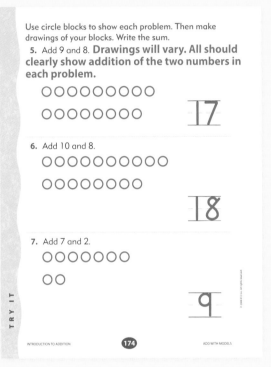

Use circle blocks to show each problem. Then make drawings of your blocks. Write the sum.

5. Add 9 and 8. **Drawings will vary. All should clearly show addition of the two numbers in each problem.**

   17

6. Add 10 and 8.

   18

7. Add 7 and 2.

   9

INTRODUCTION TO ADDITION   **174**   ADD WITH MODELS

Use Sketches to Add

Lesson Overview

Skills Update	5 minutes	ONLINE
GET READY Domino Count	10 minutes	ONLINE
LEARN Beach Addition	10 minutes	ONLINE
TRY IT Add Two Groups	5 minutes	ONLINE
LEARN Sketch the Problem	5 minutes	OFFLINE
TRY IT Use Sketches to Add Groups	10 minutes	OFFLINE

▶ Lesson Objectives

Use concrete objects or sketches to model and solve addition or subtraction computation problems involving sums or minuends up through 20.

▶ Prerequisite Skills

- Demonstrate the meaning of addition as the combining of two sets (for sums up through 20).
- Use concrete objects or sketches to represent a quantity up through 20.

▶ Common Errors and Misconceptions

- Students might have difficulty adding and subtracting with zero.
- Students might say more than one number for each object when counting objects in a group. Or they might skip objects. To avoid such problems, draw a line down the center of a sheet of paper. Have students move objects from one side of the paper to the other as they count.

▶ Content Background

Students will use models and sketches to solve addition problems with sums through 20.

Addition is combining, or putting together, groups of objects. The total number of objects is the sum.

Materials to Gather

SUPPLIED
Use Sketches to Add Groups activity page

ALSO NEEDED
crayons

Keywords

number – a quantity or value
quantity – a number or amount

GET READY **Domino Count**

Objectives

- Demonstrate the meaning of addition as the combining of two sets (for sums up through 20).
- Use concrete objects or sketches to represent a quantity up through 20.

Students will watch Rosa and Alexander use dominoes and drawings to add numbers. For each screen, point out to students that Rosa and Alexander have drawn pictures to match the dots on the dominoes. Have students say the sum before you read the text.

LEARN **Beach Addition**

Objectives

- Use concrete objects or sketches to model and solve addition or subtraction computation problems involving sums or minuends up through 20.

Students will learn that drawing pictures can be a better way to add than using objects.

TRY IT **Add Two Groups**

Objectives

- Use concrete objects or sketches to model and solve addition or subtraction computation problems involving sums or minuends up through 20.

Students will be shown an addition problem and asked to choose the picture that models the problem.

LEARN **Sketch the Problem**

Objectives

- Use concrete objects or sketches to model and solve addition or subtraction computation problems involving sums or minuends up through 20.

By drawing pictures to solve addition problems, students will learn that drawing pictures can be a better way to add than using objects.

Gather the crayons.

1. Write 14 and 3, and show the problem to students. Have student draw a picture to model the first number. Then have them draw a picture for the second number.

   Ask: Count the total number of pictures. What is the sum?
   ANSWER: 17

```
  X  X  X  X  X            X  X  X
  X  X  X  X
    X  X  X  X
       14                    3
```

2. Repeat Step 1 with the following problem: 12 and 4.

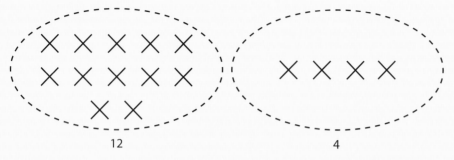

12   4

3. Repeat Step 1 with the following problem: 10 and 5.

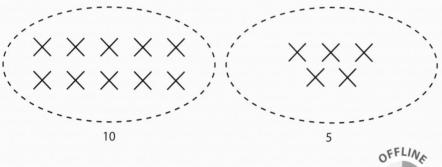

10   5

TRY IT Use Sketches to Add Groups

OFFLINE
10 min

Students will draw pictures to add numbers. Give students the Use Sketches to Add Groups activity page from their Activity Book and read the directions with them. Use the answer key to check students' answers, and then enter the results online.

Objectives

- Use concrete objects or sketches to model and solve addition or subtraction computation problems involving sums or minuends up through 20.

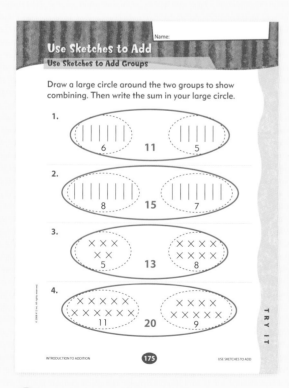

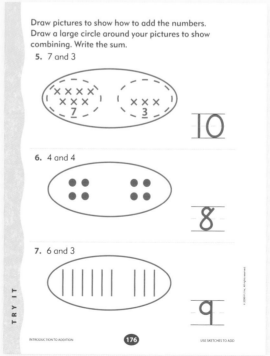

Unit Review

Lesson Overview

UNIT REVIEW Look Back	20 minutes	**ONLINE**
UNIT REVIEW Checkpoint Practice	10 minutes	**OFFLINE**
▶ **UNIT REVIEW** Prepare for the Checkpoint		

▶ Unit Objectives

This lesson reviews the following objectives:

- Demonstrate the meaning of addition as the combining of two sets (for sums up through 20).
- Demonstrate with concrete objects representing numbers up to 10 that changing the order in which numbers are added does not affect the sum.
- Use concrete objects or sketches to model and solve addition or subtraction computation problems involving sums or minuends up through 20.

▶ Advance Preparation

In this lesson, students will have an opportunity to review previous activities in the Introduction to Addition unit. Look at the suggested activities in Unit Review: Prepare for the Checkpoint online and gather any needed materials.

Materials to Gather

SUPPLIED

blocks – B (10 red, 10 blue)
blocks – O (10 green, 10 yellow)
Checkpoint Practice activity page

Keywords

add	number
addition	number line
count	quantity
count on	sum
model (noun)	total
model (verb)	

UNIT REVIEW Look Back

ONLINE 20min

In this unit, students have learned the meaning of addition by combining two groups of objects to find the total, or sum. By experimenting with groups of objects, they have learned that adding numbers in a different order does not change the sum.

Students have also learned to add numbers with sums through 20 using models, sketches, and number lines. On the number line, they added by counting on from a number by 1s and by 2s. Students will review these concepts to prepare for the Unit Checkpoint.

Objectives

- Review unit objectives.

Objectives

- Review unit objectives.

This Checkpoint Practice has two parts.

Part 1

Students will use blocks to model addition. Gather the circles and cubes.

1. Lay out 5 red circles in a group and 8 blue circles in another group.

   Ask: What will you be doing if you combine the red and blue blocks?
   ANSWER: I will be adding the two groups.

2. Clear the work area. Lay out 4 green cubes in a group to the left and 5 yellow cubes in a group to the right.

   Point to the green cubes.

   Ask: How many cubes are in the first group?
   ANSWER: 4

   Point to the yellow cubes.

   Ask: How many cubes are in the second group?
   ANSWER: 5

   Ask: How many cubes are there altogether?
   ANSWER: 9

3. Move the groups so the green cubes are to the right of the yellow cubes.

   Point to the yellow cubes.

   Ask: How many cubes are in the first group?
   ANSWER: 5

   Point to the green cubes.

   Ask: How many cubes are in the second group?
   ANSWER: 4

   Ask: How many cubes are there altogether?
   ANSWER: 9

   Ask: Did changing the order of the groups change the sum?
   ANSWER: No

4. Ask students model and add 6 and 4 using green cubes to show 6 and yellow cubes to show 4. Then have them show the same problem, but using yellow cubes for 6 and green cubes for 4.

   Ask: Did the total change when you added in a different order?
   ANSWER: No

5. **Say:** Use circles to show how to add 5 and 2. Find the sum.
   ANSWER: Students should place 5 circles next to 2 circles, and then combine them. The sum is 7.

6. **Say:** Use circles to show how to add 7 and 1.
   ANSWER: Students should place 7 circles next to 1 circle, and then combine them. The sum is 8 .

Part 2

Students will complete the Checkpoint Practice activity page to prepare for the Unit Checkpoint. If necessary, read the directions, questions, and answer choices to students. Have students answer the problems on their own. Carefully review the answers with students.

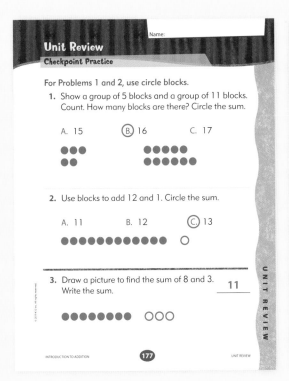

Unit Review

Checkpoint Practice

Name: _____

For Problems 1 and 2, use circle blocks.

1. Show a group of 5 blocks and a group of 11 blocks. Count. How many blocks are there? Circle the sum.

A. 15　　(B.) 16　　C. 17

2. Use blocks to add 12 and 1. Circle the sum.

A. 11　　B. 12　　(C.) 13

3. Draw a picture to find the sum of 8 and 3. Write the sum. _11_

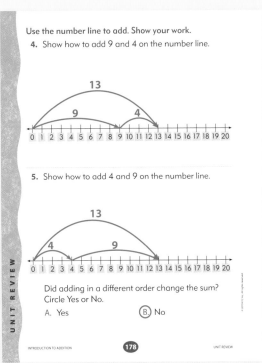

Use the number line to add. Show your work.

4. Show how to add 9 and 4 on the number line.

5. Show how to add 4 and 9 on the number line.

Did adding in a different order change the sum? Circle Yes or No.

A. Yes　　(B.) No

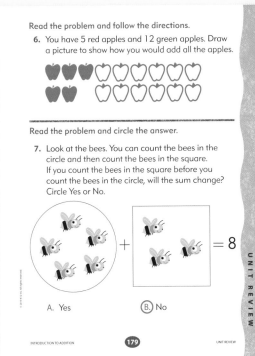

Read the problem and follow the directions.

6. You have 5 red apples and 12 green apples. Draw a picture to show how you would add all the apples.

Read the problem and circle the answer.

7. Look at the bees. You can count the bees in the circle and then count the bees in the square. If you count the bees in the square before you count the bees in the circle, will the sum change? Circle Yes or No.

A. Yes　　(B.) No

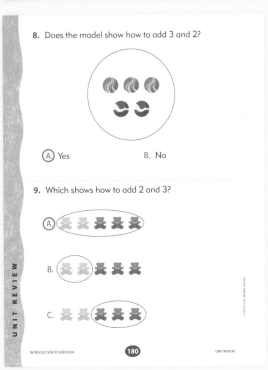

8. Does the model show how to add 3 and 2?

(A.) Yes　　　　B. No

9. Which shows how to add 2 and 3?

A.

B.

C.

⇥ UNIT REVIEW Prepare for the Checkpoint

What you do next depends on how students performed in the previous activity, Unit Review: Checkpoint Practice. If students had difficulty with any of the problems, complete the appropriate review activity listed in the table online.

Unit Checkpoint

Lesson Overview

| UNIT CHECKPOINT Offline | 40 minutes | OFFLINE |

▶ Unit Objectives

This lesson assesses the following objectives:

- Demonstrate the meaning of addition as the combining of two sets (for sums up through 20).
- Demonstrate with concrete objects representing numbers up to 10 that changing the order in which numbers are added does not affect the sum.
- Use concrete objects or sketches to model and solve addition or subtraction computation problems involving sums or minuends up through 20.

Materials to Gather

SUPPLIED
Unit Checkpoint (printout)
blocks – B (10 red , 10 blue)
blocks – O (10 green, 10 yellow)

UNIT CHECKPOINT Offline

OFFLINE 40 min

Objectives

- Assess unit objectives.

Students will complete the Unit Checkpoint offline. In Part 1, students will take a performance-based assessment. In Part 2, students will complete the problems on their own. Print the Unit Checkpoint. Read the directions, problems, and answer choices to students if necessary. Use the answer key to score the Checkpoint, and then enter the results online.

Gather the blocks.

⟳ Checkpoint   Math | Introduction to Addition | Unit Checkpoint

Name _____   Date _____

Unit Checkpoint Answer Key

Part 1
Read each problem and follow the directions.

1. Use circle blocks to show the addition problem "5 and 8."
   Show how to add all the circles together.
   (1 point)
   Students should correctly use models to represent groups of 5 and 8.
   (1 point)
   Students should combine the groups.

2. Put 5 red circles in one group and 4 blue circles in another group.
   Add the circles and say the sum.
   (1 point)
   Students should combine the groups to find the sum of 9 circles.

3. If you had groups of 4 circles and 7 circles, how would you add the groups?
   (1 point)
   Students should say they would put the two groups together.

© 2008 K12 Inc. All rights reserved.   1 of 7
Copying or distributing without K12's written consent is prohibited.

Name _____ Date _____

4. If you had groups of 8 cubes and 3 cubes, how would you add the groups?
(1 point)

Students should say they would put the two groups together.

5. Use the green and yellow cubes to show 4 plus 3. What is the sum? Now show 3 plus 4. What is the sum? Did the sum change when you added in a different order?
(1 point)

Students should say No.

6. Use the green and yellow cubes to show 8 plus 3. What is the sum? Now show 3 plus 8. What is the sum? Did the sum change when you added in a different order?
(1 point)

Students should say No.

7. Use the green and yellow cubes to show 3 plus 7. What is the sum? Now show 7 plus 3. What is the sum? Did the sum change when you added in a different order?

(1 point)

Students should say No.

Name _____ Date _____

8. Look at the cubes.
(1 point)

A. How many cubes are in the top group?

Students should say 2.

How many cubes are in the bottom group?

Students should say 6.

How many cubes are there in all?

Students should say 8.

Look at the cubes again.

(1 point)

B. How many cubes are in the top group?

Students should say 6.

How many cubes are in the bottom group?

Students should say 2.

How many cubes are there in all?

Students should say 8.

(1 point)

C. Did changing the order of the groups change the sum?

Students should say No.

Name _____ Date _____

9. Use the green and yellow cubes to show 7 plus 4. What is the sum? Now show 4 plus 7. What is the sum? Did the sum change when you added in a different order?
(1 point)

Students should say No.

10. Use circles to show how to add 6 and 5. What is the sum?
(1 point)

Students should show 6 circles next to 5 circles, and then move the circles together.

(1 point)

Students should state the sum as 11.

11. Use circles to show how to add 4 and 8. What is the sum?
(1 point)

Students should show 4 circles next to 8 circles, and then move the circles together.

(1 point)

Students should state the sum as 12.

Name _____ Date _____

12. Use cubes to show how to add 9 and 3. What is the sum?
(1 point)

Students should show 9 cubes next to 3 cubes, and then move the cubes together.

(1 point)

Students should state the sum as 12.

13. Use cubes to show how to add 8 and 6. What is the sum?
(1 point)

Students should show 8 cubes next to 6 cubes, and then move the cubes together.

(1 point)

Students should state the sum as 14.

Give students Part 2 of the assessment.

Name _____   Date _____

Part 2

Read each problem and follow the directions.
(1 point)
14. Draw a picture to show how to add 5 red balls and 5 blue balls.

●●●●● **Students should show 1**
○○○○○ **group with 5 red balls and**
5 blue balls.

(1 point)
15. Maria has 3 red apples and 4 green apples. Draw a picture to show how Maria can add her apples together. **Students**
🍎🍎🍎 **should show 1 group with 3**
○○○○ **red apples and 4 green apples.**

(1 point)
16. Look at the hearts below. You can count hearts in the square and then count hearts in the circle. If you count the hearts in the circle before you count the hearts in the square, will the sum change?

Circle the answer.

A. Yes
(B.) No

[square with hearts] + [circle with hearts] = 9

(1 point)
17. Look at the dots below. You can count dots in the circle and then count dots in the square. If you count the dots in the square before you count the dots in the circle, will the sum change?

Circle the answer.

A. Yes
(B.) No

[square with dots] + [circle with dots] = 10

Name _____   Date _____

(1 point)
18. Draw a picture to show 7 and 2.

Sketches vary.

(○○○○○○○ ●●)

(1 point)
19. Which shows how to add 5 and 7? Circle the answer.

(A.)   B.   C.

(1 point)
20. Which shows how to add 3 and 7? Circle the answer.

A.

B.

(C.)

Problem Solving with Addition

There are 9 boys at the park. There are 8 girls at the park. How many children in all are at the park?

▶ Unit Objectives

- Use concrete objects to explain how to solve addition and subtraction problem-solving situations involving numbers up through 10.

- Recognize and solve word problems involving sums up through 20 in which two quantities are combined.

- Make reasonable estimates for the solutions to addition problems (for sums up through 20).

- Check the accuracy of calculations for the solutions to addition problems with sums up through 20.

▶ Big Ideas

- Counting principles and numbers can be used to solve addition and subtraction problems.

- Addition represents the combining of two sets.

▶ Unit Introduction

Students will use concrete objects to solve addition story problems that involve combining groups. They will learn how to explain how they are solving these story problems. They will also solve missing-addend problems, which are problems in which one of the groups being added is unknown. Students will then learn how to estimate sums and to check the accuracy of their work.

Addition Problem Solving

Lesson Overview

Skills Update	5 minutes	ONLINE
GET READY Add Red and White Circles	5 minutes	ONLINE
LEARN Addition Story Problems	10 minutes	ONLINE
LEARN Represent Story Problems with Cubes	10 minutes	ONLINE
TRY IT Snack on Story Problems	15 minutes	OFFLINE

▶ Lesson Objectives

Use concrete objects to explain how to solve addition and subtraction problem-solving situations involving numbers up to 10.

▶ Prerequisite Skills

Use concrete objects or sketches to model and solve addition or subtraction computation problems involving sums or minuends up through 20.

▶ Common Errors and Misconceptions

Students might say more than one number for each object when counting objects in a group. Or they might skip objects. To avoid such problems, draw a line down the center of a sheet of paper. Have students move objects from one side of the paper to the other as they count.

▶ Content Background

Students will use concrete objects to solve an addition story problem.

Keywords	
	add – to combine, or put together, groups of objects or numbers
	addition – the process of combining, or putting together, groups of objects or numbers; a mathematical operation
	sum – the solution to an addition problem

Materials to Gather

SUPPLIED

blocks – O (10 red, 10 blue)

Snack on Story Problems activity page

blocks – B (10 red, 10 blue)

GET READY Add Red and White Circles

ONLINE 5min

Students will use red and white circle blocks to model and solve addition problems.

Objectives

- Use concrete objects or sketches to model and solve addition or subtraction computation problems involving sums or minuends up through 20.

LEARN Addition Story Problems

ONLINE 10min

Students will learn how to use objects to solve story problems by watching Rosa and Serena solve story problems while playing dress up.

Objectives

- Use concrete objects to explain how to solve addition and subtraction problem-solving situations involving numbers up to 10.

LEARN Represent Story Problems with Cubes

ONLINE 10min

Students will read addition story problems on online flash cards. They will use cubes to model these problems offline. Gather the cubes.

Read the story problem on the flash card. Have students choose a different color cube to represent each quantity in the problem. Then have them count the cubes altogether to find the sum. Have students flip the flash card to check their answer.

Objectives

- Use concrete objects to explain how to solve addition and subtraction problem-solving situations involving numbers up to 10.

TRY IT Snack on Story Problems

Students will solve addition story problems. Give students the circles and the Snack on Story Problems activity page from their Activity Book. Read the directions with them. Use the answer key to score the Try It, and then enter the results online.

Objectives

• Use concrete objects to explain how to solve addition and subtraction problem-solving situations involving numbers up through 10.

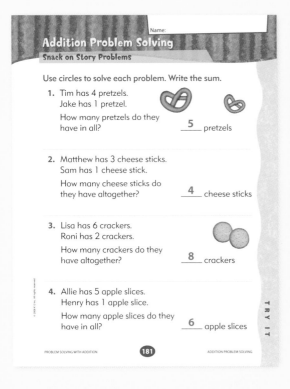

Name: _____

Addition Problem Solving

Snack on Story Problems

Use circles to solve each problem. Write the sum.

1. Tim has 4 pretzels.
   Jake has 1 pretzel.
   How many pretzels do they have in all? __5__ pretzels

2. Matthew has 3 cheese sticks.
   Sam has 1 cheese stick.
   How many cheese sticks do they have altogether? __4__ cheese sticks

3. Lisa has 6 crackers.
   Roni has 2 crackers.
   How many crackers do they have altogether? __8__ crackers

4. Allie has 5 apple slices.
   Henry has 1 apple slice.
   How many apple slices do they have in all? __6__ apple slices

PROBLEM SOLVING WITH ADDITION **181** ADDITION PROBLEM SOLVING

T R Y   I T

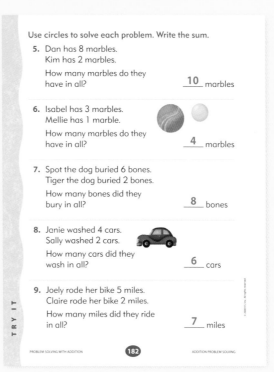

Use circles to solve each problem. Write the sum.

5. Dan has 8 marbles.
   Kim has 2 marbles.
   How many marbles do they have in all? __10__ marbles

6. Isabel has 3 marbles.
   Mellie has 1 marble.
   How many marbles do they have in all? __4__ marbles

7. Spot the dog buried 6 bones.
   Tiger the dog buried 2 bones.
   How many bones did they bury in all? __8__ bones

8. Janie washed 4 cars.
   Sally washed 2 cars.
   How many cars did they wash in all? __6__ cars

9. Joely rode her bike 5 miles.
   Claire rode her bike 2 miles.
   How many miles did they ride in all? __7__ miles

T R Y   I T

PROBLEM SOLVING WITH ADDITION **182** ADDITION PROBLEM SOLVING

Addition Story Problems

▶ Lesson Objectives

Use concrete objects to explain how to solve addition and subtraction problem-solving situations involving numbers up to 10.

▶ Prerequisite Skills

Use concrete objects or sketches to model and solve addition or subtraction computation problems involving sums or minuends up through 20.

▶ Common Errors and Misconceptions

Students might say more than one number for each object when counting objects in a group. Or they might skip objects. To avoid such problems, draw a line down the center of a sheet of paper. Have students move objects from one side of the paper to the other as they count.

▶ Content Background

Students will use objects to solve addition story problems.

Keywords

model (noun) – a physical object, diagram, or picture that represents an amount, an expression, an equation, or a problem situation

model (verb) – to use physical objects, diagrams, or pictures to represent an amount, an expression, an equation, or a problem situation

Materials to Gather

SUPPLIED

blocks – O (10 blue, 10 green)
Sketch to Solve activity page
Model It or Sketch It activity page

ONLINE
5 min

GET READY Garden Animals

Students will learn how to model addition story problems with cubes. They will solve story problems about garden animals.

Objectives

- Use concrete objects or sketches to model and solve addition or subtraction computation problems involving sums or minuends up through 20.

LEARN Flower Story Problems

ONLINE 10min

Students will learn how to model and solve story problems using sketches and objects. They will solve story problems with Alexander in the garden.

Objectives

- Use concrete objects to explain how to solve addition and subtraction problem-solving situations involving numbers up to 10.

LEARN Sketch to Solve

OFFLINE 15min

Students will draw sketches to solve addition story problems. Give students the Sketch to Solve activity page and read the directions with them. Have students use simple sketches such as lines, dots, X's, or circles to show each group.

Objectives

- Use concrete objects to explain how to solve addition and subtraction problem-solving situations involving numbers up to 10.

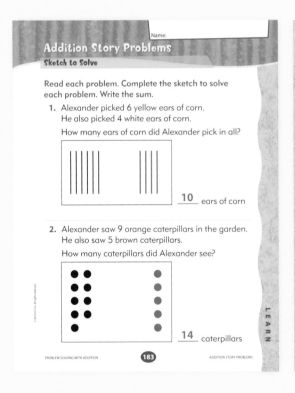

Name: _____

Addition Story Problems
Sketch to Solve

Read each problem. Complete the sketch to solve each problem. Write the sum.

1. Alexander picked 6 yellow ears of corn.
   He also picked 4 white ears of corn.

   How many ears of corn did Alexander pick in all?

   10 ears of corn

2. Alexander saw 9 orange caterpillars in the garden.
   He also saw 5 brown caterpillars.

   How many caterpillars did Alexander see?

   14 caterpillars

Read each problem. Use sketches to solve each problem. Write the sum.

3. Alexander dug 8 white potatoes from the garden.
   He also dug 7 red potatoes.

   How many potatoes did Alexander dig in all from the garden?

   15 potatoes

4. Alexander picked 10 red tomatoes off the vine.
   He also picked 2 yellow tomatoes.

   How many tomatoes did Alexander pick in all?

   12 tomatoes

5. Alexander saw 6 beetles.
   He also saw 3 spiders.

   How many bugs did Alexander see altogether?

   9 bugs

TRY IT Model It or Sketch It

Objectives

Students will use objects and sketches to solve addition story problems. Give students the Model It or Sketch It activity page from their Activity Book and the cubes. Read the directions with them. Use the answer key to check students' answers, and then enter the results online.

- Use concrete objects to explain how to solve addition and subtraction problem-solving situations involving numbers up to 10.

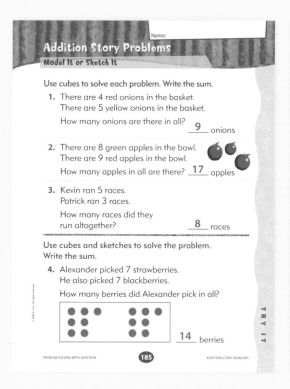

Name: _____

Addition Story Problems

Model It or Sketch It

Use cubes to solve each problem. Write the sum.

1. There are 4 red onions in the basket.
   There are 5 yellow onions in the basket.
   How many onions are there in all? __9__ onions

2. There are 8 green apples in the bowl.
   There are 9 red apples in the bowl.
   How many apples in all are there? __17__ apples

3. Kevin ran 5 races.
   Patrick ran 3 races.
   How many races did they run altogether? __8__ races

Use cubes and sketches to solve the problem. Write the sum.

4. Alexander picked 7 strawberries.
   He also picked 7 blackberries.
   How many berries did Alexander pick in all?

   __14__ berries

T R Y   I T

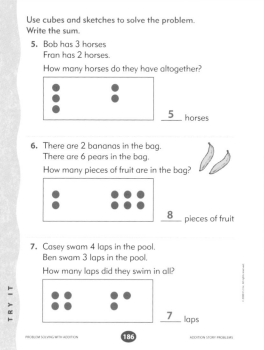

Use cubes and sketches to solve the problem. Write the sum.

5. Bob has 3 horses
   Fran has 2 horses.
   How many horses do they have altogether?

   __5__ horses

6. There are 2 bananas in the bag.
   There are 6 pears in the bag.
   How many pieces of fruit are in the bag?

   __8__ pieces of fruit

7. Casey swam 4 laps in the pool.
   Ben swam 3 laps in the pool.
   How many laps did they swim in all?

   __7__ laps

Explain Addition Solutions

Lesson Overview

Skills Update	5 minutes	ONLINE
LEARN Solve with Serena and Johnny	15 minutes	ONLINE
LEARN My Story Problems	10 minutes	OFFLINE
TRY IT Create Problems and Solve	15 minutes	OFFLINE

▶ Lesson Objectives

Use concrete objects to explain how to solve addition and subtraction problem-solving situations involving numbers up to 10.

▶ Prerequisite Skills

Use concrete objects or sketches to model and solve addition or subtraction computation problems involving sums or minuends up through 20.

▶ Common Errors and Misconceptions

Students might say more than one number for each object when counting objects in a group. Or they might skip objects. To avoid such problems, draw a line down the center of a sheet of paper. Have students move objects from one side of the paper to the other as they count.

▶ Content Background

Students will learn to explain how to solve a story problem by watching Serena and Johnny explain how to solve story problems. Students will also write and explain how to solve their own story problems.

Materials to Gather

SUPPLIED

My Story Problems activity page
Create Problems and Solve activity page
blocks – B (10 red, 10 blue)

ONLINE
15min

LEARN Solve with Serena and Johnny

Students will learn how to solve an addition story problem. Serena and Johnny will take them through three steps: draw, explain, and solve.

Objectives

- Use concrete objects to explain how to solve addition and subtraction problem-solving situations involving numbers up to 10.

LEARN My Story Problems

Objectives

• Use concrete objects to explain how to solve addition and subtraction problem-solving situations involving numbers up to 10.

Students will use pictures to complete and solve addition story problems. Then students will create their own story problems and solve them using sketches.

Give students the My Story Problems activity page and read the directions with them. For Problems 1–3, students may write the name of a friend or family member in the blank at the beginning of each sentence.

Name: _____

Explain Addition Solutions

My Story Problems

Look at the pictures. Fill in the blanks to write an addition story problem about the pictures. Then solve it.

1.

_____Name_____ has ___5___ bananas.

_____Name_____ has ___4___ bananas.

How many bananas do they have in all? ___9___ bananas

2.

_____Name_____ has ___2___ water bottles.

_____Name_____ has ___6___ water bottles.

How many water bottles do they have in all? ___8___ water bottles

---

Look at the pictures. Fill in the blanks to write an addition story problem about the pictures. Then solve it.

3.

_____Name_____ has ___4___ basketballs.

_____Name_____ has ___2___ baseballs.

How many balls do they have in all? ___6___ balls

4. Look at the numbers. Tell an addition story problem by using the numbers. Then use sketches to solve it.

3   **See below.**   7

5. Make up your own addition story problem. Then solve it.

Think: What are the numbers? What are the objects?   **See below.**

Sketches will vary.   **Sketches will vary.**

Additional Answers

4. Students should tell a story about 3 objects and 7 objects. Then students should ask a question about the total number of objects.

   Students should sketch a group of 3 and a group of 7 and explain that the sum of 3 and 7 is 10.

5. Students should tell a story about two groups of objects. Then students should ask a question about the total number of objects. To solve the problem, students should combine the groups and tell the sum.

TRY IT Create Problems and Solve

Objectives

Students will create and solve their own addition story problems. They will use sketches and circle blocks to solve the problems. Give students the blocks and the Create Problems and Solve activity page from their Activity Book. Read the directions with them. Use the answer key to check students' answers, and then enter the results online.

- Use concrete objects to explain how to solve addition and subtraction problem-solving situations involving numbers up to 10.

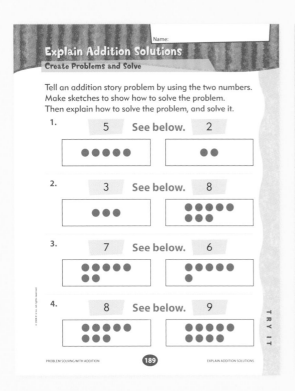

Additional Answers

1. Students should tell an addition story problem about groups of 5 and 2 objects. They should sketch the amounts to find that 5 plus 2 equals 7.

2. Students should tell an addition story problem about groups of 3 and 8 objects. They should sketch the amounts to find that 3 plus 8 equals 11.

3. Students should tell an addition story problem about groups of 7 and 6 objects. They should sketch the amounts to find that 7 plus 6 equals 13.

4. Students should tell an addition story problem about groups of 8 and 9 objects. They should sketch the amounts to find that 8 plus 9 equals 17.

5. Students should show 6 circles next to 4 circles, and then move the circles together to find how many stuffed animals there are in all.

6. Students should show 3 circles next to 5 circles, and then move the circles together to find how many trucks there are in all.

7. Students should show 5 circles next to 4 circles, and then move the circles together to find how many pencils there are in all.

Combine to Find Totals

Lesson Overview

Skills Update	5 minutes	**ONLINE**
GET READY Piecing It Together	5 minutes	**ONLINE**
LEARN Parts and Totals in Problems	5 minutes	**ONLINE**
LEARN Find the Total	10 minutes	**ONLINE**
LEARN Model and Solve	10 minutes	**OFFLINE**
TRY IT Toy Problems	10 minutes	**OFFLINE**

▶ Lesson Objectives

Recognize and solve word problems involving sums up through 20 in which two quantities are combined.

▶ Prerequisite Skills

Demonstrate the meaning of addition as the combining of two sets (for sums up through 20).

▶ Advance Preparation

Print the Part-Part-Total Sheet.

▶ Content Background

Students will combine two parts to find the sum, or total, in addition story problems.

Every addition and subtraction number sentence has a total and at least two parts. In addition, the sum is the total, and the numbers being added, or addends, are the parts. For example, in $5 = 4 + 1$, the total is 5, and the parts are 4 and 1. In a subtraction sentence, one part is subtracted from the total to get the other part. For example, in $5 - 1 = 4$, again the total is 5, and the parts are 4 and 1. This part-part-total relationship can help students understand the opposite or inverse relationship between addition and subtraction.

Materials to Gather

SUPPLIED

blocks – B (10 red, 10 blue)
blocks – O (10 green, 10 blue)
Part-Part-Total Sheet (printout)
Toy Problems activity page

Keywords	**part-part-total** – two groups (parts) that combine to create the whole (total)

GET READY Piecing It Together

ONLINE
5min

Students will watch puzzle pieces being combined to make a puzzle. This activity introduces students to combining parts to make a total, or sum, in addition story problems.

Objectives

- Demonstrate the meaning of addition as the combining of two sets (for sums up through 20).

LEARN Parts and Totals in Problems

ONLINE
5min

Students will learn how to identify the parts and total in an addition story problem. They will learn how to model the parts with objects and how to combine the objects to find the total. Gather the red and blue circles.

Follow the directions on each screen. Students will need the circles on the last screen, but they may use the circles throughout the activity if they wish.

Objectives

- Recognize and solve word problems involving sums up through 20 in which two quantities are combined.

LEARN Find the Total

ONLINE
10min

Students will watch addition story problems being modeled and solved.

Objectives

- Recognize and solve word problems involving sums up through 20 in which two quantities are combined.

LEARN Model and Solve

OFFLINE
10min

Students will use the cubes and Part-Part-Total Sheet to model and solve addition story problems.

Gather the cubes and Part-Part-Total Sheet, and give these materials to students.

1. **Say:** Johnny has 6 marbles and Ron has 4 marbles. Use the cubes to show the problem.

   Students should place 6 cubes of one color in one Part section and 4 cubes of another color in the other.

2. **Ask:** How would you find the total?
   ANSWER: I would move all the cubes to the Total section and count them.

   Have students move the cubes to the Total section and count them.

   Ask: How many marbles do Johnny and Ron have altogether?
   ANSWER: 10

3. Repeat Steps 1 and 2 with the following story problems:

   Serena saw 4 blue birds today, and Winnie saw 4 black birds. Use the cubes to show the problem.

   There are 7 puppies in the pet store window. There are also 5 kittens in the pet store window. Use the cubes to show the problem.

Objectives

- Recognize and solve word problems involving sums up through 20 in which two quantities are combined.

Tips

When students use the Part-Part-Total Sheet, make sure they move the cubes from each Part section to the Total section rather than placing new cubes in the Total section.

Students will solve story problems by modeling each part and combining the parts to find the total. Give students the Part-Part-Total Sheet, cubes, and the Toy Problems activity page from their Activity Book. Read the directions with them. Use the answer key to check students' answers, and then enter the results online.

Objectives

- Recognize and solve word problems involving sums up through 20 in which two quantities are combined.

Tips

When students use the Part-Part-Total Sheet, make sure they move the cubes from each Part section to the Total section rather than placing new cubes in the Total section.

Combine to Find Totals

Name:

Toy Problems

Use the Part-Part-Total Sheet and cubes to solve each problem. Then write the answer on the line.

1. Winnie has 6 dominoes.
Serena has 7 dominoes.

How many dominoes do Winnie and
Serena have in all? ___13___ dominoes

2. There are 3 black checkers on the board.
There are 6 red checkers on the board.

How many checkers are on
the board? ___9___ checkers

3. Serena has 4 jacks.
Winnie has 8 jacks.

How many jacks do Winnie and
Serena have altogether? ___12___ jacks

4. There are 5 black cards in Winnie's hand.
There are 9 red cards in Winnie's hand.

How many cards are in Winnie's hand? ___14___ cards

Use the Part-Part-Total Sheet and cubes to solve each problem. Then circle the answer.

5. Pedro has 14 books.
Shay has 6 books.

How many do they have altogether?

A. 8   (B.) 20   C. 16

6. A pet store has 12 hamsters in one habitat
and 7 hamsters in another habitat.

How many hamsters are there in the two habitats?

(A.) 19   B. 15   C. 4

7. A cat ate 8 treats.
A dog ate 7 treats.

How many treats did they eat altogether?

A. 14   (B.) 15   C. 1

8. The Best Berry Farm baked 10 apple pies.
The farm also baked 3 peach pies.

How many pies did the farm bake in all?

A. 7   B. 8   (C.) 13

Recognize Combine Problems

Lesson Overview

Skills Update	5 minutes	ONLINE
GET READY Playground Parts and Totals	5 minutes	ONLINE
LEARN Part-Part-Total or Not?	15 minutes	ONLINE
LEARN Same-Number Problems	10 minutes	OFFLINE
TRY IT Snack-Time Problems	10 minutes	OFFLINE

▶ Lesson Objectives

Recognize and solve word problems involving sums up through 20 in which two quantities are combined.

▶ Prerequisite Skills

Demonstrate the meaning of addition as the combining of two sets (for sums up through 20).

▶ Advance Preparation

Print the Part-Part-Total Sheet.

▶ Content Background

Students are familiar with story problems that involve combining two parts to find the sum, or total. In this lesson, they will learn that they cannot combine parts to solve every story problem. Students will begin to recognize which problems they can solve with a part-part-total chart.

Materials to Gather

SUPPLIED
Part-Part-Total Sheet (printout)
blocks – O (10 green, 10 blue)
Same-Number Problems activity page
Snack-Time Problems activity page

GET READY Playground Parts and Totals

ONLINE **5** min

Students will learn that they can solve only some story problems by combining parts by attempting to solve two problems using a part-part-total chart.

Objectives

- Demonstrate the meaning of addition as the combining of two sets (for sums up through 20).

LEARN Part-Part-Total or Not?

ONLINE **15** min

Students will learn when story problems can be solved by combining parts.

Objectives

- Recognize and solve word problems involving sums up through 20 in which two quantities are combined.

LEARN Same-Number Problems

Objectives

- Recognize and solve word problems involving sums up through 20 in which two quantities are combined.

Students will learn about a special type of addition story problems: same-number problems. Problems with the same numbers will result in the same sum, even if the numbers represent different things (e.g., 2 pigs and 4 pigs makes **6** pigs; 4 books and 2 books makes **6** books). Then students will write their own sets of same-number problems.

Give students the Part-Part-Total Sheet, cubes, and Same-Number Problems activity page. Read the directions with them.

Tips

Make a list of objects (e.g., cars, foods, animals) that students can use for ideas when writing their own story problems.

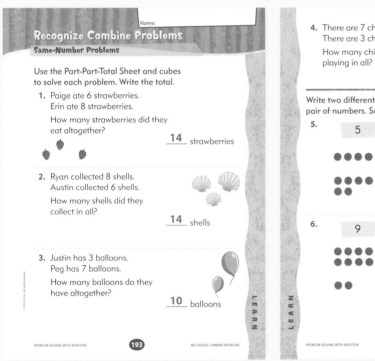

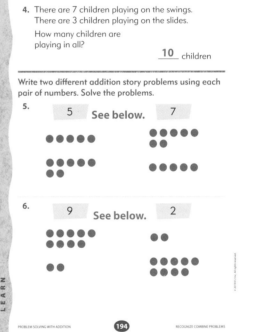

Additional Answers

5. Students should make up two addition problems in which the numbers 5 and 7 are combined. Examples: There were 5 frogs on a log. Seven more frogs jumped on the log. How many frogs are on the log in all? Janice ate 5 pretzels. Jack ate 7 pretzels. How many pretzels did they eat in all?

6. Students should make up two addition problems in which the numbers 9 and 2 are combined. Examples: Henry has 9 toy cars. His brother gives him 2 more cars. How many toy cars does Henry have altogether? There are 9 ants near the pond. 2 more ants join them. How many ants in all are near the pond?

TRY IT Snack-Time Problems

Objectives

- Recognize and solve word problems involving sums up through 20 in which two quantities are combined.

Students will decide if they can solve an addition story problem by combining. Give students the Part-Part-Total Sheet, cubes, and Snack-Time Problems activity page. Read the directions with them. Use the answer key to check students' answers, and then enter the results online.

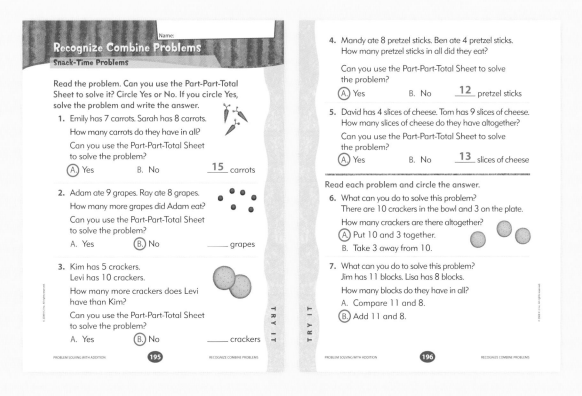

Name:

Recognize Combine Problems
Snack-Time Problems

Read the problem. Can you use the Part-Part-Total Sheet to solve it? Circle Yes or No. If you circle Yes, solve the problem and write the answer.

1. Emily has 7 carrots. Sarah has 8 carrots.

   How many carrots do they have in all?

   Can you use the Part-Part-Total Sheet to solve the problem?

   (A.) Yes   B. No   __15__ carrots

2. Adam ate 9 grapes. Ray ate 8 grapes.

   How many more grapes did Adam eat?

   Can you use the Part-Part-Total Sheet to solve the problem?

   A. Yes   (B.) No   _____ grapes

3. Kim has 5 crackers.
   Levi has 10 crackers.

   How many more crackers does Levi have than Kim?

   Can you use the Part-Part-Total Sheet to solve the problem?

   A. Yes   (B.) No   _____ crackers

TRY IT

4. Mandy ate 8 pretzel sticks. Ben ate 4 pretzel sticks. How many pretzel sticks in all did they eat?

   Can you use the Part-Part-Total Sheet to solve the problem?

   (A.) Yes   B. No   __12__ pretzel sticks

5. David has 4 slices of cheese. Tom has 9 slices of cheese. How many slices of cheese do they have altogether?

   Can you use the Part-Part-Total Sheet to solve the problem?

   (A.) Yes   B. No   __13__ slices of cheese

Read each problem and circle the answer.

6. What can you do to solve this problem?
   There are 10 crackers in the bowl and 3 on the plate.

   How many crackers are there altogether?

   (A.) Put 10 and 3 together.
   B. Take 3 away from 10.

7. What can you do to solve this problem?
   Jim has 11 blocks. Lisa has 8 blocks.

   How many blocks do they have in all?

   A. Compare 11 and 8.
   (B.) Add 11 and 8.

TRY IT

Missing Parts Problems

Lesson Overview

Skills Update	5 minutes	**ONLINE**
GET READY Build a Wagon	10 minutes	**ONLINE**
LEARN Identify Parts and Total	15 minutes	**ONLINE**
TRY IT Name the Missing Part	15 minutes	**ONLINE**

▶ Lesson Objectives

Recognize and solve word problems involving sums up through 20 in which two quantities are combined.

▶ Prerequisite Skills

Demonstrate the meaning of addition as the combining of two sets (for sums up through 20).

▶ Content Background

Students have solved story problems in which they've combined parts to find the total. Now students will learn about story problems in which the total is given and they must solve for a missing part.

Materials to Gather

There are no materials to gather for this lesson.

GET READY Build a Wagon

ONLINE 10min

By watching someone try to build a wagon using only 3 wheels, students will learn that in some story problems, the total is given and they must solve for the missing part.

Objectives

- Demonstrate the meaning of addition as the combining of two sets (for sums up through 20).

LEARN Identify Parts and Total

ONLINE 15min

Students will learn how to identify the total, part, and missing part in a story problem.

Objectives

- Recognize and solve word problems involving sums up through 20 in which two quantities are combined.

Students will answer questions online in which they must identify the number of missing parts in a picture. They will also be asked to identify the total as if no parts were missing from the picture.

Objectives

- Recognize and solve word problems involving sums up through 20 in which two quantities are combined.

Tips

Before students begin, review the Part-Part-Total Sheet. Explain that each part is an addend, or number being added, and the total is the sum.

Estimate Sums Through 20

Lesson Overview

Skills Update	5 minutes	ONLINE
GET READY About How Many Jelly Beans?	5 minutes	ONLINE
LEARN Estimate to the Nearest 5	10 minutes	OFFLINE
LEARN Estimate Sums of Story Problems	10 minutes	OFFLINE
TRY IT Estimate Sums	10 minutes	OFFLINE
CHECKPOINT	5 minutes	OFFLINE

▶ Lesson Objectives

Make reasonable estimates for the solutions to addition problems (for sums up through 20).

▶ Prerequisite Skills

Recognize and solve word problems involving sums up through 20 in which two quantities are combined.

▶ Advance Preparation

Make two trains of 5 yellow cubes and two trains of 10 green cubes. Number index cards 1 through 20, or gather the number cards you created previously.

▶ Content Background

Students will learn how to estimate to find a sum.

Estimates, or approximate calculations, are sufficient and appropriate in many everyday situations. One way to estimate sums or quantities is to choose the nearest target number, such as the nearest 5 or 10. This target number is called a benchmark.

Throughout this lesson you will see the word *estimate* and the phrase *about how many* used interchangeably. Students should understand that *estimate* is a mathematical term that means *about how many*.

Materials to Gather

SUPPLIED

blocks – O (10 yellow, 20 green, 20 blue)

Checkpoint (printout)

Estimate Sums of Story Problems activity page

Estimate Sums activity page

ALSO NEEDED

index cards – numbered 1–20

Keywords

estimate (noun) – the answer to an approximation or rough calculation

estimate (verb) – to approximate or perform a rough calculation

GET READY About How Many Jelly Beans?

Objectives

- Make reasonable estimates for the solutions to addition problems (for sums up through 20).

Students will estimate numbers to the nearest 5 by estimating the number of jelly beans in a jar. For example, a jar of 4 jelly beans has about 5 jelly beans.

Tips

Have students count the jelly beans to check that the exact number is nearest to the estimated number.

LEARN Estimate to the Nearest 5

Objectives

- Make reasonable estimates for the solutions to addition problems (for sums up through 20).

Students will use benchmarks of 5 and 10 to estimate sums. They will compare cube trains that represent the exact sum to cube trains that represent the benchmarks.

Gather the cube trains you prepared, blue cubes, and number cards.

1. Display a train of 5 yellow cubes. Ask students how many cubes are in the train. (5) Put the 5 card above the one yellow train.

2. Display the second train of 5 yellow cubes. Ask students how many cubes are in the train. (5)

3. Point to the two yellow trains.
   Ask: How many is 5 and 5?
   ANSWER: 10
   Have students count the cubes to check their answer.

4. Display one train of 10 green cubes. Ask students how many cubes are in the train. (10)

5. Point to the green train and one yellow train.
   Ask: How many is 10 and 5?
   ANSWER: 15
   Have students count the cubes to check their answer.

6. Display the two green trains.
   Ask: How many is 10 and 10?
   ANSWER: 20
   Have students count the cubes to check their answer.

7. Display a yellow train and a green train. Remind students of the number of cubes in each train.
   Say: We'll use the 5-train and 10-train to help us estimate, or find, about how many blue cubes we will show.

8. Display the 4 card. Have students choose 4 blue cubes and snap them to make a train.

9. Point to the 4-train.
   Ask: Is your train of 4 cubes closer to the length of the 5-train or the 10-train?
   ANSWER: 5-train

Tips

Students can add or take away cubes from the addend trains to help decide whether the addend is nearer to 5 or 10. For example, students would add 1 cube to the 9 train to make 10. They would take away 4 cubes from the 9 train to make 5. So 10 is the nearer benchmark because they must add or take away fewer cubes.

Say: We can estimate that 4 is a number closer to 5 than it is to 10. An estimate is a number that is about as many as a target number. We can use numbers like 5, 10, 15, and 20 as target numbers, just like we did when you said 4 is close to the target number 5. Estimating is different from counting. When you estimate, you do not count every object. An estimate is a very good guess of how many you have.

10. **Say:** Let's look at our yellow 5-train together with our blue 4-train.

11. Point to the yellow and blue trains.

    Ask: We know that the yellow train is 5 and we estimated that the blue train was close to 5. So, are the two trains together about 5 or 10?
    ANSWER: 10

12. Point to the 5 and 4 cards.

    Say: The sum of 5 and 4 is about 10.

13. Clear the work area except for the yellow and green trains. Display the 9 and 7 number cards.

    Say: Let's estimate the sum of 9 and 7.

14. Have students make trains to show 9 and 7.

15. Explain that first students will estimate each number. Have students compare each train to the yellow and green trains.

    Ask: What is your estimate for 9? For 7?
    ANSWER: 10 for 9 and 5 for 7

    Ask: Why did you choose 10 for 9 and 5 for 7?
    ANSWER: The 9-train is closer in length to the 10-train than the 5-train. The 7-train is closer in length to the 5-train than the 10-train.

16. **Ask:** What is a good estimate for the sum of 9 and 7?
    ANSWER: 15

17. Repeat Steps 13–16 with the numbers 11 and 9.

18. Show the students 1 blue cube with the 1 card and a 5-train with the 5 card.

    Say: Now, let's estimate the sum of 1 and 5.

19. **Ask:** Is 1 closer to 0 or to 5?
    ANSWER: 0

20. **Ask:** So, what's the estimate of the sum of 1 and 5?
    ANSWER: 5

OFFLINE
10 min

LEARN Estimate Sums of Story Problems

Students will use benchmarks of 5, 10, 15, and 20 to estimate sums of addition problems. Give students the Estimate Sums of Story Problems activity page, cube trains you prepared, and blue cubes. Read the directions with them.

Objectives

- Make reasonable estimates for the solutions to addition problems (for sums up through 20).

Tips

To help students understand benchmarks of 15 and 20, review that 5 and 5 is 10, 10 and 5 is 15, and 10 and 10 is 20.

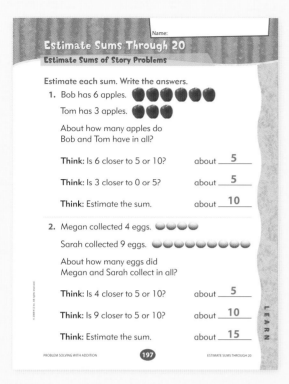

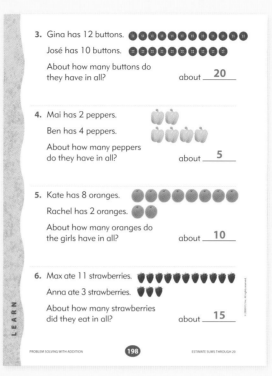

TRY IT Estimate Sums

OFFLINE
10 min

Objectives

- Make reasonable estimates for the solutions to addition problems (for sums up through 20).

Students will use benchmarks to practice estimating sums. Give students the Estimate Sums activity page from their Activity Book and read the directions with them.

If students have difficulty estimating, have them show each addend with cubes and decide which benchmark is closer in length to the actual number. Then have them add their benchmarks to estimate the sum.

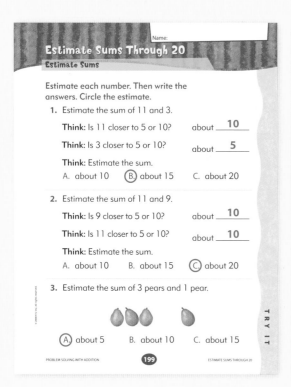

Estimate Sums Through 20

Estimate Sums

Estimate each number. Then write the answers. Circle the estimate.

1. Estimate the sum of 11 and 3.

   Think: Is 11 closer to 5 or 10?   about ___10___

   Think: Is 3 closer to 5 or 10?   about ___5___

   Think: Estimate the sum.
   A. about 10   (B.) about 15   C. about 20

2. Estimate the sum of 11 and 9.

   Think: Is 9 closer to 5 or 10?   about ___10___

   Think: Is 11 closer to 5 or 10?   about ___10___

   Think: Estimate the sum.
   A. about 10   B. about 15   (C.) about 20

3. Estimate the sum of 3 pears and 1 pear.

   (A.) about 5   B. about 10   C. about 15

T R Y   I T

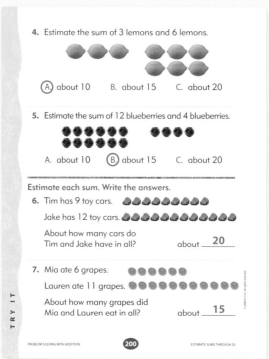

4. Estimate the sum of 3 lemons and 6 lemons.

   (A.) about 10   B. about 15   C. about 20

5. Estimate the sum of 12 blueberries and 4 blueberries.

   A. about 10   (B.) about 15   C. about 20

Estimate each sum. Write the answers.

6. Tim has 9 toy cars.

   Jake has 12 toy cars.

   About how many cars do
   Tim and Jake have in all?   about ___20___

7. Mia ate 6 grapes.

   Lauren ate 11 grapes.

   About how many grapes did
   Mia and Lauren eat in all?   about ___15___

T R Y   I T

OFFLINE
5min

CHECKPOINT

Objectives

Print the Checkpoint and have students complete it on their own. Read the directions, problems, and answer choices to students if necessary. Use the answer key to score the Checkpoint, and then enter the results online.

- Make reasonable estimates for the solutions to addition problems (for sums up through 20).

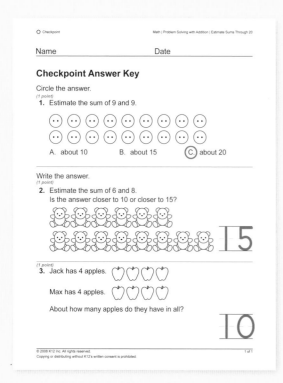

Checkpoint   Math | Problem Solving with Addition | Estimate Sums Through 20

Name   Date

Checkpoint Answer Key

Circle the answer.
(1 point)
1. Estimate the sum of 9 and 9.

   A. about 10   B. about 15   (C.) about 20

Write the answer.
(1 point)
2. Estimate the sum of 6 and 8.
   Is the answer closer to 10 or closer to 15?

   15

(1 point)
3. Jack has 4 apples.

   Max has 4 apples.

   About how many apples do they have in all?

   10

Check the Accuracy of Calculations

Lesson Overview

Skills Update	5 minutes	ONLINE
LEARN Check Story Problems	10 minutes	ONLINE
LEARN Check Problems	10 minutes	OFFLINE
TRY IT Check Answers	10 minutes	OFFLINE
CHECKPOINT	10 minutes	OFFLINE

▶ **Lesson Objectives**

- Check the accuracy of calculations for the solutions to addition problems with sums up through 20.
- Make reasonable estimates for the solutions to addition problems (for sums up through 20).

▶ **Prerequisite Skills**

Recognize and solve word problems involving sums up through 20 in which two quantities are combined.

▶ **Content Background**

Students will learn how to use models and sketches to check answers to addition story problems.

Keywords

check – to examine for accuracy

Materials to Gather

SUPPLIED

blocks – O (10 green, 10 blue)
Check Problems activity page
Check Answers activity page
Checkpoint (printout)

ALSO NEEDED

paper, drawing – 1 sheet

LEARN Check Story Problems

ONLINE **10**min

Students will learn how to check answers using models and sketches by watching Serena check Alexander's answers to story problems. Then students will try checking answers to story problems using models and sketches.

Gather the cubes and drawing paper. Students will use these materials in the second part of the activity. Follow the directions on each screen.

Objectives

- Check the accuracy of calculations for the solutions to addition problems with sums up through 20.

Tips

To prevent students from counting the same object twice, have them touch each object as they count it.

LEARN Check Problems

OFFLINE **10**min

Students will practice checking addition problems. They will choose the correct problem from a group of three problems.

Give students the cubes and the Check Problems activity page. Read the directions with them.

Objectives

- Check the accuracy of calculations for the solutions to addition problems with sums up through 20.

Tips

When students add with cubes, have them count on from the greater number of cubes rather than mixing the cubes and counting them as a single group.

Name:

Check the Accuracy of Calculations
Check Problems

Use cubes to check each problem. Circle the problem that has a correct answer.

1. Which math problem is correct?
   A. 4 cups and 2 cups makes 7 cups.
   B. 8 cups and 3 cups makes 12 cups.
   C. 9 cups and 5 cups makes 14 cups.

2. Which math problem is correct?
   A. 2 plates and 3 plates makes 5 plates.
   B. 6 plates and 7 plates makes 14 plates.
   C. 8 plates and 9 plates makes 18 plates.

3. Which math problem is correct? Use cubes to show how you know your answer is correct.
   A. 6 spoons and 3 spoons makes 10 spoons.
   B. 7 spoons and 7 spoons makes 15 spoons.
   C. 9 spoons and 10 spoons makes 19 spoons.

4. Which math problem is correct?
   A. 1 bowl and 6 bowls makes 7 bowls.
   B. 8 bowls and 5 bowls makes 11 bowls.
   C. 6 bowls and 4 bowls makes 9 bowls.

PROBLEM SOLVING WITH ADDITION 201 CHECK THE ACCURACY OF CALCULATIONS

PROBLEM SOLVING WITH ADDITION 202 CHECK THE ACCURACY OF CALCULATIONS

TRY IT Check Answers

Students will practice checking answers to story problems. Give students the cubes, drawing paper, and Check Answers activity page. Read the directions with them.

Objectives

- Check the accuracy of calculations for the solutions to addition problems with sums up through 20.

Tips

Students should use a different color of cubes to show each number in the story problem.

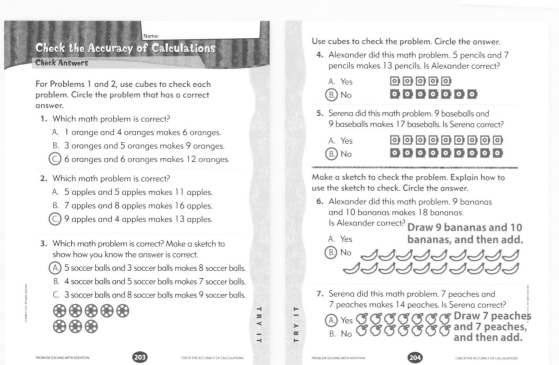

Check the Accuracy of Calculations

Check Answers

Name:

For Problems 1 and 2, use cubes to check each problem. Circle the problem that has a correct answer.

1. Which math problem is correct?
   A. 1 orange and 4 oranges makes 6 oranges.
   B. 3 oranges and 5 oranges makes 9 oranges.
   C. 6 oranges and 6 oranges makes 12 oranges.

2. Which math problem is correct?
   A. 5 apples and 5 apples makes 11 apples.
   B. 7 apples and 8 apples makes 16 apples.
   C. 9 apples and 4 apples makes 13 apples.

3. Which math problem is correct? Make a sketch to show how you know the answer is correct.
   A. 5 soccer balls and 3 soccer balls makes 8 soccer balls.
   B. 4 soccer balls and 5 soccer balls makes 7 soccer balls.
   C. 3 soccer balls and 8 soccer balls makes 9 soccer balls.

PROBLEM SOLVING WITH ADDITION　　203　　CHECK THE ACCURACY OF CALCULATIONS

TRY IT

Use cubes to check the problem. Circle the answer.

4. Alexander did this math problem. 5 pencils and 7 pencils makes 13 pencils. Is Alexander correct?
   A. Yes
   B. No

5. Serena did this math problem. 9 baseballs and 9 baseballs makes 17 baseballs. Is Serena correct?
   A. Yes
   B. No

Make a sketch to check the problem. Explain how to use the sketch to check. Circle the answer.

6. Alexander did this math problem. 9 bananas and 10 bananas makes 18 bananas. Is Alexander correct?
   A. Yes
   B. No
   Draw 9 bananas and 10 bananas, and then add.

7. Serena did this math problem. 7 peaches and 7 peaches makes 14 peaches. Is Serena correct?
   A. Yes
   B. No
   Draw 7 peaches and 7 peaches, and then add.

PROBLEM SOLVING WITH ADDITION　　204　　CHECK THE ACCURACY OF CALCULATIONS

TRY IT

CHECKPOINT

Print the Checkpoint and have students complete it on their own. Read the directions, problems, and answer choices to students, if necessary. Use the answer key to score the Checkpoint, and then enter the results online.

Gather the cubes. Students will use cubes to check answers in Problems 1 and 2.

Objectives

- Check the accuracy of calculations for the solutions to addition problems with sums up through 20.

Tips

To help students understand benchmarks of 15 and 20, review that 5 and 5 is 10, 10 and 5 is 15, and 10 and 10 is 20.

Name _____ Date _____

Checkpoint Answer Key

(1 point)
1. Alexander did this math problem.
   5 birds and 9 birds makes 12 birds.
   Use cubes to check his work.
   Is Alexander correct?

   A. Yes   (B.) No

(1 point)
2. Serena did this math problem.
   4 flowers and 7 flowers makes 11 flowers.
   Use cubes to check her work.
   Is Serena correct?

   (A.) Yes   B. No

Name _____ Date _____

(1 point)
3. Which problem is correct? Make a sketch to show how you know the answer is correct.

   A. 4 footballs and 2 footballs makes 7 footballs.
   (B.) 10 footballs and 10 footballs makes 20 footballs.
   C. 9 footballs and 8 footballs makes 15 footballs.

(1 point)
4. Which problem is correct? Make a sketch to show how you know the answer is correct.

   (A.) 7 crackers and 7 crackers makes 14 crackers.
   B. 4 crackers and 9 crackers makes 14 crackers.
   C. 6 crackers and 0 crackers makes 7 crackers.

Unit Review

Lesson Overview

UNIT REVIEW Look Back	20 minutes	ONLINE
UNIT REVIEW Checkpoint Practice	10 minutes	OFFLINE
➡ UNIT REVIEW Prepare for the Checkpoint		

▶ Unit Objectives

This lesson reviews the following objectives:

- Use concrete objects to explain how to solve addition and subtraction problem-solving situations involving numbers up to 10.
- Recognize and solve word problems involving sums up through 20 in which two quantities are combined.
- Make reasonable estimates for the solutions to addition problems (for sums up through 20).
- Check the accuracy of calculations for the solutions to addition problems with sums up through 20.

▶ Advance Preparation

In this lesson, students will have an opportunity to review previous activities in the Problem Solving with Addition unit. Look at the suggested activities in Unit Review: Prepare for the Checkpoint online and gather any needed materials.
   Print the Part-Part-Total Sheet.

Keywords		
add	model (noun)	
addition	model (verb)	
check	part-part-total	
estimate (noun)	sum	
estimate (verb)		

Materials to Gather

SUPPLIED

blocks – O (10 red, 10 blue)
Part-Part-Total Sheet (printout)
Checkpoint Practice activity page

ONLINE
20min

UNIT REVIEW Look Back

Objectives

- Review unit objectives.

Students used concrete objects to solve addition story problems that involve combining groups. They learned how to explain how they are solving these story problems. They also solved missing-addend problems, which are problems in which one of the groups being added is unknown. Students then learned how to estimate sums and check the accuracy of their work. Students will review these concepts to prepare for the Unit Checkpoint.

UNIT REVIEW Checkpoint Practice

Objectives

- Review unit objectives.

Students will complete a Checkpoint Practice activity page to prepare for the Unit Checkpoint. If necessary, read the directions, questions, and answer choices to students. Have students answer the problems on their own. Carefully review the answers with students.

Gather the cubes and Part-Part-Total Sheet, and give these materials to students.

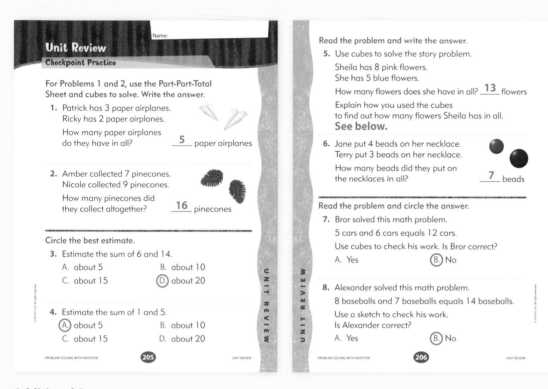

Unit Review
Checkpoint Practice

Name: _____

For Problems 1 and 2, use the Part-Part-Total Sheet and cubes to solve. Write the answer.

1. Patrick has 3 paper airplanes.
   Ricky has 2 paper airplanes.
   How many paper airplanes
   do they have in all? __5__ paper airplanes

2. Amber collected 7 pinecones.
   Nicole collected 9 pinecones.
   How many pinecones did
   they collect altogether? __16__ pinecones

Circle the best estimate.

3. Estimate the sum of 6 and 14.
   A. about 5   B. about 10
   C. about 15   (D.) about 20

4. Estimate the sum of 1 and 5.
   (A.) about 5   B. about 10
   C. about 15   D. about 20

PROBLEM SOLVING WITH ADDITION   (205)   UNIT REVIEW

Read the problem and write the answer.

5. Use cubes to solve the story problem.
   Sheila has 8 pink flowers.
   She has 5 blue flowers.
   How many flowers does she have in all? __13__ flowers
   Explain how you used the cubes
   to find out how many flowers Sheila has in all.
   See below.

6. Jane put 4 beads on her necklace.
   Terry put 3 beads on her necklace.
   How many beads did they put on
   the necklaces in all? __7__ beads

Read the problem and circle the answer.

7. Bror solved this math problem.
   5 cars and 6 cars equals 12 cars.
   Use cubes to check his work. Is Bror correct?
   A. Yes   (B.) No

8. Alexander solved this math problem.
   8 baseballs and 7 baseballs equals 14 baseballs.
   Use a sketch to check his work.
   Is Alexander correct?
   A. Yes   (B.) No

PROBLEM SOLVING WITH ADDITION   (206)   UNIT REVIEW

Additional Answers

5. Put 8 cubes in one group and 5 cubes in a second group. Move the groups together and count them to find how many flowers in all.

➡ UNIT REVIEW Prepare for the Checkpoint

What you do next depends on how students performed in the previous activity, Unit Review: Checkpoint Practice. If students had difficulty with any of the problems, complete the appropriate review activity listed in the table online.

Unit Checkpoint

UNIT CHECKPOINT   40 minutes : OFFLINE

▶ Unit Objectives

This lesson assesses the following objectives:

- Use concrete objects to explain how to solve addition and subtraction problem-solving situations involving numbers up to 10.

- Recognize and solve word problems involving sums up through 20 in which two quantities are combined.

- Make reasonable estimates for the solutions to addition problems (for sums up through 20).

- Check the accuracy of calculations for the solutions to addition problems with sums up through 20.

Materials to Gather

SUPPLIED

Unit Checkpoint (printout)

blocks – B (10 green, 10 blue)

blocks – O (10 red, 10 yellow)

UNIT CHECKPOINT Offline

OFFLINE
40 min

Objectives

- Assess unit objectives.

Students will complete the Unit Checkpoint offline. In Part 1, students will take a performance-based assessment. In Part 2, students will complete the problems on their own. Print the Unit Checkpoint. Read the directions, problems, and answer choices to students if necessary. Use the answer key to score the Checkpoint, and then enter the results online.

Gather the cubes. Have students use circles for Problems 1–4 and cubes for Problems 13–16.

Checkpoint   Math | Problem Solving with Addition | Unit Checkpoint

Name _____ Date _____

Unit Checkpoint Answer Key

Part 1
Read each story problem. Show and tell how to use circles to solve the problem.

1. Mona has 6 small stuffed animals. She has 4 large stuffed animals. How many stuffed animals does Mona have in all?
   (1 point)
   Put 6 circles next to 4 circles. Move the groups together to find how many stuffed animals in all.

2. Charlie has 3 toy trucks. Tom has 5 toy trucks. How many trucks do they have in all?
   (1 point)
   Put 3 circles next to 5 circles. Move the groups together to find how many toy trucks in all.

Checkpoint   Math | Problem Solving with Addition | Unit Checkpoint

Name _____ Date _____

3. Clara has 4 marbles. Sue has 5 marbles. How many marbles do they have in all?
   (1 point)
   Put 4 circles next to 5 circles. Move the groups together to find how many marbles in all.

4. Lily has 7 stickers. Stella has 3 stickers. How many stickers do they have in all?
   (1 point)
   Put 7 circles next to 3 circles. Move the groups together to find how many stickers in all.

Give students Part 2 of the Unit Checkpoint.

Name _____ Date _____

Part 2
Circle the answer.
(1 point)
5. Lisa has 5 cats and Mary has 11. How many cats do
   they have altogether?
   A. 5   B. 6   C. 11   (D.) 16

(1 point)
6. Nina has 12 books. Todd has 7 books. How many books
   do they have in all?
   (A.) 19   B. 12   C. 7   D. 5

(1 point)
7. David collected 6 sticks. Max collected 7 sticks. How
   many sticks did they collect in all?
   A. 1   B. 6   C. 9   (D.) 13

(1 point)
8. Dina bought 4 stickers yesterday. She bought 7 stickers today.
   How many stickers did she buy on both days?
   A. 9   (B.) 11   C. 14   D. 10

(1 point)
9. Estimate the sum of 4 and 2.
   (A.) about 5   B. about 10   C. about 15

(1 point)
10. Estimate the sum of 11 and 4.
    A. about 10   (B.) about 15   C. about 20

Name _____ Date _____

Write the answer.
(1 point)
11. Estimate the sum of 10 and 9.

                                              about __20__

(1 point)
12. Estimate the sum of 1 and 8.

                                              about __10__

For Problems 13–16, use cubes. Circle the answer.
(1 point)
13. Bror did this math problem: The sum of 7 marbles and 3 marbles is
    9 marbles. Use cubes to check his work. Is Bror correct?

    A. Yes   (B.) No

(1 point)
14. Bror did this math problem: The sum of 8 stickers and 4 stickers is
    12 stickers. Use cubes to check his work. Is Bror correct?
    (A.) Yes   B. No

(1 point)
15. Serena did this math problem: The sum of 7 books and 9 books is
    16 books. Use cubes to check her work. Is Serena correct?

    (A.) Yes   B. No

(1 point)
16. Serena did this math problem: The sum of 9 bears and 5 bears is
    15 bears. Use cubes to check her work. Is Serena correct?
    A. Yes   (B.) No

Introduction to Subtraction

10 take away 7 is 3.

▶ Unit Objectives

- Demonstrate the meaning of subtraction as taking away an amount from a given quantity (with minuends up through 20).
- Use concrete objects or sketches to model and solve addition or subtraction computation problems involving sums or minuends up through 20.
- Make reasonable estimates for the solutions to subtraction problems with minuends up through 20.
- Check the accuracy of the calculations for the solutions to subtraction problems with minuends up through 20.

▶ Big Ideas

- Subtraction represents taking away. Subtraction can find a mystery addend.
- Counting principles and numbers can be used to solve addition and subtraction problems.
- Estimation is a useful tool in problem solving.

▶ Unit Introduction

Students will learn to take away objects and to find how many are left. Students will learn to take away objects and tell how many are left, and will use sketches and countable objects to model subtraction problems. They will learn that they can use subtraction to find the amount of a mystery addend in an addition problem. They will learn to find how many cubes are hidden for problems in which one part is hidden, one part is visible, and they know the total.

Students will learn to estimate answers and to check the accuracy of their work. They will also learn that counting principles and numbers can be used to solve subtraction story problems.

Take Away to Subtract

▶ Lesson Objectives

Demonstrate the meaning of subtraction as taking away an amount from a given quantity (with minuends up through 20).

▶ Prerequisite Skills

- Count aloud a number of objects up through 20.
- Use concrete objects or sketches to represent a quantity up through 10.

▶ Content Background

Students will use concrete objects to learn how to take away and find how many are left.

Materials to Gather

SUPPLIED

blocks – O (any color)
Take Away Cubes activity page
blocks – B (10 red, 10 blue)

ALSO NEEDED

household objects – bowl
card stock – 1 sheet

Keywords

operation – a process or action, such as addition, subtraction, multiplication, or addition, performed in a specified sequence and in accordance with specific rules; also called a mathematical operation

part-part-total – two groups (parts) that combine to create the whole (total)

subtract – to take away objects from a group or to find a difference between two groups

subtraction – the process of taking away objects from a group or finding the difference between two groups; a mathematical operation

take away – in subtraction, to separate a group from the total

GET READY Button Count   ONLINE 5 min

Objectives

- Count aloud a number of objects up through 20.

Students will practice counting up through 20.

Encourage students to click the buttons in a sequence by either going down the screen or across the screen.

LEARN Cube Cover Up

OFFLINE
10min

Objectives

- Demonstrate the meaning of subtraction as taking away an amount from a given quantity (with minuends up through 20).

Tips

If students have difficulty counting, review counting up from 1 to 20 and counting back from 20 to 1.

Students will find the number of hidden cubes for problems where they can see some cubes and know the total.

Gather the cubes and a sheet of card stock.

1. Place 10 cubes on the table in groups of 6 and 4. Explain that you are going to take away some of the cubes, and cover the group of 4 with the card stock. Have students tell you how many cubes they can see. Have them tell you how many cubes are hidden.

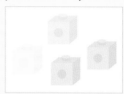

2. While students hide their eyes, place 9 cubes on the table. Cover a group of 3 cubes, leaving 6 cubes visible. Tell students that you started with 9 cubes.

   Ask: How many cubes can you see?
   ANSWER: 6 cubes

3. Ask students how they would find what number added to 6 to make 9. Explain that they can count up to find how many cubes are hidden.

4. Explain that when you take away some objects from a group of objects you are subtracting.

   Say: 9 take away 3 is 6.

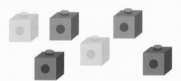 

5. Repeat Steps 2–4 with the following problems:
   - 11 cubes total with 8 visible and 3 hidden
   - 14 cubes total with 9 visible and 5 hidden
   - 16 cubes total with 8 visible and 8 hidden

LEARN Circle Subtraction

OFFLINE **15min**

Students will take away circles to find how many are left.
Gather the circles and the bowl. Place the circles in the bowl.

1. Place 9 circles on the table. Tell students to take away 2 circles. Then have them count the circles that are left.

   Say: 9 take away 2 is 7. In this problem, 9 is the total. You took away a part and were left with a part.

2. Place 8 circles on the table. Tell students to take away 2 circles. Then have them count the circles that are left.

3. Repeat the process with 7 circles, taking away 2 circles.

   Ask: What pattern did you see as you took away 2 circles each time?
   ANSWER: The number left was 1 less than the answer before.

4. Place 15 circles on the table. Tell students to take away 7 circles. Then have them count the circles that are left.

   Say: 15 take away 7 is 8.

5. Repeat Step 4, but this time have students take away 8 circles. Repeat again and have students take away 9 circles.

   Ask: What pattern do you see?
   ANSWER: I started with 15. I took 1 more away each time, and the number left was 1 less.

6. Have students use the circles to show 8 take away 6. Have them tell how many are left.

   Say: Describe the take away problem you just showed.
   ANSWER: 8 take away 6 is 2.

7. Repeat Step 6 with the following problems:

   - 9 take away 5

   - 12 take away 8

   Say: Each time you started with a total, took away a part, and were left with a part.

Objectives

- Demonstrate the meaning of subtraction as taking away an amount from a given quantity (with minuends up through 20).

Tips

Return the circles to the bowl after each problem to make sure that only the circles needed for the problem are on the table.

Tips

To prevent students from counting the circles that have been taken away, cover them with your hand or a sheet of paper.

TRY IT Take Away Cubes

Students will practice taking away objects and finding how many are left. Give students the cubes and the Take Away Cubes activity page from their Activity Book. Read the directions with them.

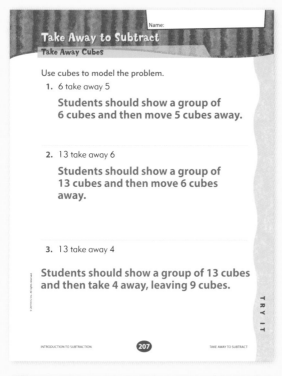

Take Away to Subtract
Take Away Cubes

Name:

Use cubes to model the problem.

1. 6 take away 5

   Students should show a group of 6 cubes and then move 5 cubes away.

2. 13 take away 6

   Students should show a group of 13 cubes and then move 6 cubes away.

3. 13 take away 4

   Students should show a group of 13 cubes and then take 4 away, leaving 9 cubes.

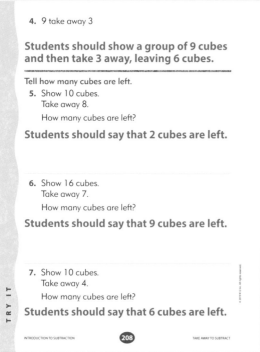

4. 9 take away 3

   Students should show a group of 9 cubes and then take 3 away, leaving 6 cubes.

Tell how many cubes are left.

5. Show 10 cubes.
   Take away 8.
   How many cubes are left?

   Students should say that 2 cubes are left.

6. Show 16 cubes.
   Take away 7.
   How many cubes are left?

   Students should say that 9 cubes are left.

7. Show 10 cubes.
   Take away 4.
   How many cubes are left?

   Students should say that 6 cubes are left.

Objectives

- Demonstrate the meaning of subtraction as taking away an amount from a given quantity (with minuends up through 20).

Tips

To prevent students from counting the same cube twice, have them touch each cube as they count it.

Subtraction as Taking Away

Lesson Overview

Skills Update	5 minutes	**ONLINE**
GET READY Show Quantities Through 10	10 minutes	**ONLINE**
LEARN Model Subtraction	15 minutes	**ONLINE**
TRY IT Subtract Groups	10 minutes	**OFFLINE**
CHECKPOINT	5 minutes	**OFFLINE**

▶ Lesson Objectives

Demonstrate the meaning of subtraction as taking away an amount from a given quantity (with minuends up through 20).

▶ Prerequisite Skills

- Count aloud a number of objects up through 20.
- Use concrete objects or sketches to represent a quantity up through 10.

▶ Advance Preparation

Put 8 circles in one bag and 5 circles in another bag.

▶ Content Background

In this lesson, students will model the different parts of subtraction stories. They will use sketches and other models to show subtraction as taking away.

Keywords	**model (noun)** – a physical object, diagram, or picture that represents an amount, an expression, an equation, or a problem situation
	model (verb) – to use physical objects, diagrams, or pictures to represent an amount, an expression, an equation, or a problem situation

Materials to Gather

SUPPLIED

blocks – B (all colors)

Checkpoint (printout)

ALSO NEEDED

household objects – 1 bowl, 2 bags

GET READY Show Quantities Through 10

Students will use the Counting Learning Tool to review counting quantities through 10.

- Count aloud a number of objects up through 20.

DIRECTIONS FOR USING THE COUNTING LEARNING TOOL

1. Click Practice Mode.
   - Have students choose an object.
   - Click Yes to use ten-frames.
   - Click Start.

2. Have students count aloud as they drag 10 objects into the ten-frame.

3. Erase the objects. Have students count aloud again, varying the number of objects they put in the ten-frame. Continue as time permits.

LEARN Model Subtraction

Students will practice modeling subtraction stories. They will describe the part that is taken away and the part that is left.

- Demonstrate the meaning of subtraction as taking away an amount from a given quantity (with minuends up through 20).

TRY IT Subtract Groups

Students will practice modeling subtraction problems using circles.

Gather the circles and the bowl. Place the circles in the bowl. Read each problem to students. Then read each part of the problem again as students model it.

- Demonstrate the meaning of subtraction as taking away an amount from a given quantity (with minuends up through 20).

1. **Ask:** There are 13 ladybugs on a flower. 9 ladybugs fly away. How many ladybugs are still on the flower?
   ANSWER: 4

2. **Ask:** There are 8 spiders on a rock. 5 spiders crawl away. How many spiders are left on the rock?
   ANSWER: 3

3. **Ask:** There are 17 ants on a log. 8 ants crawl away. How many ants are left on the log?
   ANSWER: 9

4. **Ask:** There are 11 worms on the sidewalk. 4 worms crawl into the grass. How many worms are still on the sidewalk?
   ANSWER: 7

5. **Ask:** There are 10 leaves on a tree. 4 leaves fall to the ground. How many leaves are left on the tree?
   ANSWER: 6

6. **Ask:** There are 15 ducks at the pond. 5 ducks fly away. How many ducks are still at the pond?
   ANSWER: 10

Tips

Return the circles to the bowl after each problem to make sure that only the ones needed for the problem are on the table.

7. **Ask:** You have 8 pencils. You give 5 pencils to your friends.
   How many pencils do you have left?
   ANSWER: 3

8. **Ask:** You have 12 cups of lemonade. You sell 6 cups at your lemonade
   stand. How many cups of lemonade are left?
   ANSWER: 6

CHECKPOINT

Objectives

- Demonstrate the meaning of subtraction as taking away an amount from a given quantity (with minuends up through 20).

Print the Checkpoint. Students will take a performance-based assessment. Read the directions and problems to students. Use the answer key to score the Checkpoint, and then enter the results online.

Gather the bags you filled with circle blocks. Give students the bag with 8 circles for Problem 1 and the bag with 5 circles for Problem 2.

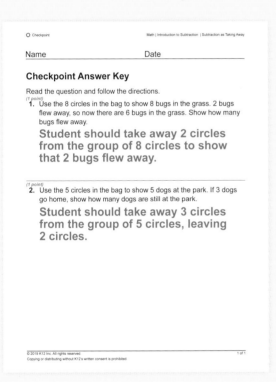

Subtract with Objects

Lesson Overview

Skills Update	5 minutes	ONLINE
GET READY Take Away Cubes	10 minutes	ONLINE
LEARN Take Away 1	10 minutes	OFFLINE
LEARN Take Away 2	10 minutes	OFFLINE
TRY IT Subtract 1 or Subtract 2	10 minutes	OFFLINE

▶ Lesson Objectives

Use concrete objects or sketches to model and solve addition or subtraction computation problems involving sums or minuends up through 20.

▶ Prerequisite Skills

Demonstrate the meaning of subtraction as taking away an amount from a given quantity (with minuends up through 20).

▶ Content Background

In this lesson, students will take away objects to subtract and will find how many objects are left.

Materials to Gather

SUPPLIED

blocks – B (10 red, 10 blue)

blocks – O (any color)

Subtract 1 or Subtract 2 activity page

GET READY Take Away Cubes

ONLINE 10min

Students will practice solving subtraction problems by taking away cubes.

Objectives

- Demonstrate the meaning of subtraction as taking away an amount from a given quantity (with minuends up through 20).

LEARN Take Away 1

Students will use cubes to model subtraction problems in which 1 is taken away. They will practice saying subtraction sentences correctly: for example, 4 take away 1 is 3.

Gather the cubes.

1. Have students place 4 cubes in a row on the table. Then have them take away the cube farthest to the right. Have students count how many cubes are left.

   Say: 4 take away 1 is 3.

2. Repeat Step 1 with the following problems:
   - 5 take away 1
   - 6 take away 1
   - 7 take away 1

3. **Ask:** What pattern did you see as you took away 1 cube each time?
   ANSWER: The number left after taking away was 1 less than the number I started with. The answer was 1 more than the answer before. For example, 4 take away 1 is 3, 5 take away 1 is 4, 6 take away 1 is 5, and 7 take away 1 is 6.

4. Have students model the following problems. Have them count aloud to find how many are left. Then ask them to say the subtraction sentence.
   - 18 take away 1
   - 12 take away 1
   - 20 take away 1

Objectives

- Use concrete objects or sketches to model and solve addition or subtraction computation problems involving sums or minuends up through 20.

Tips

After each problem, make sure that only the cubes needed for the problem are on the table.

To prevent students from counting the same cube twice, have them touch each cube as they count it.

LEARN Take Away 2

Students will model subtraction problems in which 2 is taken away.
Gather the circle blocks.

1. Explain to students that now they are going to take away 2. Have students place 10 circles in a row on the table.

2. Direct students to take away the circle farthest to the right. Then have them take away the next circle on the right. Have students count how many circles are left. Then ask them to say the subtraction sentence.
   ANSWER: 10 take away 2 is 8.

3. Repeat Step 2 with the following problems:
   - 9 take away 2
   - 8 take away 2
   - 7 take away 2

4. **Ask:** What pattern did you see as you took away 2 circles each time?
   ANSWER: The number left was 2 less than the number I started with. The answer was 1 less than the answer before. For example, 10 take away 2 is 8, 9 take away 2 is 7, 8 take away 2 is 6, and 7 take away 2 is 5.

Objectives

- Use concrete objects or sketches to model and solve addition or subtraction computation problems involving sums or minuends up through 20.

Tips

If students understand that taking away 2 circles at once is the same as taking away 1 and then another, allow them to remove 2 circles in 1 step.

TRY IT Subtract 1 or Subtract 2

Objectives

Students will practice modeling and solving subtraction problems. Give students the circle blocks and the Subtract 1 or Subtract 2 activity page from their Activity Book. Read the directions with them. Use the answer key to check students' answers, and then enter the results online.

- Use concrete objects or sketches to model and solve addition or subtraction computation problems involving sums or minuends up through 20.

Name:

Subtract with Objects
Subtract 1 or Subtract 2

Use circles to show the subtraction problem.
Write how many are left.

1. 8 take away 1 is 7 .

2. 10 take away 1 is 9 .

3. 17 take away 1 is 16 .

4. 3 take away 2 is 1 .

5. 12 take away 2 is 10 .

6. 19 take away 2 is 17 .

TRY IT

---

7. 20 take away 2 is 18 .

8. 9 take away 1 is 8 .

9. 15 take away 2 is 13 .

10. Use circles to show how to subtract 2 from 10.

   8   ● ● ● ● ● ● ● ● ● ●

11. Use circles to show how to subtract 1 from 20.

   19   ●

TRY IT

Model Subtraction

Skills Update	5 minutes	ONLINE
LEARN Sketch to Subtract	15 minutes	ONLINE
LEARN Number Line Subtraction	15 minutes	ONLINE
TRY IT Different Ways to Subtract	10 minutes	OFFLINE

▶ Lesson Objectives

Use concrete objects or sketches to model and solve addition or subtraction computation problems involving sums or minuends up through 20.

▶ Prerequisite Skills

Demonstrate the meaning of subtraction as taking away an amount from a given quantity (with minuends up through 20).

▶ Content Background

In this lesson, students will use a sketch to solve subtraction problems.

Materials to Gather

SUPPLIED
blocks – O (blue)
Different Ways to Subtract activity page

LEARN Sketch to Subtract

ONLINE **15min**

Students will practice using objects and sketches to model and solve subtraction problems.

Objectives

- Use concrete objects or sketches to model and solve addition or subtraction computation problems involving sums or minuends up through 20.

Tips

Make sure that students count only the objects that are not crossed out to find how many are left.

LEARN Number Line Subtraction

ONLINE **15min**

Students will practice using circles and a number line to solve subtraction problems.

Objectives

- Use concrete objects or sketches to model and solve addition or subtraction computation problems involving sums or minuends up through 20.

Objectives

This Try It activity has two parts.

PART 1

Students will practice modeling subtraction problems. Give students the cubes. Note how students perform, and then enter the results online.

1. **Say:** Use cubes to show 11 take away 5. How many are left?
   ANSWER: 6
   Students should model 11 cubes and then take away 5 cubes.

2. **Say:** Use cubes to show 20 take away 7. How many are left?
   ANSWER: 13
   Students should model 20 cubes and then take away 7 cubes.

3. **Say:** Use cubes to show 13 take away 8. How many are left?
   ANSWER: 5
   Students should model 13 cubes and then take away 8 cubes.

4. **Say:** Use cubes to show 19 take away 11. How many are left?
   ANSWER: 8
   Students should model 19 cubes and then take away 11 cubes.

PART 2

Students will practice modeling subtraction problems using cubes, a number line, and sketches. Give students the cubes and the Different Ways to Subtract activity page from their Activity Book. Read the directions with them. Use the answer key to check students' answers, and then enter the results online.

Name: _____

Model Subtraction
Different Ways to Subtract

Use cubes to show the subtraction problem. Write how many are left.

1. 14 take away 6 is __8__.   2. 17 take away 8 is __9__.

Use the number line to show the subtraction problem. Write how many are left.

3. 9 take away 6 is __3__.

4. 6 take away 4 is __2__.

Use sketches to show the subtraction problem. Write how many are left.

5. 12 take away 5 is __7__.

6. 10 take away 4 is __6__.

Subtract with Pictures

▶ Lesson Objectives

Use concrete objects or sketches to model and solve addition or subtraction computation problems involving sums or minuends up through 20.

▶ Prerequisite Skills

Demonstrate the meaning of subtraction as taking away an amount from a given quantity (with minuends up through 20).

▶ Content Background

In this lesson, students will use sketches to model subtraction problems.

Materials to Gather

SUPPLIED

blocks – B (all colors)

Solve with Pictures activity page

GET READY Domino Subtraction

ONLINE 15min

Students will practice subtracting using the groups of dots on two sides of a domino.

Objectives

- Demonstrate the meaning of subtraction as taking away an amount from a given quantity (with minuends up through 20).

LEARN Muffins for Sale

ONLINE 15min

Students will practice recording and solving subtraction problems using sketches.

Objectives

- Use concrete objects or sketches to model and solve addition or subtraction computation problems involving sums or minuends up through 20.

Objectives

Students will practice solving subtraction problems by using objects and sketches. Give students the circle blocks and the Solve with Pictures activity page from their Activity Book. Read the directions with them. Use the answer key to check students' answers, and then enter the results online.

- Use concrete objects or sketches to model and solve addition or subtraction computation problems involving sums or minuends up through 20.

Name:

Subtract with Pictures
Solve with Pictures

Count the objects. Cross out the number of objects to be taken away. Write how many are left.

1. 15 take away 8 is __7__.

2. 12 take away 7 is __5__.

3. 17 take away 9 is __8__.

4. 11 take away 5 is __6__.

Use circles to show the problem.
Write how many are left.

5. 15 take away 8   __7__

6. 19 take away 5   __14__

7. 13 take away 7   __6__

8. 20 take away 14   __6__

9. 14 take away 5   __9__

Students should use circles to model the greater number, and then they should take away the lesser number of circles. Students should write the difference for each problem.

Estimate and Check Differences

Lesson Overview

Skills Update	5 minutes	ONLINE
GET READY Estimate Sums	5 minutes	ONLINE
LEARN Estimate Differences	15 minutes	OFFLINE
LEARN Check Calculations	10 minutes	OFFLINE
TRY IT Estimate and Check	10 minutes	OFFLINE

▶ Lesson Objectives

- Make reasonable estimates for the solutions to subtraction problems with minuends up through 20.
- Check the accuracy of calculations for the solutions to subtraction problems with minuends up through 20.

▶ Prerequisite Skills

- Make reasonable estimates for the solutions to addition problems (for sums up through 20).
- Use concrete objects or sketches to model and solve addition or subtraction computation problems involving sums or minuends up through 20.

▶ Advance Preparation

- Number index cards 0–20, or gather the number cards you created previously.
- Make four trains of cubes to use as benchmarks: a 5-train, 10-train, 15-train, and 20-train.
- Make another train of 20 cubes.

▶ Content Background

In this lesson, students will estimate the difference by comparing numbers to the benchmarks of 5 and 10.

Materials to Gather

SUPPLIED

blocks – O (all colors)
Check Calculations activity page
blocks – B (10 blue)
Estimate and Check activity page

ALSO NEEDED

index cards – numbered 1–20

Keywords

benchmark – a target number used in estimation
difference – the solution to a subtraction problem
estimate (noun) – the answer to an approximation or rough calculation
estimate (verb) – to approximate or perform a rough calculation

GET READY **Estimate Sums**

Students will practice estimating solutions to addition problems with sums through 20.

- Make reasonable estimates for the solutions to addition problems (for sums up through 20).

LEARN **Estimate Differences**

Students will estimate differences by modeling a subtraction sentence with cubes and comparing the model to benchmarks of four trains of cubes: a 5-train, 10-train, 15-train, and 20-train.

- Make reasonable estimates for the solutions to subtraction problems with minuends up through 20.

Gather the numbered index cards, cube trains to use as benchmarks, and the additional 20-train.

1. Show students one train of 20 cubes. Have students count the cubes.

2. Have students remove 5 cubes and tell you how many are left.

    Say: 20 take away 5 is 15.

3. Replace the 5 cubes. Have students remove 10 cubes and tell you how many are left.

    Say: 20 take away 10 is 10.

4. Show students the train of 10 cubes. Have students count the cubes.

5. Have students remove 5 cubes and tell you how many are left.

    Say: 10 take away 5 is 5.

6. Show students the 5-train, 10-train, 15-train, and 20-train that they will use as benchmarks. Explain that these cube trains can help estimate answers to subtraction problems.

    Have students count the number of cubes in each train and place the corresponding numbered index card with each.

7. Show students the 9 and 4 numbered index cards. Have students make a train of 9 cubes.

    Ask: Is the train of 9 cubes closer to the size of the 5-train or 10-train?
    ANSWER: 10-train

8. **Say:** An estimate is a number that is pretty close to a target number. We can use benchmarks like 5, 10, 15, and 20 when we estimate. We can estimate that the train of 9 cubes is closest to the benchmark train of 10 cubes.

9. Have students remove 4 cubes from the train of 9 cubes.

    Ask: Are the 4 cubes you took off closer to the size of the 5-train or the 10-train?
    ANSWER: 5-train

    Say: We can estimate that you subtracted about 5 cubes.

10. Explain that students can now estimate the answer to the problem 9 take away 4.

    Say: We said that 9 is close to 10 and 4 is close to 5. About how many is 9 take away 4?
    ANSWER: 5

11. Clear the workspace, except for the benchmark cube trains. Show students the 19 and 11 numbered index cards. Explain that they are going to estimate 19 take away 11.

12. Have students make a train of 19 cubes. Then have them compare their cube train to the benchmarks.

    Ask: Which benchmark is 19 closest to?
    ANSWER: 20

13. Have students take off 11 cubes from the train of 19 cubes.

    Ask: Which benchmark is 11 closet to?
    ANSWER: 10

14. **Ask:** About how many is 19 take away 11?
    ANSWER: 10

15. Repeat Steps 11–14 with the following problems:

    • About how many is 19 take away 6? (15)
    • About how many is 11 take away 4? (5)
    • About how many is 14 take away 3? (10)
    • About how many is 12 take away 6? (5)

LEARN Check Calculations

Students will practice using models or sketches to check the accuracy of answers to subtraction word problems. Give students the circle blocks and the Check Calculations activity page from their Activity Book. Read the directions with them.

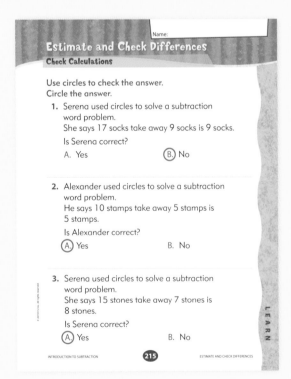

Name:

Estimate and Check Differences
Check Calculations

Use circles to check the answer.
Circle the answer.

1. Serena used circles to solve a subtraction word problem.
   She says 17 socks take away 9 socks is 9 socks.
   Is Serena correct?
   A. Yes   B. No

2. Alexander used circles to solve a subtraction word problem.
   He says 10 stamps take away 5 stamps is 5 stamps.
   Is Alexander correct?
   A. Yes   B. No

3. Serena used circles to solve a subtraction word problem.
   She says 15 stones take away 7 stones is 8 stones.
   Is Serena correct?
   A. Yes   B. No

INTRODUCTION TO SUBTRACTION   215   ESTIMATE AND CHECK DIFFERENCES

L E A R N

Tips

When students take cubes off the train of cubes that shows the subtraction sentence, move the cubes away from the train. This will help students see the part that was taken away.

To prevent students from skipping a cube or counting a cube twice, have students touch each cube as they count it.

Objectives

• Check the accuracy of calculations for the solutions to subtraction problems with minuends up through 20.

Tips

Check that students say each number in sequence as they touch each circle or draw each sketch.

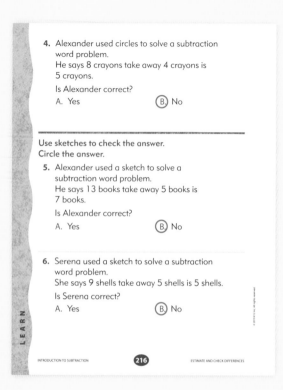

4. Alexander used circles to solve a subtraction word problem.
He says 8 crayons take away 4 crayons is 5 crayons.

Is Alexander correct?

A. Yes   Ⓑ No

Use sketches to check the answer.
Circle the answer.

5. Alexander used a sketch to solve a subtraction word problem.
He says 13 books take away 5 books is 7 books.

Is Alexander correct?

A. Yes   Ⓑ No

6. Serena used a sketch to solve a subtraction word problem.
She says 9 shells take away 5 shells is 5 shells.

Is Serena correct?

A. Yes   Ⓑ No

TRY IT   Estimate and Check

OFFLINE
10 min

Students will practice estimating and checking the answers to subtraction story problems. Give students the Estimate and Check activity page from their Activity Book and read the directions with them.

Objectives

- Make reasonable estimates for the solutions to subtraction problems with minuends up through 20.

Tips

Students may use trains of 5, 10, and 15 cubes as benchmarks to estimate the answers for Problems 1–8.

Name: _____

Estimate and Check Differences

Estimate and Check

Find the estimate.

1. Estimate the difference if you take away 3 from 9.

Is 9 closer to 5 or 10?   ___10___

Is 3 closer to 5 or 10?   ___5___

Estimate: What is the difference?
9 take away 3 is about ___5___.

2. Estimate the difference if you take away 8 from 19.

Is 19 closer to 15 or 20?   ___20___

Is 8 closer to 5 or 10?   ___10___

Estimate: What is the difference?
19 take away 8 is about ___10___.

TRY IT

3. 14 take away 8 is about _____5_____.

4. 16 take away 4 is about _____10_____.

5. About how many is 14 take away 4? ___10___

6. You had 19 stickers. You gave 4 stickers away.
About how many stickers do you have left?
Circle the answer.

A. about 20   B. about 10   C. about 15

7. Estimate the difference.
19 take away 10 is about _____10_____.

8. Estimate the difference.
15 take away 6 is about _____10_____.

Decide whether the answer is correct or
incorrect. Circle the answer.

9. Alexander did this math problem:
9 plants take away 7 plants is 2 plants.

Explain how to use a sketch to check his work.

Is Alexander correct?

A. Yes   B. No

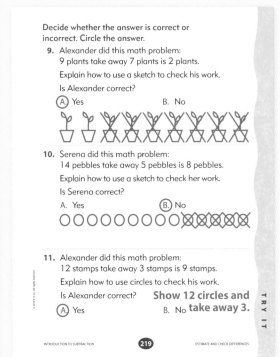

10. Serena did this math problem:
14 pebbles take away 5 pebbles is 8 pebbles.

Explain how to use a sketch to check her work.

Is Serena correct?

A. Yes   B. No

11. Alexander did this math problem:
12 stamps take away 3 stamps is 9 stamps.

Explain how to use circles to check his work.

Is Alexander correct?   **Show 12 circles and**
                                take away 3.
A. Yes   B. No

12. Serena did this math problem:
16 socks take away 7 socks is 8 socks.

Explain how to use circles to check her work.

Is Serena correct? **Show 16 circles and take**
                         away 7.
A. Yes   B. No

13. Which math problem is incorrect?

A. 8 cats take away 4 cats is 4 cats.

B. 7 cats take away 1 cat is 6 cats.

C. 9 cats take away 3 cats is 7 cats.

14. Johnny did this math problem:
15 dogs take away 3 dogs is 13 dogs.

Check his work by using the dogs shown.

Is Johnny correct?

A. Yes   B. No

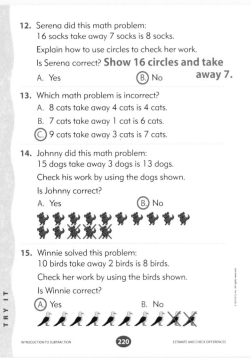

15. Winnie solved this problem:
10 birds take away 2 birds is 8 birds.

Check her work by using the birds shown.

Is Winnie correct?

A. Yes   B. No

Unit Review

Lesson Overview

UNIT REVIEW Look Back	15 minutes	**ONLINE**
UNIT REVIEW Checkpoint Practice	15 minutes	**OFFLINE**
⊡ **UNIT REVIEW** Prepare for the Checkpoint		

▶ Unit Objectives

- Demonstrate the meaning of subtraction as taking away an amount from a given quantity (with minuends up through 20).
- Use concrete objects or sketches to model and solve addition or subtraction computation problems involving sums or minuends up through 20.
- Make reasonable estimates for the solutions to subtraction problems with minuends up through 20.
- Check the accuracy of the calculations for the solutions to subtraction problems with minuends up through 20.

▶ Advance Preparation

In this lesson, students will have an opportunity to review previous activities in the Introduction to Subtraction unit. Look at the suggested activities in Unit Review: Prepare for the Checkpoint online and gather any needed materials.

Materials to Gather

SUPPLIED
blocks – B (10 red, 10 blue)
Checkpoint Practice activity page

Keywords

benchmark	operation
difference	part-part-total
estimate (noun)	subtract
estimate (verb)	subtraction
model (noun)	take away
model (verb)	

UNIT REVIEW Look Back

Objectives

- Review unit objectives.

In this unit, students were introduced to subtraction as taking away objects from a group of objects. They learned to take away objects and to tell how many are left, and then used sketches and countable objects to model subtraction problems and story problems. Students learned that they can use subtraction to find the amount of a mystery addend in an addition problem. They learned to find how many cubes are hidden for problems in which one part is hidden, one part is visible, and they know the total.

Students learned to estimate answers and to check the accuracy of their work. They also learned that counting principles and numbers can be used to solve subtraction story problems.

Students will review key concepts from the unit to prepare for the Unit Checkpoint.

UNIT REVIEW Checkpoint Practice

Objectives

- Review unit objectives.

Students will complete a Checkpoint Practice activity page to prepare for the Unit Checkpoint. If necessary, read the directions, problems, and answer choices to students. Have students answer the problems on their own. Review any missed problems with students.

Unit Review
Checkpoint Practice

Name: _____

Use circles to model the subtraction problem. Write how many are left. **Students should use circles to show the greater number and then take away the lesser number.**

1. 8 take away 6 is __2__.

2. 13 take away 8 is __5__.

3. Place 7 circles on the table. Show how to subtract 3 circles.

   7 take away 3 is __4__.

4. Place 8 circles on the table. Show how to subtract 6 circles.

   8 take away 6 is __2__.

5. Subtract 4 from 12. How many are left?

   __8__

6. Subtract 5 from 14. How many are left?

   __9__

Find the estimate. Circle the answer.

7. 19 take away 8 is about ____.
   - A. 5
   - B. 10
   - C. 15

8. 18 take away 9 is about ____.
   - A. 20
   - B. 10
   - C. 5

9. About how many is 16 take away 9?
   - A. about 15
   - B. about 10
   - C. about 5

Use sketches to solve the problem.

10. 10 take away 4 is __6__ **Sketches will vary.**

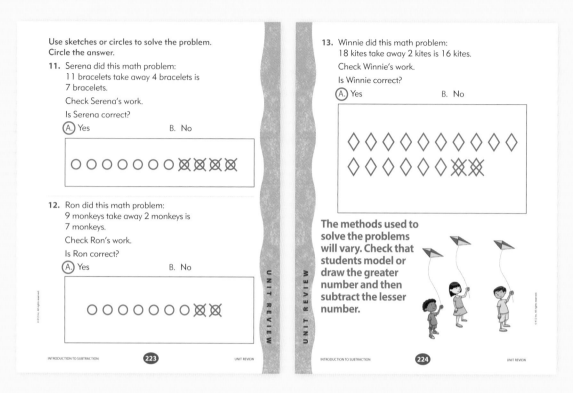

Use sketches or circles to solve the problem. Circle the answer.

11. Serena did this math problem:
11 bracelets take away 4 bracelets is 7 bracelets.

Check Serena's work.

Is Serena correct?

(A.) Yes   B. No

12. Ron did this math problem:
9 monkeys take away 2 monkeys is 7 monkeys.

Check Ron's work.

Is Ron correct?

(A.) Yes   B. No

13. Winnie did this math problem:
18 kites take away 2 kites is 16 kites.

Check Winnie's work.

Is Winnie correct?

(A.) Yes   B. No

The methods used to solve the problems will vary. Check that students model or draw the greater number and then subtract the lesser number.

→ UNIT REVIEW   Prepare for the Checkpoint

What you do next depends on how students performed in the previous activity, Unit Review: Checkpoint Practice. If students had difficulty with any of the problems, complete the appropriate review activity listed in the table online.

Unit Checkpoint

UNIT CHECKPOINT Offline   40 minutes   **OFFLINE**

▶ Unit Objectives

- Demonstrate the meaning of subtraction as taking away an amount from a given quantity (with minuends up through 20).
- Use concrete objects or sketches to model and solve addition or subtraction computation problems involving sums or minuends up through 20.
- Make reasonable estimates for the solutions to subtraction problems with minuends up through 20.
- Check the accuracy of the calculations for the solutions to subtraction problems with minuends up through 20.

▶ Advance Preparation

Put 13 circles in one bag, 18 circles in another bag, and 10 circles in a third bag.

Materials to Gather

SUPPLIED
blocks – B (all colors)
Unit Checkpoint (printout)

ALSO NEEDED
household objects – 3 bags

OFFLINE
40min

UNIT CHECKPOINT Offline

Students will complete the Unit Checkpoint offline. Print the Checkpoint and have students complete it on their own. Read the direction, problems, and answer choices to students, if necessary. Use the answer key to score the Checkpoint, and then enter the results online.

Gather the bags of circle blocks and the loose circle blocks. For Problems 1–3, give students the bags as directed. For Problems 4–6, 10, and 11, give students the loose circles.

Objectives

- Assess unit objectives.

Name   Date

Unit Checkpoint Answer Key

Read the problem and follow the directions.

(1 point)
1. Using the 13 circles in the bag, show how to subtract 10 circles.

Student should take 10 circles away from the group of 13 circles.

(1 point)
2. Using the 18 circles in the bag, show how to subtract 7 circles.

Student should take 7 circles away from the group of 18 circles.

(1 point)
3 Using the 10 circles in the bag, show how to subtract 4 circles.

Student should take 4 circles away from the group of 10 circles.

Use circles to model the subtraction. Then say the asnwer.

4. Use circles to show how to subtract 3 from 6. How many are left?
(1 point)
Students should model 6 circles and then take away 3 circles.
(1 point)
Students should say the answer is 3.

5. Use circles to show how to subtract 8 from 10. How many are left?
(1 point)
Students should model 10 circles and then take away 8 circles.
(1 point)
Students should say the answer is 2.

Name   Date

6. Use circles to show how to subtract 3 from 5. How many are left?
(1 point)
Students should model 5 circles and then take away 3 circles.
(1 point)
Students should say the answer is 2.

Say the answer.

(1 point)
7. About how many is 9 take away 4?

Students should make a reasonable estimate, such as about 5.

(1 point)
8. About how many is 14 take away 9?

Students should make a reasonable estimate, such as about 5.

(1 point)
9. About how many is 19 take away 11?

Students should make a reasonable estimate, such as about 10.

Name   Date

Sample sketches are shown.

Read the problem and follow the directions. Circle the answer.

(1 point)
10. Ron did this math problem:

15 kittens take away 4 kittens is 12 kittens.

Use a sketch or circles to check his work.

Is Ron correct?

A. Yes   (B.) No

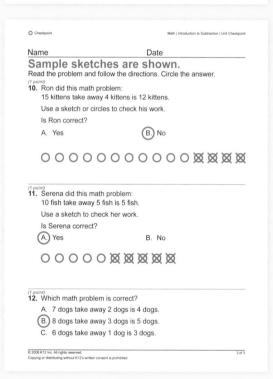

(1 point)
11. Serena did this math problem:

10 fish take away 5 fish is 5 fish.

Use a sketch to check her work.

Is Serena correct?

(A.) Yes   B. No

(1 point)
12. Which math problem is correct?

A. 7 dogs take away 2 dogs is 4 dogs.

(B.) 8 dogs take away 3 dogs is 5 dogs.

C. 6 dogs take away 1 dog is 3 dogs.

Problem Solving with Subtraction

There were 9 butterflies in the garden. ← Total

5 butterflies flew away. ← Part

How many butterflies were left in the garden?

There are 4 butterflies left in the garden.
9 take away 5 is 4.

▶ Unit Objectives

- Use concrete objects to explain how to solve addition and subtraction problem-solving situations involving numbers up to 10.
- Recognize and solve word problems involving sums or minuends up through 20 in which one quantity changes through addition or subtraction.
- Make reasonable estimates for the solutions to subtraction problems with minuends up through 20.
- Check the accuracy of calculations for the solutions to subtraction problems with minuends up through 20.

▶ Big Ideas

- Counting principles and numbers can be used to solve addition and subtraction problems.
- Estimation is a useful tool in problem solving.

▶ Unit Introduction

Students will learn to recognize and solve subtraction story problems by using concrete objects and sketches. They will create their own story problems and will solve those problems using models or sketches. They will apply that knowledge to make reasonable estimates for solutions and will check the accuracy of subtraction calculations.

Model Subtraction Stories

Lesson Overview

Skills Update	5 minutes	ONLINE
GET READY Thinking About Subtraction	10 minutes	ONLINE
LEARN Explain Subtraction Stories	10 minutes	ONLINE
LEARN Model Stories with Cubes	10 minutes	ONLINE
TRY IT Model Stories with Circles	10 minutes	ONLINE

▶ Lesson Objectives

Use concrete objects to explain how to solve addition and subtraction problem-solving situations involving numbers up to 10.

▶ Prerequisite Skills

Use concrete objects or sketches to model and solve addition or subtraction computation problems involving sums or minuends up through 20.

▶ Content Background

In this lesson, students will learn how to understand what is happening in subtraction story problems. They will model story problems with objects.

Materials to Gather

SUPPLIED
blocks – O (10 blue)
blocks – B (10 red)

Keywords

model (noun) – a physical object, diagram, or picture that represents an amount, an expression, an equation, or a problem situation

model (verb) – to use physical objects, diagrams, or pictures to represent an amount, an expression, an equation, or a problem situation

subtract – to take away objects from a group or to find a difference between two groups

subtraction – the process of taking away objects from a group or finding the difference between two groups; a mathematical operation

take away – in subtraction, to separate a group from the total

GET READY Thinking About Subtraction

ONLINE
10min

Objectives

- Use concrete objects or sketches to model and solve addition or subtraction computation problems involving sums or minuends up through 20.

Students will model subtraction on a number line.

DIRECTIONS FOR USING THE NUMBER LINE LEARNING TOOL

1. Click — and choose the following:
   - Minuends through: 20

   Click OK.

   A subtraction number sentence will be shown, such as $7 - 2 = ?$.

2. Have students click the minuend, or starting number, on the number line. Then have them count back the number being subtracted and click the answer on the number line. So for the number sentence above, students would start by clicking 7. Next they would count back 2 numbers: 6, 5. They would then click 5, which is the answer to the subtraction problem.

3. Click New Problem to continue. Continue as time allows.

LEARN Explain Subtraction Stories

ONLINE
10min

Objectives

- Use concrete objects to explain how to solve addition and subtraction problem-solving situations involving numbers up to 10.

Students will explain what is happening in subtraction story problems.

LEARN Model Stories with Cubes

ONLINE
10min

Objectives

- Use concrete objects to explain how to solve addition and subtraction problem-solving situations involving numbers up to 10.

Students will model subtraction story problems. Then they will explain how to solve the problem. Gather the cubes.

Students will model each step of the problem using cubes and then check their answer.

You may wish to provide students with a sheet of construction paper to use as a mat. Have them place cubes on the paper that represent the beginning amount. Then have students move the cubes that represent the number taken away off the paper.

TRY IT Model Stories with Circles

ONLINE
10min

Objectives

- Use concrete objects to explain how to solve addition and subtraction problem-solving situations involving numbers up to 10.

Students will practice modeling and solving story problems. Gather the circle blocks.

Students will model each step of the problem using circles and then check their answer.

Sketch Subtraction Stories

Lesson Overview

Skills Update	5 minutes	ONLINE
GET READY Model Subtraction	5 minutes	ONLINE
LEARN Solve with Circles and Sketches	10 minutes	ONLINE
LEARN Sketch Story Problems	15 minutes	ONLINE
TRY IT Model and Sketch Stories	5 minutes	OFFLINE
CHECKPOINT	5 minutes	OFFLINE

▶ Lesson Objectives

Use concrete objects to explain how to solve addition and subtraction problem-solving situations involving numbers up to 10.

▶ Prerequisite Skills

Use concrete objects or sketches to model and solve addition or subtraction computation problems involving sums or minuends up through 20.

▶ Content Background

In this lesson, students will model subtraction story problems with objects and sketches.

Materials to Gather

SUPPLIED

Model and Sketch Stories activity page

blocks – O (10 red)

Checkpoint (printour)

ALSO NEEDED

paper, drawing – 3 sheets

crayons

GET READY Model Subtraction

ONLINE 5 min

Students will review modeling a subtraction story problem with cubes.

Objectives

- Use concrete objects or sketches to model and solve addition or subtraction computation problems involving sums or minuends up through 20.

LEARN Solve with Circles and Sketches

ONLINE 10 min

Students will go to the batting cages with Ron. Working with Ron, they'll learn how to make sketches to solve subtraction story problems.

Objectives

- Use concrete objects to explain how to solve addition and subtraction problem-solving situations involving numbers up to 10.

LEARN Sketch Story Problems

Objectives

- Use concrete objects to explain how to solve addition and subtraction problem-solving situations involving numbers up to 10.

Students will make sketches to solve subtraction story problems. Gather the drawing paper and crayons.

Follow the directions on each screen.

TRY IT Model and Sketch Stories

OFFLINE
5 min

Objectives

- Use concrete objects to explain how to solve addition and subtraction problem-solving situations involving numbers up to 10.

Students will practice modeling and sketching subtraction story problems. Give students the cubes and the Model and Sketch Stories activity page from their Activity Book. Read the directions with them.

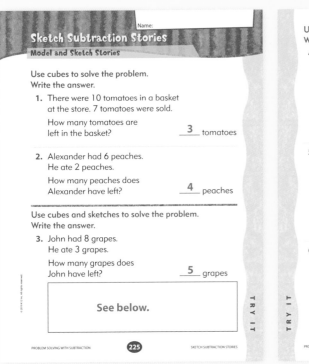

Sketch Subtraction Stories
Model and Sketch Stories

Name: _____

Use cubes to solve the problem.
Write the answer.

1. There were 10 tomatoes in a basket at the store. 7 tomatoes were sold.

   How many tomatoes are left in the basket? ___3___ tomatoes

2. Alexander had 6 peaches. He ate 2 peaches.

   How many peaches does Alexander have left? ___4___ peaches

Use cubes and sketches to solve the problem.
Write the answer.

3. John had 8 grapes. He ate 3 grapes.

   How many grapes does John have left? ___5___ grapes

   See below.

PROBLEM SOLVING WITH SUBTRACTION 225 SKETCH SUBTRACTION STORIES

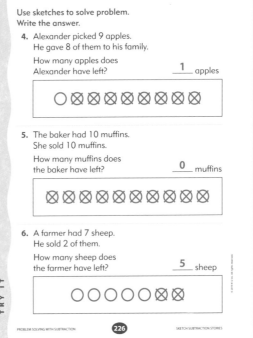

Use sketches to solve problem.
Write the answer.

4. Alexander picked 9 apples. He gave 8 of them to his family.

   How many apples does Alexander have left? ___1___ apples

5. The baker had 10 muffins. She sold 10 muffins.

   How many muffins does the baker have left? ___0___ muffins

6. A farmer had 7 sheep. He sold 2 of them.

   How many sheep does the farmer have left? ___5___ sheep

PROBLEM SOLVING WITH SUBTRACTION 226 SKETCH SUBTRACTION STORIES

Additional Answers

3. Students should model the subtraction problem with 8 cubes and then move 3 cubes to the right. Then students should sketch 8 simple objects and cross out 3.

CHECKPOINT

Objectives

- Use concrete objects to explain how to solve addition and subtraction problem-solving situations involving numbers up to 10.

Print the Checkpoint and have students complete it on their own. Read the directions, problems, and answer choices to students, if necessary. Use the answer key to score the Checkpoint, and then enter the results online.

Gather the circle blocks, cubes, drawing paper, and crayons.

⚙ Checkpoint   Math | Problem Solving with Subtraction | Sketch Subtraction Story Problems

Name _____ Date _____

Checkpoint Answer Key

Read the question and follow the directions.
(1 point)

1. Use circles to explain how to solve this problem:
   If 9 lemons were on the tree, and 4 lemons fell to the ground, how many lemons are still on the tree?

   Students should count out 9 circles and then explain they can take away 4, leaving 5 circles.

(1 point)

2. Use circles to explain how to solve this problem:
   If 3 cats were sitting on the back porch, and 1 cat walked away, how many cats are left on the porch?

   Students should count out 3 circles and then explain they can take away 1, leaving 2 circles.

(1 point)

3. Use cubes and draw a sketch to show how to solve this problem:
   If there were 4 puzzles in the toy store, and 4 puzzles were sold, how many puzzles are left in the store?

   Students should model 4 take away 4 with cubes, and then draw a sketch that shows 4 objects drawn and 4 objects crossed out.

⚙ Checkpoint   Math | Problem Solving with Subtraction | Sketch Subtraction Story Problems

Name _____ Date _____

(1 point)

4. Use cubes and then draw a sketch to show how to solve this problem:
   If Terrance had 5 fish in his tank, and he gave 2 to Marly to put in her tank, how many fish does Terrance have left in his tank?

   Students should model 5 take away 2 with cubes, and then draw a sketch that shows 5 objects drawn and 2 objects crossed out.

(1 point)

5. Draw a sketch to show how to solve this problem:
   If William made 3 model cars to sell at the fair, and he sold 2 of them, how many model cars does William have left?

   Students should draw a sketch to show 3 take away 2.

Take-Away Stories

Lesson Overview

Skills Update	5 minutes	ONLINE
GET READY Serena's Marbles	5 minutes	ONLINE
LEARN Total and Parts	20 minutes	ONLINE
TRY IT Story Problem Explanations	15 minutes	OFFLINE

▶ **Lesson Objectives**

Recognize and solve word problems involving sums or minuends up through 20 in which one quantity changes through addition or subtraction.

▶ **Prerequisite Skills**

- Demonstrate the meaning of subtraction as taking away an amount from a given quantity (with minuends up through 20).
- Demonstrate the meaning of addition as the combining of two sets (for sums up through 20).
- Use concrete objects or sketches to model and solve addition or subtraction computation problems involving sums or minuends up through 20.

▶ **Content Background**

In this lesson, students will learn what is happening in subtraction story problems and will model the problems with objects.

Materials to Gather

SUPPLIED

Story Problem Explanations activity page

blocks – O (10 blue)

GET READY Serena's Marbles

ONLINE 5 min

Students will practice using a model to describe a subtraction story problem.

Objectives

- Recognize and solve word problems involving sums or minuends up through 20 in which one quantity changes through addition or subtraction.

LEARN Total and Parts

ONLINE 20 min

Students will identify the total and parts of subtraction story problems. Then they will model and solve the problems. Gather the cubes.
   Follow the directions on each screen.

Objectives

- Recognize and solve word problems involving sums or minuends up through 20 in which one quantity changes through addition or subtraction.

TRY IT Story Problem Explanations

Students will practice modeling subtraction story problems. They will identity the total and the part. Then they will solve the problem. Give students the cubes and the Story Problem Explanations activity page from their Activity Book. Read the directions with them.

Use the steps shown for the example for all problems.

Example: Jill had 10 grapes.
She ate 6 grapes.

How many grapes does Jill have left?

1. **Ask:** What is the total you start with in this story problem?
   ANSWER: 10

2. Have students show the total using cubes.

3. **Ask:** What part is given in this story problem?
   ANSWER: 6

4. Have students say and underline the part on the activity page. Then have students take away the part from the total.

5. Have students count the cubes that are left.

   Ask: What part is left?
   ANSWER: 4

Take-Away Stories
Story Problem Explanations

Tell about the steps.
Use cubes to solve the problem.

Example: Jill had 10 grapes.
She ate 6 grapes.

How many grapes does
Jill have left?   __4__ grapes

---

1. There were 8 postage stamps.
   Ken used 5 stamps on his letters.

   How many postage stamps
   are left?   __3__ stamps
   See below.

2. There were 4 turtles on the grass.
   Then 3 turtles went into the pond.

   How many turtles are left
   on the grass?   __1__ turtles
   See below.

3. There were 7 strawberries in a bowl.
   Tom ate 2 strawberries.

   How many strawberries
   are left in the bowl?   __5__ strawberries
   See below.

T R Y   I T

---

4. Mandy had 9 hats.
   She sold 4 hats.

   How many hats does she have left?   __5__ hats
   See below.

Solve the problem. Write or circle the answer.

5. Mark had 7 carrots.
   He ate 3 carrots at lunchtime.

   How many carrots does Mark have left?   __4__ carrots

6. James had 8 trucks.
   He gave 2 trucks to his sister.

   How many trucks does James have now?   __6__ trucks

7. Therese made 6 pizzas.
   5 pizzas got eaten.

   How many pizzas does Therese have left? __1__ pizzas

8. Javier made 9 paintings to sell at the fair.
   He sold 8 of them.

   How many paintings does Javier have left?
   (A) 1   B. 4   C. 17

9. Sophie had 6 blocks.
   She gave 2 blocks to Molly.

   How many blocks does Sophie have now?   __4__ blocks

T R Y   I T

Additional Answers

1. Students should explain that they start with a total of 8. Then they take away a part that is given in the problem. When that part (5) is taken away, the other part is left. There are 3 stamps left.

2. Students should explain that they start with a total of 4. Then they take away a part that is given in the problem. When that part (3) is taken away, the other part is left. There is 1 turtle left on the grass.

3. Students should explain that they start with a total of 7. Then they take away a part that is given in the problem. When that part (2) is taken away, the other part is left. There are 5 strawberries left in the bowl.

4. Students should explain that they start with a total of 9. Then they take away a part that is given in the problem. When that part (4) is taken away, the other part is left. There are 5 hats left.

Compare Take-Away and Combine

Lesson Overview

Skills Update	5 minutes	ONLINE
GET READY Combine Problems	5 minutes	ONLINE
LEARN Recognize Take-Away or Combine	15 minutes	ONLINE
LEARN Tell What's Happening	10 minutes	ONLINE
TRY IT Add or Subtract?	10 minutes	OFFLINE

▶ ## Lesson Objectives

Recognize and solve word problems involving sums or minuends up through 20 in which one quantity changes through addition or subtraction.

▶ ## Prerequisite Skills

Use concrete objects or sketches to model and solve addition or subtraction computation problems involving sums or minuends up through 20.

▶ ## Advance Preparation

Gather 5–10 stuffed animals or other objects to act out addition and subtraction story problems.

▶ ## Content Background

In this lesson, students will compare addition and subtraction story problems. They will tell whether they should add or subtract to solve a problem.

Materials to Gather

SUPPLIED

Add or Subtract? activity page
blocks – O (20 all colors)

ALSO NEEDED

household objects – 5 stuffed animals or other objects

Keywords

add – to combine, or put together, groups of objects or numbers
addition – the process of combining, or putting together, groups of objects or numbers; a mathematical operation
combine problems – a classification of addition problems in which two numbers are put together to find a sum

---

ONLINE
5min

GET READY Combine Problems

Students will practice solving an addition story problem. They will review that a combine problem is a problem where you put two numbers together to find a sum.

Objectives

- Recognize and solve word problems involving sums or minuends up through 20 in which one quantity changes through addition or subtraction.

LEARN Recognize Take-Away or Combine

ONLINE 15min

Objectives

Students will use stuffed animals to model a subtraction story problem. Then they will explain the difference between combine and take away problems. Gather the stuffed animals.

Follow the directions on each screen.

- Recognize and solve word problems involving sums or minuends up through 20 in which one quantity changes through addition or subtraction.

LEARN Tell What's Happening

ONLINE 10min

Objectives

Student will use cubes to practice modeling story problems. Based on what is happening in the problem, students will tell whether it is an addition story problem or a subtraction story. Gather the cubes.

Follow the directions on each screen.

- Recognize and solve word problems involving sums or minuends up through 20 in which one quantity changes through addition or subtraction.

TRY IT Add or Subtract?

OFFLINE 10min

Objectives

Students will practice modeling and solving addition and subtraction problems. They will explain how they solved each problem. Give students the cubes and the Add or Subtract? activity page. Read the directions with them.

- Recognize and solve word problems involving sums or minuends up through 20 in which one quantity changes through addition or subtraction.

Name: _____

Compare Take-Away and Combine

Add or Subtract?

Use the picture and your cubes to act out the problem. Then circle the way you found the answer.

1. There were 8 bees on a flower.
   5 more bees flew over.
   Now how many bees are on the flower?
   A. I put the parts together.
   B. I took away a part from the total.

TRY IT

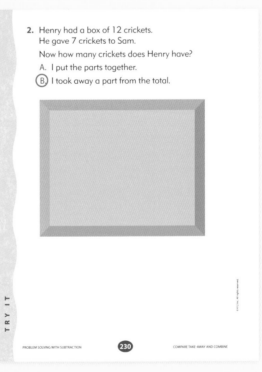

2. Henry had a box of 12 crickets.
   He gave 7 crickets to Sam.
   Now how many crickets does Henry have?
   A. I put the parts together.
   B. I took away a part from the total.

TRY IT

3. There were 13 monkeys in a tree.
Then 4 monkeys jumped off the tree.

How many monkeys are left?

A. I combined 13 and 4.

B. I took away 4 from 13.

4. There were 7 toads in the pond.
Then 3 more toads jumped into the pond.

How many toads are in the pond altogether?

A. I combined 7 and 3.

B. I took away 3 from 7.

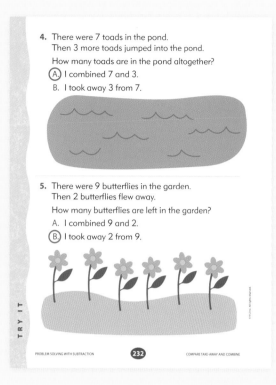

5. There were 9 butterflies in the garden.
Then 2 butterflies flew away.

How many butterflies are left in the garden?

A. I combined 9 and 2.

B. I took away 2 from 9.

T R Y   I T

Recognize and Solve Problems

Lesson Overview

Skills Update	5 minutes	ONLINE
LEARN Take-Away and Combine Problems	15 minutes	ONLINE
TRY IT Solve Problems	15 minutes	ONLINE
CHECKPOINT	10 minutes	OFFLINE

▶ Lesson Objectives

Recognize and solve word problems involving sums or minuends up through 20 in which one quantity changes through addition or subtraction.

▶ Prerequisite Skills

Use concrete objects or sketches to model and solve addition or subtraction computation problems involving sums or minuends up through 20.

▶ Content Background

In this lesson, students will recognize whether a story problem is an addition problem or a subtraction problem. They will model and solve the problems.

Materials to Gather

SUPPLIED
blocks – O (red)
Checkpoint (printout)

ALSO NEEDED
paper, drawing –1 sheet

LEARN Take-Away and Combine Problems

ONLINE
15min

Students will use cubes and sketches to model and to solve take-away and story problems. Gather the cubes and drawing paper.
　　Follow the directions on each screen.

Objectives

- Recognize and solve word problems involving sums or minuends up through 20 in which one quantity changes through addition or subtraction.

TRY IT Solve Problems

ONLINE 15 min

Objectives

- Recognize and solve word problems involving sums or minuends up through 20 in which one quantity changes through addition or subtraction.

Students will answer questions online to demonstrate what they remember about recognizing and solving addition and subtraction problems.

Tips

Students should start by showing the first part a problem. Then, if it is an addition problem, they should add the second number. If it is a subtraction problem, they should cross out the second number.

OFFLINE 10 min

CHECKPOINT

Objectives

- Recognize and solve word problems involving sums or minuends up through 20 in which one quantity changes through addition or subtraction.

Print the Checkpoint and have students complete it on their own. Read the directions, problems, and answer choices to students, if necessary. Use the answer key to score the Checkpoint, and then enter the results online.

Gather the cubes.

Checkpoint   Math | Problem Solving with Subtraction | Recognize and Solve Problems

Name _____ Date _____

Checkpoint Answer Key

Read the problem. Circle the answer.
(1 point)
1. What can you do to solve this problem?

   Ella made 12 quilts.
   She gave 5 to her friends.

   How many quilts does Ella have now?
   A. Compare 12 and 5 to see which is larger.
   B. Put 12 and 5 together.
   C. Take away 5 from 12. *(circled)*

(1 point)
2. Which best describes what is happening in this problem?

   Yasmin had 8 stickers.
   She bought 8 more.

   How many stickers does Yasmin have now?
   A. Yasmin now has more than 8 stickers. *(circled)*
   B. Yasmin now has 8 stickers.
   C. Yasmin now has fewer than 8 stickers.

Read the problem. Use cubes to solve the problem.
Circle the answer.
(1 point)
3. Taylor had 9 crayons.
   Her friend gave her 5 more.

   How many crayons does Taylor have now?
   A. 4   B. 5   C. 14 *(circled)*

1 of 3

Name _____   Date _____

(1 point)
4. Sandro had 14 baseball cards.
He gave 9 cards to his brother.

How many cards does Sandro have now?

Ⓐ 5   B. 9   C. 14

Read the problem. Use sketches to solve the problem.
Circle the answer. **Sketches will vary.**

(1 point)
5. Cara baked 15 muffins.
She gave 7 to her neighbor.

How many muffins does Cara have left?

A. 2   Ⓑ 8   C. 12

⬠⬠⬠⬠⬠⬠⬠⬠☒☒☒☒☒☒☒

(1 point)
6. There were 9 stickers in Jackie's album.
She bought 7 more stickers. **Sketches will vary.**

How many stickers does Jackie have in all?

Ⓐ 16   B. 7   C. 2

○○○○○○○○○   ○○○○○○○

Name _____   Date _____

Read the problem. Write the answer on the line.
(1 point)
7. Karen had 6 pencils in her pencil box.
She put 5 more pencils in her box.

How many pencils are in her pencil box now?   __11__ pencils

(1 point)
8. Terrance had 9 pencils.
Then 8 of them broke.

How many unbroken pencils does
Terrance have left?   __1__ pencils

(1 point)
9. Sarah had 19 apples.
She used 15 of them to make a pie.

How many apples does Sarah have left?   __4__ apples

(1 point)
10. 5 squirrels ran up a tree.
Then 2 more squirrels ran up the tree.

How many squirrels are in the tree altogether?   __7__ squirrels

---

Make Estimates and Check Answers

Lesson Overview

Skills Update	5 minutes	ONLINE
GET READY Check Sums	10 minutes	ONLINE
LEARN Estimate What's Left	10 minutes	ONLINE
LEARN Accurate Answers	10 minutes	OFFLINE
TRY IT Estimate and Check Answers	10 minutes	OFFLINE

▶ Lesson Objectives

- Make reasonable estimates for the solutions to subtraction problems with minuends up through 20.
- Check the accuracy of calculations for the solutions to subtraction problems with minuends up through 20.

▶ Prerequisite Skills

- Make reasonable estimates for the solutions to addition problems (for sums up through 20).
- Check the accuracy of calculations for the solutions to addition problems with sums up through 20.

▶ Content Background

In this lesson, students will estimate the difference by comparing numbers to the benchmarks of 5 and 10.

Keywords	**benchmark** – a target number used in estimation
	check – to examine for accuracy
	difference – the solution to a subtraction problem
	estimate (verb) – to approximate or perform a rough calculation
	estimate (noun) – the answer to an approximation or rough calculation

Materials to Gather

SUPPLIED

blocks – B (10 red, 10 blue)

Accurate Answers activity page

Estimate and Check Answers activity page

blocks – O (blue, red)

ALSO NEEDED

paper, drawing – 3 sheets

GET READY Check Sums

ONLINE
10 min

Students will use circles and sketches to check addition problems. Gather the circles and drawing paper.

Follow the directions on each screen. Students will model problems and compare their answers to the solutions shown.

Objectives

- Check the accuracy of calculations for the solutions to addition problems with sums up through 20.

Tips

Have students start with the greater number and count on to find the sum.

To prevent students from skipping an object or counting an object twice, have students touch each object as they count it.

LEARN Estimate What's Left

ONLINE
10 min

Students will use cubes to model subtraction story problems and estimate the difference. Gather the cubes.

Follow the directions on each screen.

Objectives

- Make reasonable estimates for the solutions to subtraction problems with minuends up through 20.

LEARN Accurate Answers

OFFLINE
10 min

Students will use models and sketches to check answers to subtraction story problems. They will tell whether each answer is correct or incorrect. Give students the circles, drawing paper, and the Accurate Answers activity page from their Activity Book. Read the directions with them.

Objectives

- Check the accuracy of calculations for the solutions to subtraction problems with minuends up through 20.

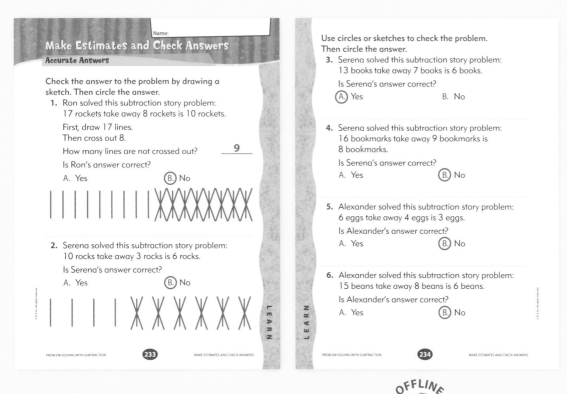

Make Estimates and Check Answers

Accurate Answers

Name:

Check the answer to the problem by drawing a sketch. Then circle the answer.

1. Ron solved this subtraction story problem:
17 rockets take away 8 rockets is 10 rockets.

First, draw 17 lines.
Then cross out 8.

How many lines are not crossed out?   **9**

Is Ron's answer correct?

A. Yes   B. No

2. Serena solved this subtraction story problem:
10 rocks take away 3 rocks is 6 rocks.

Is Serena's answer correct?

A. Yes   B. No

233 MAKE ESTIMATES AND CHECK ANSWERS

LEARN

Use circles or sketches to check the problem.
Then circle the answer.

3. Serena solved this subtraction story problem:
13 books take away 7 books is 6 books.

Is Serena's answer correct?

A. Yes   B. No

4. Serena solved this subtraction story problem:
16 bookmarks take away 9 bookmarks is
8 bookmarks.

Is Serena's answer correct?

A. Yes   B. No

5. Alexander solved this subtraction story problem:
6 eggs take away 4 eggs is 3 eggs.

Is Alexander's answer correct?

A. Yes   B. No

6. Alexander solved this subtraction story problem:
15 beans take away 8 beans is 6 beans.

Is Alexander's answer correct?

A. Yes   B. No

LEARN

234 MAKE ESTIMATES AND CHECK ANSWERS

TRY IT Estimate and Check Answers

OFFLINE
10 min

Objectives

Students will practice estimating answers and solving subtraction story problems. Give students the circles, drawing paper, and Estimate and Check Answers activity page from their Activity Book. Read the directions with them.

- Make reasonable estimates for the solutions to subtraction problems with minuends up through 20.

- Check the accuracy of calculations for the solutions to subtraction problems with minuends up through 20.

Make Estimates and Check Answers

Estimate and Check Answers

Use models or sketches to estimate or check the problem. Then circle the answer.

1. You had 19 baseball cards.
   You gave 6 baseball cards to a friend.

   About how many baseball cards do you have left?

   A. about 5   B. about 10   (C.) about 15

2. Maria saw 18 birds.
   Then 9 birds flew away.

   About how many birds are left?

   A. about 5   (B.) about 10   C. about 15

3. Rosa solved this subtraction story problem.
   18 blocks take away 9 blocks is 9 blocks.

   Is Rosa's answer correct?

   (A.) Yes   B. No

4. Winnie solved this subtraction story problem.
   14 marbles take away 6 marbles is 9 marbles.

   Is Winnie's answer correct?

   A. Yes   (B.) No

TRY IT

5. You had 18 crackers.
   Your friend ate 9 of your crackers.

   About how many crackers are left?

   A. about 20   (B.) about 10   C. about 0

6. You had 19 stamps.
   You gave 4 stamps away.

   About how many stamps do you have left?

   A. about 20   B. about 10   (C.) about 15

7. Which subtraction story problem is correct?

   A. 8 cookies take away 3 cookies is 4 cookies.
   (B.) 9 cookies take away 6 cookies is 3 cookies.
   C. 7 cookies take away 2 cookies is 6 cookies.

8. Which subtraction story problem is correct?

   (A.) 13 bananas take away 2 bananas is 11 bananas.
   B. 18 bananas take away 3 bananas is 14 bananas.
   C. 20 bananas take away 5 bananas is 16 bananas.

TRY IT

Unit Review

UNIT REVIEW Look Back	15 minutes	**ONLINE**
UNIT REVIEW Checkpoint Practice	15 minutes	**OFFLINE**
⏩ **UNIT REVIEW** Prepare for the Checkpoint		

▶ Lesson Objectives

This lesson reviews the following objectives:

- Use concrete objects to explain how to solve addition and subtraction problem-solving situations involving numbers up to 10.
- Recognize and solve word problems involving sums or minuends up through 20 in which one quantity changes through addition or subtraction.
- Make reasonable estimates for the solutions to subtraction problems with minuends up through 20.
- Check the accuracy of calculations for the solutions to subtraction problems with minuends up through 20.

▶ Advance Preparation

In this lesson, students will have an opportunity to review previous activities in the Problem Solving with Subtraction unit. Look at the suggested activities in Unit Review: Prepare for the Checkpoint online and gather any needed materials.

Materials to Gather

SUPPLIED

blocks – O (10 red, 10 blue)
Checkpoint Practice activity page

Keywords		
add	estimate (verb)
addition	model (noun)
benchmark	model (verb)
check	subtract
combine problems	subtraction
difference	take away
estimate (noun)	

UNIT REVIEW **Look Back**

ONLINE 15min

Objectives

- Review unit objectives.

In this unit, students have learned to recognize and solve subtraction story problems by using concrete objects and sketches. They have created their own story problems and have solved those problems using models or sketches. They have applied that knowledge to make reasonable estimates for solutions and have checked the accuracy of subtraction calculations. Students will review these concepts to prepare for the Unit Checkpoint.

UNIT REVIEW Checkpoint Practice

Objectives

- Review unit objectives.

Students will complete a Checkpoint Practice activity page to prepare for the Unit Checkpoint. If necessary, read the directions, problems, and answer choices to students. Have students answer the problems on their own. Carefully review the answers with students.

Gather the cubes.

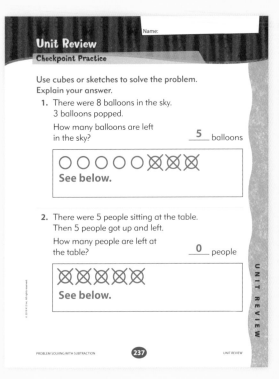

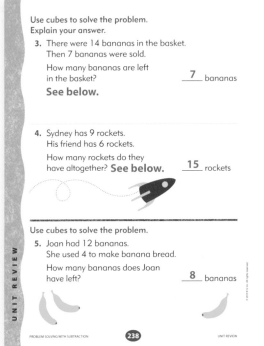

Additional Answers

1. Students should explain that this is a subtraction story problem. They start with a total and take away a part. 8 take away 3 is 5. There are 5 balloons left in the sky.

2. Students should explain that this is a subtraction story problem. They start with a total and take away a part. 5 take away 5 is 0. There are 0 people left at the table.

3. Students should explain that this is a subtraction story problem. They start with a total and take away a part. 14 take away 7 is 7. There are 7 bananas left in the basket.

4. Students should explain that this is an addition story problem. To find how many rockets Sydney and his friend have altogether, they combine two amounts. 9 and 6 is 15.

Read the problem. Circle the answer.

6. Ryan had 19 straws.
   He gave 4 to some friends.
   About how many straws does Ryan have left?
   A. about 5   B. about 10   (C.) about 15

7. Jean has 15 bows.
   She gives Susie 8 bows.
   About how many bows does Jean have left?
   (A.) about 5   B. about 10   C. about 15

8. Alexander solved this problem:
   13 hats take away 5 hats is 7 hats.
   Check Alexander's answer with cubes.
   Is Alexander's answer correct?
   A. Yes   (B.) No

9. Fred baked 9 mini pizzas.
   He and his family ate 3 of them.
   Which shows how many mini pizzas Fred has left?

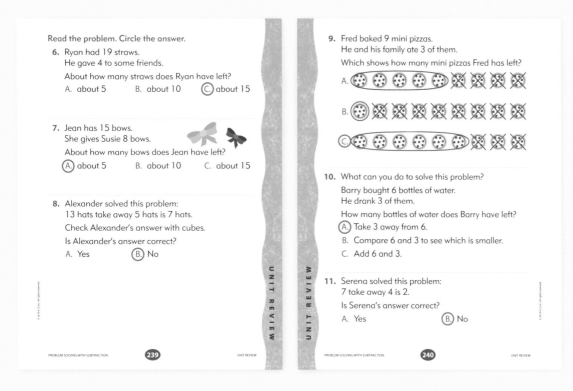

10. What can you do to solve this problem?
    Barry bought 6 bottles of water.
    He drank 3 of them.
    How many bottles of water does Barry have left?
    (A.) Take 3 away from 6.
    B. Compare 6 and 3 to see which is smaller.
    C. Add 6 and 3.

11. Serena solved this problem:
    7 take away 4 is 2.
    Is Serena's answer correct?
    A. Yes   (B.) No

> **UNIT REVIEW** Prepare for the Checkpoint

What you do next depends on how students performed in the previous activity, Unit Review: Checkpoint Practice. If students had difficulty with any of the problems, complete the appropriate review activity listed in the table online.

Unit Checkpoint

Lesson Overview

UNIT CHECKPOINT Offline | 45 minutes | **OFFLINE**

▶ Unit Objectives

This lesson assesses the following objectives:

- Use concrete objects to explain how to solve addition and subtraction problem-solving situations involving numbers up to 10.
- Recognize and solve word problems involving sums or minuends up through 20 in which one quantity changes through addition or subtraction.
- Make reasonable estimates for the solutions to subtraction problems with minuends up through 20.
- Check the accuracy of calculations for the solutions to subtraction problems with minuends up through 20.

Materials to Gather

SUPPLIED
Unit Checkpoint (printout)
blocks – B (10 green, 10 yellow)

UNIT CHECKPOINT Offline

OFFLINE 45 min

Objectives

- Assess unit objectives.

Students will complete the Unit Checkpoint offline. Print the Checkpoint and have students complete it on their own. Read the directions, problems, and answer choices to students, if necessary. Use the answer key to score the Checkpoint, and then enter the results online.

Gather the circle blocks.

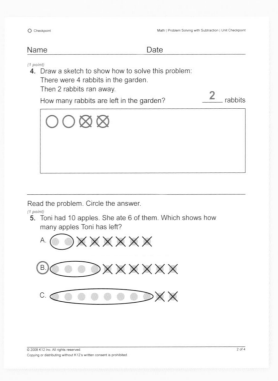

Name _____ Date _____

(1 point)
6. What can you do to solve this problem?

There were 7 children at the playground.
Then 3 of them went home for lunch.

How many children are left at the playground?

  A. Add 7 and 3.

  Ⓑ Take 3 away from 7.

  C. Compare 7 and 3 to see which is smaller.

(1 point)
7. What can you do to solve this problem?

Farmer Glen had 10 rows of corn.
He planted 10 more rows of corn.

How many rows of corn does Farmer Glen have in all?

  Ⓐ Put 10 and 10 together.

  B. Take 10 away from 10.

  C. Compare 10 and 10.

(1 point)
8. Solve the problem.

Tory made 8 greeting cards.
She gave 4 of the cards to her friends.

How many greeting cards does Tory have left?

  A. 12

  B. 10

  Ⓒ 4

Name _____ Date _____

Estimate the answer. Circle the answer.
(1 point)
9. You had 18 crackers.
Your friend ate 9 of your crackers.

About how many crackers are left?

  A. about 20   Ⓑ about 10   C. about 5

(1 point)
10. Cassidy made 16 birthday invitations.
She mailed 9 of them.

About how many birthday invitations does Cassidy have left?

  Ⓐ about 5   B. about 10   C. about 15

Read the problem. Circle the answer.
(1 point)
11. Which math problem is correct?

  A. 7 take away 2 is 4.

  Ⓑ 8 take away 3 is 5.

  C. 6 take away 1 is 3.

(1 point)
12. Use circles to solve this problem.

Alexander did this math problem.
16 marbles take away 7 marbles is 10 marbles.

Check Alexander's work.

Is Alexander's answer correct?

  A. Yes   Ⓑ No

Subtraction as Comparison

▶ Unit Objectives

- Use concrete objects or sketches to model and solve addition or subtraction computation problems involving sums or minuends up through 20.

- Demonstrate the meaning of subtraction as comparing two quantities to find the difference (with minuends up through 20).

▶ Big Ideas

- Counting principles and numbers can be used to solve addition and subtraction problems.

- Show the meaning of subtraction (taking away, comparing, finding the difference).

▶ Unit Introduction

Students will use models and sketches to solve comparison subtraction problems using one-to-one-correspondence. They will use pairs of numbers to create addition and subtraction problems, exploring the differences among comparing, combining, and take-away problems.

Compare and Subtract

Lesson Overview		
Skills Update	5 minutes	ONLINE
GET READY Party Math	5 minutes	ONLINE
LEARN Envelope Math	5 minutes	ONLINE
LEARN Pair Objects to Solve	10 minutes	OFFLINE
LEARN Model and Compare	10 minutes	OFFLINE
TRY IT Compare and Solve	10 minutes	OFFLINE

▶ Lesson Objectives

Use concrete objects or sketches to model and solve addition or subtraction computation problems involving sums or minuends up through 20.

▶ Prerequisite Skills

- Demonstrate the meaning of addition as the combining of two sets (for sums up through 20).
- Demonstrate the meaning of subtraction as taking away an amount from a given quantity (with minuends up through 20).

▶ Advance Preparation

Cut out the stamps and envelopes from the Pair Objects to Solve activity page. Save envelopes and stamps for use in several activities.

▶ Content Background

In this lesson, students will use models to solve compare problems by subtracting.

In compare problems, students must compare two groups to determine how many more or fewer objects are in one group. To compare, students may subtract.

Students will first compare groups using models that are aligned so that the objects in the two groups match one-to-one. To find how many more or fewer, students will count the unmatched objects. When comparing greater numbers, counting isn't practical. Students will learn that they can subtract, rather than count, to solve compare problems.

Keywords	**compare problem** – a problem in which two quantities are compared by finding the difference
	fewer – a lesser number than another
	more – a greater number or amount than another

Materials to Gather

SUPPLIED

Pair Objects to Solve activity page

Compare and Solve activity page

ALSO NEEDED

scissors, adult

GET READY Party Math

ONLINE 5min

Students will watch how Rosa combines two groups of objects to solve an addition story problem. They will also see one group of objects taken away from another to show take-away subtraction.

Objectives

- Demonstrate the meaning of addition as the combining of two sets (for sums up through 20).
- Demonstrate the meaning of subtraction as taking away an amount from a given quantity (with minuends up through 20).

LEARN Envelope Math

ONLINE 5min

Students will watch how Rosa compares two groups of objects to solve a comparison subtraction story problem.

Explain to students that greater numbers describe groups with *more* objects, and lesser numbers describe groups with *fewer* objects.

Objectives

- Use concrete objects or sketches to model and solve addition or subtraction computation problems involving sums or minuends up through 20.

LEARN Pair Objects to Solve

OFFLINE 10min

Students will use concrete objects (stamps and envelopes) to compare to solve subtraction problems.

Gather the cut-out stamps and envelopes from the Pair Objects to Solve activity page.

1. **Say:** We will use stamps and envelopes to solve problems that ask "how many more" and "how many fewer."
2. Lay out 8 envelopes and 5 stamps.
3. **Say:** Find how many more 8 is than 5. You have 8 envelopes and 5 stamps. Match each stamp with an envelope to find how many more envelopes you have. Place 1 stamp on each envelope.
4. **Ask:** Which do you have more of, envelopes or stamps?
   ANSWER: envelopes

   Ask: How many envelopes do not have stamps?
   ANSWER: 3
5. **Say:** You have 3 more envelopes than stamps. So 8 is 3 more than 5.

   Repeat Steps 2–4 for the following problems:
   - 6 envelopes and 2 stamps
   - 4 envelopes and 1 stamp
6. **Say:** Now let's compare two groups of objects to find how many fewer one number is than another number.
7. Lay out 2 envelopes and 4 stamps.
8. **Say:** Find how many fewer 2 is than 4. You have 2 envelopes and 4 stamps. Match each stamp with an envelope. Place 1 stamp on each envelope.
9. **Ask:** Which do you have fewer of, envelopes or stamps?
   ANSWER: envelopes

Objectives

- Use concrete objects or sketches to model and solve addition or subtraction computation problems involving sums or minuends up through 20.

Tips

Show students where a stamp goes on an envelope if they do not know.

Ask: How many stamps do not have envelopes?
ANSWER: 2

10. **Say:** You do not have enough envelopes for the stamps. You have 2 fewer envelopes than stamps. So 2 is 2 fewer than 4.

Have students repeat Steps 7–9 for the following problems:

- 7 envelopes and 8 stamps

- 1 envelope and 5 stamps

- 3 envelopes and 10 stamps

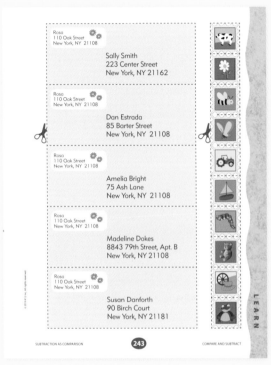

LEARN Model and Compare

OFFLINE 10 min

Objectives

- Use concrete objects or sketches to model and solve addition or subtraction computation problems involving sums or minuends up through 20.

Students will use envelopes and stamps to compare to solve subtraction problems. They should make the connection that "How many more?" problems can be reversed to become "How many fewer?" problems.

Gather the cut-out stamps and envelopes from the Pair Objects to Solve activity page.

1. **Say:** 8 is 3 more than 5. You can use this fact to find how many fewer 5 is than 8.

2. Lay out groups of 5 envelopes and 8 stamps. Then help students align the envelopes and stamps in each group so that they match one-to-one.

3. **Say:** You can pair up the stamps so that it is easy to see how many fewer envelopes than stamps I have. I can see there are 3 fewer envelopes, so I know that 5 is 3 fewer than 8.

4. **Say:** We know that 8 is 3 more than 5 and that 5 is 3 fewer than 8. In both facts, the amount that is more or fewer is the same number—3. When you compare two numbers, the amount that is more or fewer will be the same number.

5. Repeat Steps 1–3 for the following problems:
   - 2 envelopes and 6 stamps
   - 1 envelope and 4 stamps

6. Lay out 4 envelopes and 2 stamps.

7. **Say:** 2 is 2 fewer than 4. You can use this fact to find how many more 4 is than 2.

   Help students align the stamps and envelopes in each group so that they match one-to-one.

8. **Ask:** How many more envelopes are there than stamps?
   ANSWER: 2

   Ask: How can you tell there are 2 more envelopes?
   SAMPLE ANSWER: I paired up the envelopes and stamps, and there are 2 extra envelopes.

9. Have students repeat Steps 6–8 for the following problems:
   - 8 envelopes and 7 stamps
   - 5 envelopes and 1 stamp
   - 6 envelopes and 3 stamps

TRY IT Compare and Solve

OFFLINE

10 min

Students will practice using models to compare to solve subtraction problems. Give students the stamps, envelopes, and Compare and Solve activity page from their Activity Book. Read the directions with them.

Objectives

- Use concrete objects or sketches to model and solve addition or subtraction computation problems involving sums or minuends up through 20.

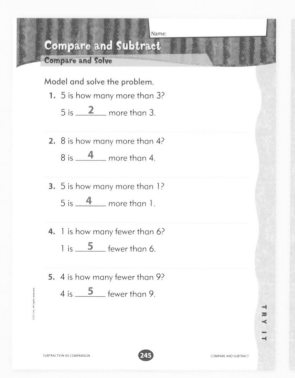

Name:

Compare and Subtract
Compare and Solve

Model and solve the problem.

1. 5 is how many more than 3?
   5 is __2__ more than 3.

2. 8 is how many more than 4?
   8 is __4__ more than 4.

3. 5 is how many more than 1?
   5 is __4__ more than 1.

4. 1 is how many fewer than 6?
   1 is __5__ fewer than 6.

5. 4 is how many fewer than 9?
   4 is __5__ fewer than 9.

SUBTRACTION AS COMPARISON   245   COMPARE AND SUBTRACT

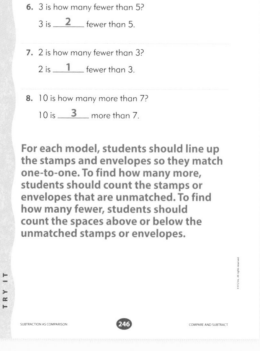

6. 3 is how many fewer than 5?
   3 is __2__ fewer than 5.

7. 2 is how many fewer than 3?
   2 is __1__ fewer than 3.

8. 10 is how many more than 7?
   10 is __3__ more than 7.

For each model, students should line up the stamps and envelopes so they match one-to-one. To find how many more, students should count the stamps or envelopes that are unmatched. To find how many fewer, students should count the spaces above or below the unmatched stamps or envelopes.

SUBTRACTION AS COMPARISON   246   COMPARE AND SUBTRACT

Sketch Subtraction Problems

Lesson Overview

Skills Update	5 minutes	ONLINE
LEARN Sketch to Subtract	10 minutes	ONLINE
LEARN Compare Numbers	15 minutes	OFFLINE
TRY IT Sketch and Solve	15 minutes	OFFLINE

▶ Lesson Objectives

Use concrete objects or sketches to model and solve addition or subtraction computation problems involving sums or minuends up through 20.

▶ Prerequisite Skills

- Demonstrate the meaning of addition as the combining of two sets (for sums up through 20).
- Demonstrate the meaning of subtraction as taking away an amount from a given quantity (with minuends up through 20).

▶ Content Background

In this lesson, students will draw sketches to solve subtraction problems by comparing.

Subtraction problems may be *take-away problems* or *compare problems*. In take-away problems, students must take away from a group to determine how many objects are left in the group. In compare problems, students must compare two groups to determine how many more or fewer objects are in one group. To compare, students may subtract.

Students will first compare groups using models that are aligned so that the objects in the two groups match one-to-one. To find how many more or fewer, students will count the unmatched objects. When comparing greater numbers, counting isn't practical. Students will learn that they can subtract, rather than count, to solve compare problems.

Materials to Gather

SUPPLIED

Compare Numbers activity page

Sketch and Solve activity page

Centimeter Grid Paper (optional printout)

LEARN Sketch to Subtract

ONLINE 10 min

Students will see comparison subtraction problems modeled with square blocks and sketches. To find the difference, they will learn how to match one-to-one in their models and sketches and count the unmatched objects.

Objectives

- Use concrete objects or sketches to model and solve addition or subtraction computation problems involving sums and minuends up through 20.

LEARN Compare Numbers

OFFLINE 15 min

Students will draw sketches to help them compare numbers. They will then solve the problem by subtracting to learn the connection between comparing and subtracting. Emphasize this connection with students.

Give students the Compare Numbers activity page from their Activity Book and read the directions with them.

Objectives

- Use concrete objects or sketches to model and solve addition or subtraction computation problems involving sums and minuends up through 20.

1. Read Problem 1. Have students draw a row of 14 circles.

   Ask: How many circles should you draw below the 14 circles?
   ANSWER: 3

   Ask: How many circles are matched up?
   ANSWER: 3

   Ask: How many circles are **not** matched up?
   ANSWER: 11

2. **Say:** We can say 14 is 11 more than 3. We can also say 3 is 11 fewer than 14.

3. Point to the blank number sentence.

4. **Say:** We can write a subtraction sentence to compare 14 and 3. The sentence "14 minus 3 is 11" shows that 14 is 11 more than 3 and that 3 is 11 fewer than 14.

   Have students write the number sentence in the boxes.

5. Point to the completed number sentence.

   Say: 14 is the number of circles in the first row. 3 is the number of circles in the second row.

   Ask: What does the number 11 tell us?
   ANSWER: how many circles are not matched

6. **Say:** We can use sketches or subtraction to compare numbers.

7. Repeat Steps 1–4 for Problems 2 and 3.

8. Have students try to complete Problems 4–8 on their own. Assist students as needed so that they can complete the activity page successfully.

Tips

Students should match up exactly one object in the top row with another object in the bottom row.

If students have difficulty lining up their sketches, use the Centimeter Grid Paper and have students draw one sketch in each box of the grid.

Tips

Students do not have to sketch circles; they may sketch whatever is easiest for them.

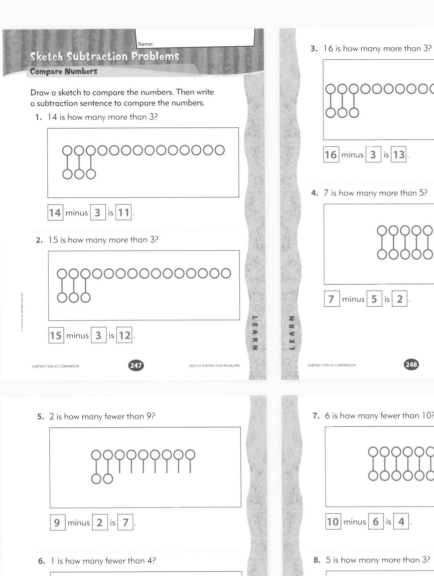

Sketch Subtraction Problems

Compare Numbers

Draw a sketch to compare the numbers. Then write a subtraction sentence to compare the numbers.

1. 14 is how many more than 3?

14 minus 3 is 11 .

2. 15 is how many more than 3?

15 minus 3 is 12 .

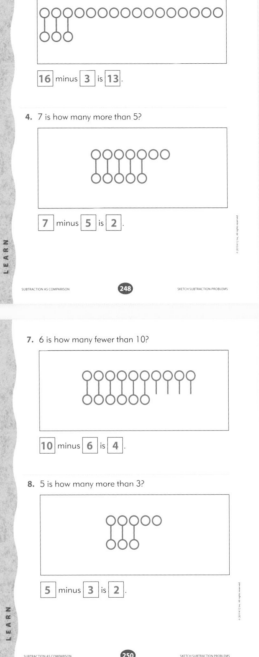

3. 16 is how many more than 3?

16 minus 3 is 13 .

4. 7 is how many more than 5?

7 minus 5 is 2 .

5. 2 is how many fewer than 9?

9 minus 2 is 7 .

6. 1 is how many fewer than 4?

4 minus 1 is 3 .

7. 6 is how many fewer than 10?

10 minus 6 is 4 .

8. 5 is how many more than 3?

5 minus 3 is 2 .

TRY IT Sketch and Solve

Objectives

Students will draw a sketch to compare numbers. They will then write a subtraction sentence to compare the numbers and complete a subtraction statement.

Give students the Sketch and Solve activity page from their Activity Book and read the directions with them.

- Use concrete objects or sketches to model and solve addition or subtraction computation problems involving sums and minuends up through 20.

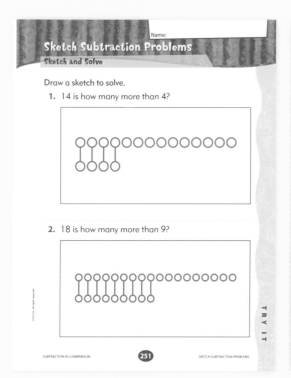

Name:

Sketch Subtraction Problems

Sketch and Solve

Draw a sketch to solve.

1. 14 is how many more than 4?

2. 18 is how many more than 9?

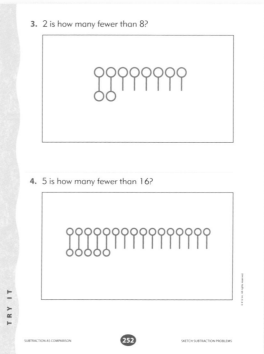

3. 2 is how many fewer than 8?

4. 5 is how many fewer than 16?

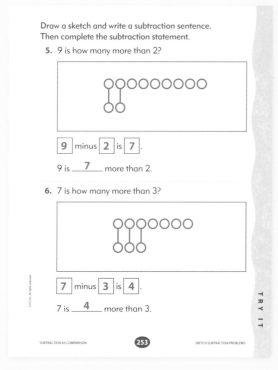

Draw a sketch and write a subtraction sentence. Then complete the subtraction statement.

5. 9 is how many more than 2?

9 minus 2 is 7 .

9 is ___7___ more than 2.

6. 7 is how many more than 3?

7 minus 3 is 4 .

7 is ___4___ more than 3.

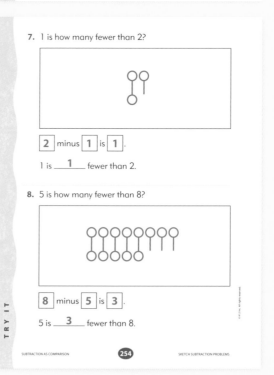

7. 1 is how many fewer than 2?

2 minus 1 is 1 .

1 is ___1___ fewer than 2.

8. 5 is how many fewer than 8?

8 minus 5 is 3 .

5 is ___3___ fewer than 8.

9. 18 is how many more than 7?

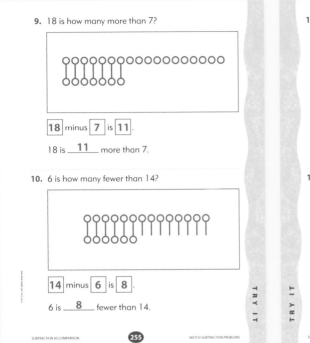

18 minus 7 is 11 .

18 is __11__ more than 7.

10. 6 is how many fewer than 14?

14 minus 6 is 8 .

6 is __8__ fewer than 14.

11. 8 is how many fewer than 17?

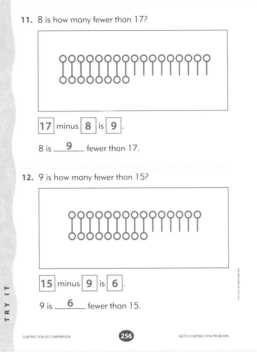

17 minus 8 is 9 .

8 is __9__ fewer than 17.

12. 9 is how many fewer than 15?

15 minus 9 is 6 .

9 is __6__ fewer than 15.

Take Away, Combine, and Compare

Lesson Overview

Skills Update	5 minutes	ONLINE
GET READY Rainy Day Add and Subtract	5 minutes	ONLINE
LEARN Solve Using a Set of Numbers	10 minutes	ONLINE
TRY IT Solve Different Types of Problems	15 minutes	OFFLINE
CHECKPOINT	10 minutes	OFFLINE

▶ Lesson Objectives

Use concrete objects or sketches to model and solve addition or subtraction computation problems involving sums or minuends up through 20.

▶ Prerequisite Skills

- Demonstrate the meaning of addition as the combining of two sets (for sums up through 20).
- Demonstrate the meaning of subtraction as taking away an amount from a given quantity (with minuends up through 20).

▶ Misconceptions

Students might have difficulty seeing the connection between addition and subtraction situations.

▶ Content Background

Students will model, explain, and solve the following types of problems: combine problems, take-away problems, and compare problems.

Subtraction problems may be *take-away problems* or *compare problems*. In take-away problems, students must take away from a group to determine how many objects are left in the group. In compare problems, students must compare two groups to determine how many more or fewer objects are in one group. To compare, students may subtract.

Materials to Gather

SUPPLIED

blocks – B (red, blue)

Solve Different Types of Problems activity page

Checkpoint (printout)

ALSO NEEDED

paper, drawing – 1 sheet

GET READY Rainy Day Add and Subtract

ONLINE 5 min

Students will review how to use pictures to solve compare, take-away, and combine problems. For each problem, have students say aloud how they would solve it. Then have them watch how to solve the problem.

Objectives

- Demonstrate the meaning of addition as the combining of two sets (for sums up through 20).
- Demonstrate the meaning of subtraction as taking away an amount from a given quantity (with minuends up through 20).

LEARN Solve Using a Set of Numbers

ONLINE 10 min

Students will review how to solve a combine addition problem, take-away subtraction problem, and compare subtraction problem.
   Follow the directions on each screen.

Objectives

- Use concrete objects or sketches to model and solve addition or subtraction computation problems involving sums and minuends up through 20.

Tips

Students may also use blocks or sketches to solve the problems.

TRY IT Solve Different Types of Problems

OFFLINE 15 min

Students will practice solving compare, take-away, and combine problems.
   Give students the circle blocks and Solve Different Types of Problems activity page from their Activity Book. Read the directions with them.

Objectives

- Use concrete objects or sketches to model and solve addition or subtraction computation problems involving sums and minuends up through 20.

Tips

Students may also sketch their answers.

Take Away, Combine, and Compare
Solve Different Types of Problems

Name:

Use circle blocks or a sketch to solve.

1. Combine 5 and 13. What is the answer?   18

2. Take away 6 from 16. What is the answer?   10

3. 7 is how many fewer than 10?   3

4. What is 8 take away 2?   6

5. Add 4 and 9. What is the answer?   13

6. 18 is how many more than 14?   4

7. 11 is how many more than 6?   5

8. Combine 12 and 8. What is the answer?   20

9. What is 15 take away 14?   1

Models and sketches will vary.
Check students' work.

T R Y   I T

CHECKPOINT

OFFLINE
10 min

Objectives

Print the Checkpoint and have students complete it on their own. Read the directions, problems, and answer choices to students, if necessary. Use the answer key to score the Checkpoint, and then enter the results online.

Give students the circle blocks and drawing paper.

- Use concrete objects or sketches to model and solve addition or subtraction computation problems involving sums or minuends up through 20.

Checkpoint   Math | Subtraction as Comparison | Take Away, Combine, and Compare

Name _____   Date _____

Checkpoint Answer Key

Use circle blocks or a sketch to solve.
(2 points)
1. 5 is how many more than 3?   2

(2 points)
2. 19 is how many more than 9?   10

(2 points)
3. 3 is how many fewer than 16?   13

(2 points)
4. Add 17 and 2. What is the answer?   19

(2 points)
5. Add 5 and 11. What is the answer?   16

(2 points)
6. Subtract 6 from 12. What is the answer?   6

(2 points)
7. Subtract 1 from 13. What is the answer?   12

(2 points)
8. 9 is how many fewer than 20?   11

Compare to Subtract

Lesson Overview

Skills Update	5 minutes	ONLINE
GET READY Take Away to Subtract	10 minutes	ONLINE
LEARN Compare Cube Trains	10 minutes	OFFLINE
LEARN How Much More or Less?	10 minutes	OFFLINE
TRY IT Compare Numbers of Cubes	10 minutes	OFFLINE

▶ Lesson Objectives

Demonstrate the meaning of subtraction as comparing two quantities to find the difference (with minuends up through 20).

▶ Prerequisite Skills

Demonstrate the meaning of subtraction as taking away an amount from a given quantity (with minuends up through 20).

▶ Advance Preparation

Number index cards 1 through 20, or gather the cards you created previously.

▶ Content Background

In this lesson, students will learn to use subtraction to compare two quantities and find the difference.

Materials to Gather

SUPPLIED

blocks – B (10 red, 10 blue, 10 green)

blocks – O (red, blue)

Compare Numbers of Cubes activity page

ALSO NEEDED

index cards – numbered 1–20

Keywords

compare – to find the similarities or differences among sizes, values, or amounts

difference – the solution to a subtraction problem

model (noun) – a physical object, diagram, or picture that represents an amount, an expression, an equation, or a problem situation

model (verb) – to use physical objects, diagrams, or pictures to represent an amount, an expression, an equation, or a problem situation

quantity – a number or amount

subtraction – the process of taking away objects from a group or finding the difference between two groups; a mathematical operation

GET READY Take Away to Subtract

Students will use circles to model and solve subtraction problems. Gather the circles.

  Follow the directions on each screen.

Objectives

- Demonstrate the meaning of subtraction as taking away an amount from a given quantity (with minuends up through 20).

Tips

To make sure that students model the problems correctly, have students touch each object and count aloud.

OFFLINE
10min

LEARN Compare Cube Trains

Students will compare two quantities. They will write subtraction sentences and find the difference.

  Gather the cubes and a sheet of paper.

1. Have students make a train of 10 blue cubes and a train of 8 red cubes.

2. Have students line up the cube trains, so that each red cube is matched to a blue cube. Have students compare the cube trains.

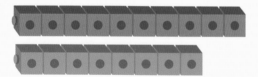

  Ask: Compare the cube trains. Which color cube do you have more of? (blue)

3. **Ask:** How many more blue cubes do you have than red cubes? (2)

4. **Ask:** What number did you use to say how many blue cubes there are? (10)

  Ask: What number did you use to say how many red cubes there are? (8)

  Ask: What number did you use to say the difference between the number of blue cubes and the number of red cubes? (2)

5. Have students write the numbers 2, 10, and 8 on a sheet of paper. Explain that you can use these numbers to write number sentences. Give the example that 2 and 8 is 10.

  Ask: What other number sentences can you make with these three numbers?
  ANSWER: 8 and 2 is 10, 10 take away 2 is 8, and 10 take away 8 is 2.

  Record each sentence on the paper.

6. **Ask:** Can we say that 10 is 2 more than 8?
  ANSWER: Yes. Write that sentence on the paper.

7. **Ask:** What sentence can you use with the words *less than* and the three numbers?
  ANSWER: 8 is 2 less than 10; 2 is 8 less than 10.

Objectives

- Demonstrate the meaning of subtraction as comparing two quantities to find the difference (with minuends up through 20).

Tips

Put red cubes in one bag and blue cubes in another bag. Have students remove the number of cubes they need for each problem.

  To make sure that students model the problems correctly, have students touch each object and count aloud.

8. Have students touch each cube train as you say that 10 is 2 more than 8. Then have them touch the cube trains as you say that 8 is 2 less than 10.

Say: Touch the cube train again as I say 8 is 2 less than 10.

LEARN How Much More or Less?

Students will compare two quantities to find the difference. They will learn to use subtraction to determine whether an amount is greater than or less than another amount.

Gather the cubes and the index cards.

1. Show students the index cards labeled 14 and 5. Have students model each number with cubes, counting aloud as they make a train of 14 red cubes and a train of 5 blue cubes.

2. Have students line up the cube trains, so that each red cube is matched to a blue cube. Have students compare the cube trains.

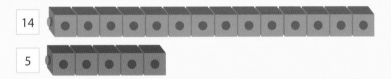

3. **Ask:** How many red cubes are there? (14)

   Ask: How many blue cubes are there? (5)

   Ask: How many cubes are not matched? (9)

   Ask: How many more cubes are in the group of 14 than in the group of 5? (9)

4. **Say:** Another way to say this is that the difference between 14 and 5 is 9.

   Ask: How many more is 14 than 5? (9)

   Ask: How much greater is 14 than 5 (9)

   Ask: How much less is 5 than 14? (9)

5. Repeat Steps 1–4 using the following quantities:

   • 15 and 8

   • 16 and 7

   • 11 and 5

   • 13 and 9

Objectives

• Demonstrate the meaning of subtraction as comparing two quantities to find the difference (with minuends up through 20).

Tips

To help students make a comparison, have them line up the cube trains in horizontal rows so that the ends of the trains are lined up vertically and the longer train is above the shorter train.

Compare Numbers of Cubes

OFFLINE

10min

Students will practice solving subtraction problems by comparing two numbers. Give students the cubes and the Compare Numbers of Cubes activity page from their Activity Book. Read the directions with them.

Objectives

- Demonstrate the meaning of subtraction as comparing two quantities to find the difference (with minuends up through 20).

Tips

Put red cubes in one bag and blue cubes in another bag. Have students remove the number of cubes they need for each problem.

To make sure that students model the problems correctly, have students touch each object and count aloud.

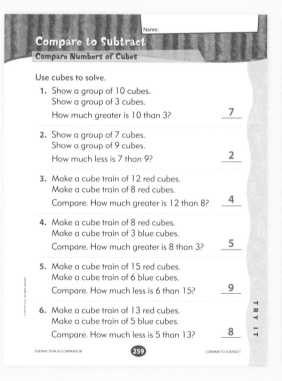

Compare to Subtract

Compare Numbers of Cubes

Name:

Use cubes to solve.

1. Show a group of 10 cubes.
   Show a group of 3 cubes.
   How much greater is 10 than 3? **7**

2. Show a group of 7 cubes.
   Show a group of 9 cubes.
   How much less is 7 than 9? **2**

3. Make a cube train of 12 red cubes.
   Make a cube train of 8 red cubes.
   Compare. How much greater is 12 than 8? **4**

4. Make a cube train of 8 red cubes.
   Make a cube train of 3 blue cubes.
   Compare. How much greater is 8 than 3? **5**

5. Make a cube train of 15 red cubes.
   Make a cube train of 6 blue cubes.
   Compare. How much less is 6 than 15? **9**

6. Make a cube train of 13 red cubes.
   Make a cube train of 5 blue cubes.
   Compare. How much less is 5 than 13? **8**

SUBTRACTION AS COMPARISON   259   COMPARE TO SUBTRACT

Draw a picture or use cubes to solve.

7. How much less is 10 than 19?
   See below.

8. How much less is 5 than 7?
   See below.

9. How much more is 14 than 7?
   See below.

10. How much more is 16 than 11?
    See below.

SUBTRACTION AS COMPARISON   260   COMPARE TO SUBTRACT

Additional Answers

7. Students should model the numbers 19 and 10 with cubes and match the cube trains to find that 9 cubes are left. They might also draw 19 objects and 10 objects. Then they should draw a line between each of the 10 objects to one of the 19 objects to find that 9 objects are left.

8. Students should model the numbers 7 and 5 with cubes or objects. They will find that the difference is 2.

9. Students should model the numbers 14 and 7 with cubes or objects. They will find that the difference is 7.

10. Students should model the numbers 16 and 11 with cubes or objects. They will find that the difference is 5.

Subtraction as Comparing

Lesson Overview

Skills Update	5 minutes	ONLINE
GET READY Take Away Pictures	10 minutes	ONLINE
LEARN Compare with Pictures	10 minutes	ONLINE
LEARN Draw Pictures to Compare	10 minutes	OFFLINE
TRY IT Compare Numbers of Pictures	10 minutes	OFFLINE

▶ Lesson Objectives

Demonstrate the meaning of subtraction as comparing two quantities to find the difference (with minuends up through 20).

▶ Prerequisite Skills

Demonstrate the meaning of subtraction as taking away an amount from a given quantity (with minuends up through 20).

▶ Content Background

In this lesson, students will compare groups of objects and find the difference.

Materials to Gather

SUPPLIED

Draw Pictures to Compare activity page

Compare Numbers of Pictures activity page

GET READY Take Away Pictures

ONLINE
10 min

Students will practice showing subtraction problems by crossing out pictured objects. Then they will select the number that shows the difference.

Objectives

- Demonstrate the meaning of subtraction as taking away an amount from a given quantity (with minuends up through 20).

LEARN Compare with Pictures

ONLINE
10 min

Objectives

- Demonstrate the meaning of subtraction as comparing two quantities to find the difference (with minuends up through 20).

Students will match pictures to solve subtraction problems where they will compare two quantities to find the difference.

Tips

To make sure that students accurately find the difference, have students touch each unmatched object online.

LEARN Draw Pictures to Compare

OFFLINE
10 min

Objectives

- Demonstrate the meaning of subtraction as comparing two quantities to find the difference (with minuends up through 20).

Students will draw pictures to solve comparison subtraction problems. Give students the Draw Pictures to Compare activity page from their Activity Book and read the directions with them.

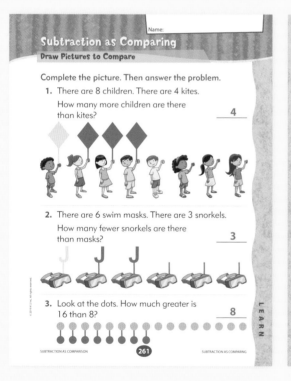

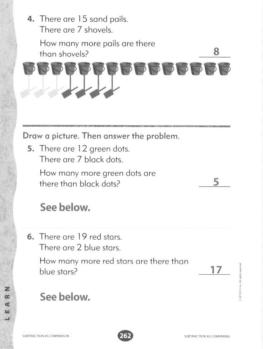

Additional Answers

5. Students should draw a row of 12 dots and a second row of 7 dots. Then they should draw a line between each of the 7 dots to one of the 12 dots to find that 5 dots are unmatched.

6. Students should draw a row of 19 stars and a second row of 2 stars. Then they should draw a line between each of the 2 stars to one of the 19 stars to find that 17 stars are unmatched.

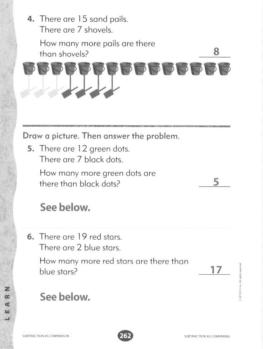

TRY IT Compare Numbers of Pictures

OFFLINE
10min

Objectives

- Demonstrate the meaning of subtraction as comparing two quantities to find the difference (with minuends up through 20).

Students will practice comparing two amounts to find the difference. Give students the Compare Numbers of Pictures activity page from their Activity Book and read the directions with them.

Have students draw two rows of objects representing the numbers in the subtraction problem. Then have students draw vertical lines to match the objects, one-to-one, to find how many are left.

Name:

Subtraction as Comparing

Compare Numbers of Pictures

Complete the picture. Then answer the problem.

1. There are 12 baseballs. There are 9 bats.

How many more baseballs are there than bats?

_____ 3

2. There are 13 basketball hoops.
There are 9 basketballs.

How many fewer basketballs are there than hoops?

4

Draw a picture. Then answer the problem.

3. There are 16 green circles.
There are 8 yellow circles.   **See below.**

How many more green circles are there than yellow circles?

_____ 8

SUBTRACTION AS COMPARISON   263   SUBTRACTION AS COMPARING

T R Y   I T

---

4. There are 10 red circles.
There are 7 blue circles.

How many more red circles are there than blue circles? **See below.**

_____ 3

5. There are 12 blue dots.
There are 4 green dots.

How many more blue dots are there than green dots? **See below.**

_____ 8

6. There are 11 green dots and 5 blue dots.

How much more is 11 green dots than 5 blue dots?   **See below.**

_____ 6

T R Y   I T

SUBTRACTION AS COMPARISON   264   SUBTRACTION AS COMPARING

Additional Answers

3.

4.

5.

6.

Comparison Subtraction

Lesson Overview

Skills Update	5 minutes	**ONLINE**
GET READY Solve Take-Away Problems	5 minutes	**OFFLINE**
LEARN Solve Comparison Problems	10 minutes	**OFFLINE**
LEARN Animal Story Problems	10 minutes	**OFFLINE**
TRY IT Compare and Subtract	10 minutes	**OFFLINE**
CHECKPOINT	5 minutes	**OFFLINE**

▶ Lesson Objectives

Demonstrate the meaning of subtraction as comparing two quantities to find the difference (with minuends up through 20).

▶ Prerequisite Skills

Demonstrate the meaning of subtraction as taking away an amount from a given quantity (with minuends up through 20).

▶ Content Background

In this lesson, students will solve subtraction problems. They will use models and pictures to compare groups and find the difference.

Materials to Gather

SUPPLIED

Solve Comparison Problems activity page

blocks – O (all colors)

Compare and Subtract activity page

Checkpoint (printout)

ALSO NEEDED

craft sticks – 20

paper, drawing – 1 sheet

GET READY Solve Take-Away Problems

OFFLINE
5 min

Objectives

- Use models to represent numbers (to 1,000).
- Use expanded forms.

Students will solve subtraction story problems. They will learn that subtraction means taking away an amount from a given quantity to find the difference.
  Gather the craft sticks.

1. Read the following story problem to students:
   There were 11 dogs playing in the yard.
   Then 3 dogs went into the house.
   How many dogs are left playing in the yard?

2. Have students model the problem with craft sticks.

   Ask: How many sticks should you use to show the number of dogs in the yard? (11)

   Ask: How many sticks should you take away? (3)

   Ask: How many sticks are left? (8)

   Ask: How many dogs are left playing in the yard? (8)

3. Read the following story problem to students:
   There were 11 birds in a tree.
   Then 9 birds flew away.
   How many birds are still in the tree?

4. Have students model the problem with craft sticks.

Ask: How many sticks should you use to show the number of birds in the tree? (11)

Ask: How many sticks should you take away? (9)

5. Ask: Why did you take away 9 sticks?
ANSWER: 9 birds flew away.

Ask: What does the number 2 show?
ANSWER: the number of birds still in the tree

Ask: How many birds are still in the tree? (2)

LEARN Solve Comparison Problems

OFFLINE 10 min

Objectives

- Demonstrate the meaning of subtraction as comparing two quantities to find the difference (with minuends up through 20).

Students will use models or pictures to solve story problems. They will compare two groups to find the difference. Give students the cubes and the Solve Comparison Problems activity page. Read the directions with them.

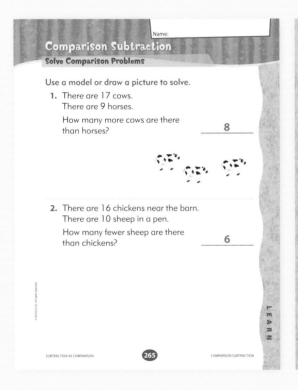

Name:

Comparison Subtraction

Solve Comparison Problems

Use a model or draw a picture to solve.

1. There are 17 cows.
There are 9 horses.

How many more cows are there than horses?   _____8_____

2. There are 16 chickens near the barn.
There are 10 sheep in a pen.

How many fewer sheep are there than chickens?   _____6_____

265

SUBTRACTION AS COMPARISON   COMPARISON SUBTRACTION

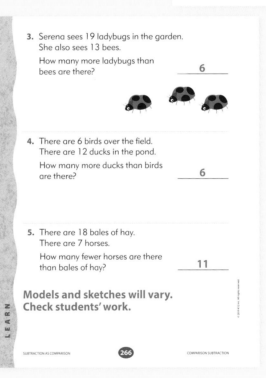

3. Serena sees 19 ladybugs in the garden.
She also sees 13 bees.

How many more ladybugs than bees are there?   _____6_____

4. There are 6 birds over the field.
There are 12 ducks in the pond.

How many more ducks than birds are there?   _____6_____

5. There are 18 bales of hay.
There are 7 horses.

How many fewer horses are there than bales of hay?   _____11_____

**Models and sketches will vary.
Check students' work.**

266

SUBTRACTION AS COMPARISON   COMPARISON SUBTRACTION

LEARN Animal Story Problems

Objectives

- Demonstrate the meaning of subtraction as comparing two quantities to find the difference (with minuends up through 20).

Tips

Have students count the objects in each row to make sure they have the correct number of objects before they compare to find the difference.

Students will solve subtraction story problems to find the difference between two numbers.

Gather the cubes and drawing paper.

1. Read the following story problem to students:
   There are 20 lions roaring.
   There are 9 lions eating.
   How many more lions are roaring than eating?

   (If necessary, read the problem again.)

2. Have students model the problem with cubes, placing a train of 9 cubes under the train of 20 cubes.

   Ask: How many lions are roaring? (20)

   Ask: How many lions are eating? (9)

3. Have students compare the two cube trains.

   Ask: How many cubes are unmatched? (11)

   Ask: How many more lions are roaring than eating? (11)

4. **Say:** You can say that 20 is 11 more than 9.

5. Read the following story problem to students:
   There are 14 monkeys swinging in trees.
   There are 6 monkeys sleeping.
   How many more monkeys are swinging in trees than sleeping?

6. Guide students to model the problem with cubes and explain their solution.

   Ask: How would you set up the problem?
   ANSWER: Make a train of 14 cubes.

   Ask: How do you show the 6 monkeys that are sleeping?
   ANSWER: Make a train of 6 cubes.

   Ask: How do you solve the problem?
   ANSWER: Compare the two cube trains. The number of cubes that are unmatched is the answer.

   Ask: How many more monkeys are swinging than sleeping? (8)

   Ask: What is the subtraction sentence for this problem?
   ANSWER: 14 is 8 more than 6.

7. Read the following story problem to students:
   There are 17 penguins in the water.
   There are 10 penguins near the water.
   How many fewer penguins are near the water than in the water?

8. Guide students to draw a sketch to solve the problem and have them explain their solution.

TRY IT Compare and Subtract

Students will practice solving subtraction story problems that compare two quantities. Give students the cubes and the Compare and Subtract activity page from their Activity Book. Read the directions with them.

- Demonstrate the meaning of subtraction as comparing two quantities to find the difference (with minuends up through 20).

Tips

If students choose to draw pictures, encourage them to use simple drawings, such as dots, circles, lines, or Xs.

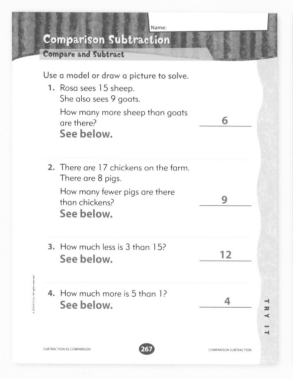

Name:

Comparison Subtraction
Compare and Subtract

Use a model or draw a picture to solve.

1. Rosa sees 15 sheep.
   She also sees 9 goats.
   How many more sheep than goats
   are there?   6
   See below.

2. There are 17 chickens on the farm.
   There are 8 pigs.
   How many fewer pigs are there
   than chickens?   9
   See below.

3. How much less is 3 than 15?
   See below.   12

4. How much more is 5 than 1?
   See below.   4

SUBTRACTION AS COMPARISON   267   COMPARISON SUBTRACTION

Circle the answer.

5. Barb has 9 flowers. John has 7 flowers.
   How many more flowers does
   Barb have than John?
   Which of the following describes this situation?
   A. Two numbers are added.
   (B.) Two numbers are compared.

6. Caden has 4 trucks. Coleman has 11 trucks.
   How many fewer trucks does Caden
   have than Coleman?
   Which of the following describes this situation?
   A. Two numbers are added.
   (B.) Two numbers are compared.

SUBTRACTION AS COMPARISON   268   COMPARISON SUBTRACTION

Additional Answers

1. If students use cubes, they should make a train of 15 cubes and another train of 9 cubes. Then they should compare the cube trains. If students use a sketch, they should draw a row of 15 dots and a second row of 9 dots. Then they should draw a line between each of the 9 dots to one of the 15 dots.

2. If students use cubes, they should make a train of 17 cubes and another train of 8 cubes. Then they should compare the cube trains. If students use a sketch, they should draw a row of 17 dots and a second row of 8 dots. Then they should draw a line down from each of the 17 dots. To find how many fewer, they should count the lines that aren't matched to dots.

3. If students use cubes, they should make a train of 15 cubes and another train of 3 cubes. Then they should compare the cube trains. If students use a sketch, they should draw a row of 15 dots and a second row of 3 dots. Then they should draw a line between each of the 3 dots to one of the 15 dots.

4. If students use cubes, they should make a train of 5 cubes and put 1 cube underneath. If students use a sketch, they should draw a row of 5 dots and a second row of 1 dot. Then they should draw a line between the 1 dot to one of the 5 dots.

OFFLINE
5min

Print the Checkpoint and have students complete it on their own. Read the directions, problems, and answer choices to students, if necessary. Use the answer key to score the Checkpoint, and then enter the results online.
    Give students the cubes.

- Demonstrate the meaning of subtraction as comparing two quantities to find the difference (with minuends up through 20).

○ Checkpoint   Math | Subtraction as Comparison | Comparison Subtraction

Name _____ Date _____

Checkpoint Answer Key

Write the answer on the line. Then draw a picture or use cubes to show how to solve the problem.

(1 point)
1. How much greater is 15 than 7? __8__

If students use cubes, they should make a train of 15 cubes and another train of 7 cubes. Then they should compare the cube trains. If students use a sketch, they should draw a row of 15 dots and a second row of 7 dots. Then they should draw a line between each of the 7 dots to one of the 15 dots.

(1 point)
2. How much less is 12 than 16? __4__

If students use cubes, they should make a train of 16 cubes and another train of 12 cubes. Then they should compare the cube trains. If students use a sketch, they should draw a row of 16 dots and a second row of 12 dots. Then they should draw a line between each of the 12 dots to one of the 16 dots.

1 of 2

○ Checkpoint   Math | Subtraction as Comparison | Comparison Subtraction

Name _____ Date _____

(1 point)
3. How much more is 9 than 3? __6__

If students use cubes, they should make a train of 9 cubes and another train of 3 cubes. Then they should compare the cube trains. If students use a sketch, they should draw a row of 9 dots and a second row of 3 dots. Then they should draw a line between each of the 3 dots to one of the 9 dots.

2 of 2

Unit Review

UNIT REVIEW Look Back	15 minutes	ONLINE
UNIT REVIEW Checkpoint Practice	15 minutes	OFFLINE
⏩ **UNIT REVIEW** Prepare for the Checkpoint		

▶ Unit Objectives

This lesson reviews the following objectives:

- Use concrete objects or sketches to model and solve addition or subtraction computation problems involving sums or minuends up through 20.
- Demonstrate the meaning of subtraction as comparing two quantities to find the difference (with minuends up through 20).

▶ Advance Preparation

In this lesson, students will have an opportunity to review previous activities in the Subtraction as Comparison unit. Look at the suggested activities in Unit Review: Prepare for the Checkpoint online and gather any needed materials.

Materials to Gather

SUPPLIED

Checkpoint Practice activity page

blocks – B (red, blue)

Keywords

compare	model (verb)
compare problem	more
difference	quantity
fewer	subtraction
model (noun)	

UNIT REVIEW Look Back

ONLINE 15min

Objectives

- Review unit objectives.

In this unit, students have learned to use models and sketches to solve comparison subtraction problems using one-to-one-correspondence. They used pairs of numbers to create addition and subtraction problems, exploring the differences among compare, combine, and take-away problems. Students will review these concepts to prepare for the Unit Checkpoint.

OFFLINE
15 min

Objectives

- Review unit objectives.

Students will complete a Checkpoint Practice activity page to prepare for the Unit Checkpoint. If necessary, read the directions, problems, and answer choices to students. Have students answer the problems on their own. Carefully review the answers with students.

Give students the circle blocks.

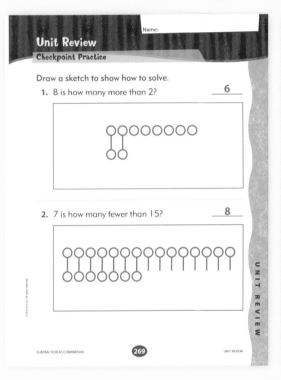

Unit Review
Checkpoint Practice

Name:

Draw a sketch to show how to solve.

1. 8 is how many more than 2?   6

2. 7 is how many fewer than 15?   8

Use circle blocks to solve.

3. 10 is how many more than 5?   5
   See below.

4. 7 is how many more than 6?   1
   See below.

5. 6 is how many fewer than 9?   3
   See below.

6. 7 is how many more than 2?   5
   See below.

7. 4 is how many fewer than 10?   6
   See below.

8. 7 is how many more than 5?   2
   See below.

9. 4 is how many fewer than 15?   11
   See below.

10. 19 is how many more than 6?   13
    See below.

269   270

Additional Answers

3., 4., 6., 8., 10.

Students should create two rows of blocks and line up the rows one-to-one. To find how many more, students should count the unmatched blocks.

5., 7., 9.

Students should create two rows of blocks and line up the rows one-to-one. To find how many fewer, students should count the spaces above or below the unmatched blocks.

⮕ UNIT REVIEW Prepare for the Checkpoint

What you do next depends on how students performed in the previous activity, Unit Review: Checkpoint Practice. If students had difficulty with any of the problems, complete the appropriate review activity listed in the table online.

Unit Checkpoint

Lesson Overview

| **UNIT CHECKPOINT** Offline | 40 minutes | **OFFLINE** |

▶ Unit Objectives

This lesson assesses the following objectives:

- Use concrete objects or sketches to model and solve addition or subtraction computation problems involving sums or minuends up through 20.
- Demonstrate the meaning of subtraction as comparing two quantities to find the difference (with minuends up through 20).

UNIT CHECKPOINT Offline

Objectives

- Assess unit objectives.

Students will complete the Unit Checkpoint offline. Print the Checkpoint and have students complete it on their own. Read the directions, problems, and answer choices to students, if necessary. Use the answer key to score the Checkpoint, and then enter the results online.

Give students the blocks.

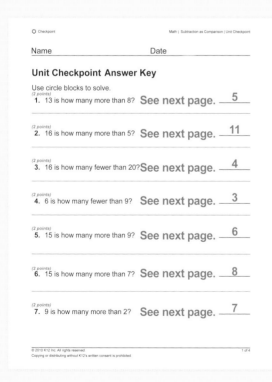

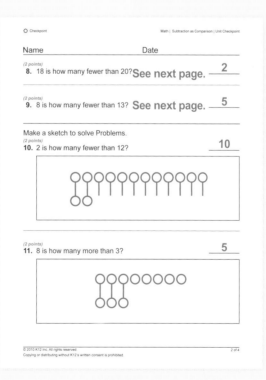

Name _____ **Date** _____

(2 points)
12. 17 is how many more than 12?   _____5_____

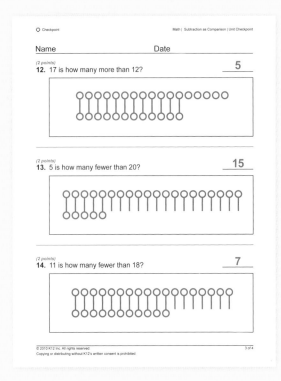

(2 points)
13. 5 is how many fewer than 20?   _____15_____

(2 points)
14. 11 is how many fewer than 18?   _____7_____

Name _____ **Date** _____

Use cubes to solve.
(2 points)
15. 4 is how many fewer than 15?   **See below.**   _____11_____

(2 points)
16. 20 is how many more than 7?   **See below.**   _____13_____

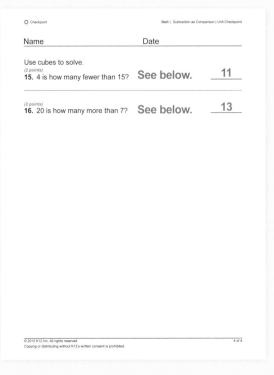

Additional Answers

1., 2., 5., 6., 7., 16.

Students should create two rows of blocks and line up the rows one-to-one.
To find how many more, students should count the unmatched blocks.

3., 4., 8., 9., 15.

Students should create two rows of blocks and line up the rows one-to-one.
To find how many fewer, students should count the spaces above or below
the unmatched blocks.

Comparison Subtraction: Story Problems

▶ Unit Objectives

- Use concrete objects to explain how to solve addition and subtraction problem-solving situations involving numbers up to 10.
- Recognize and solve word problems involving numbers up to 10 in which two quantities are compared by the use of addition or subtraction.
- Make reasonable estimates for the solutions to subtraction problems with minuends up through 20.
- Check the accuracy of calculations for the solutions to subtraction problems with minuends up through 20.

▶ Big Ideas

- Counting principles and numbers can be used to solve addition and subtraction problems.
- Estimation is a useful tool in problem solving.

▶ Unit Introduction

In this unit, students will learn how to identify, model, and solve combine, take-away, and compare addition and subtraction story problems involving numbers to 10. They will then learn how to estimate solutions to subtraction problems and then check the accuracy of their estimates.

What's the Difference?

Lesson Overview

Skills Update	5 minutes	ONLINE
LEARN Solve Story Problems	10 minutes	ONLINE
LEARN Compare Stories with Cubes and Sketches	15 minutes	OFFLINE
TRY IT Solve Compare Problems	15 minutes	OFFLINE

▶ Lesson Objectives

Use concrete objects to explain how to solve addition and subtraction problem-solving situations involving numbers up to 10.

▶ Prerequisite Skills

Use concrete objects or sketches to model and solve addition or subtraction computation problems involving sums or minuends up through 20.

▶ Advance Preparation

Print two copies of the Inch Grid Paper.

▶ Content Background

Students will use objects and sketches to solve compare problems. Subtraction problems may be *change problems* involving taking away an amount or *compare problems*. In change problems, students must take away from a group to determine how many objects are left in the group. In compare problems, students must compare two groups to determine how many more or fewer objects are in one group. To compare, they may subtract.

Keywords	**compare** – to find the similarities or differences among sizes, values, or amounts
	take away – in subtraction, to separate a group from the total

Materials to Gather

SUPPLIED

blocks – O (red, yellow)

Compare Stories with Cubes and Sketches activity page

Solve Compare Problems activity page

ALSO NEEDED

Inch Grid Paper (printout) – 2 copies

ONLINE
10min

LEARN Solve Story Problems

Students will learn how to solve compare problems. They will also see the connection between solving computation compare problems and story problems. Remind students that *more* means a greater number of objects, and *fewer* means a lesser number of objects.

Objectives

- Use concrete objects to explain how to solve addition and subtraction problem-solving situations involving numbers up to 10.

OFFLINE

15 min

LEARN **Compare Stories with Cubes and Sketches**

Students will practice solving compare problems using cubes and sketches. Give students the cubes, Inch Grid Paper printout, and Compare Stories with Cubes and Sketches activity page from their Activity Book. Read the directions with them.

1. Guide students to use a sketch for any three of the problems and cubes for the other three problems.

2. Turn the Inch Grid Paper printout so that there are 8 sections across. Students can use the paper for both their sketches and aligning their cubes.

Objectives

- Use concrete objects to explain how to solve addition and subtraction problem-solving situations involving numbers up to 10.

Tips

For each problem, first have students name the groups that they must compare. Then have them tell how many are in each group.

What's the Difference?

Name: ____

Compare Stories with Cubes and Sketches

Model the problem with cubes or sketches. Write the answer. **Check students' models or sketches.**

1. Ethan has 7 fish. He also has 2 crabs.

   How many more fish than crabs does Ethan have? **Sample sketch for**

   __5__ more fish **Problem 1:**

2. Jack saw 2 blue boats. He saw 4 red boats.

   How many fewer blue boats than red boats did Jack see?

   __2__ fewer blue boats

3. Emily picked 5 strawberries. Ashley picked 8 strawberries.

   How many fewer strawberries did Emily pick than Ashley?

   __3__ fewer strawberries

4. Ricky has 3 toy trucks. Al has 7 toy trucks.

   How many more toy trucks does Al have than Ricky?

   __4__ more trucks

5. Michael has 8 crayons. Beth has 2 crayons.

   How many more crayons does Michael have than Beth?

   __6__ more crayons

6. Beth has 3 stuffed animals. Taylor has 6 stuffed animals.

   How many fewer stuffed animals does Beth have than Taylor?

   __3__ fewer stuffed animals

COMPARISON SUBTRACTION: STORY PROBLEMS   **271**   WHAT'S THE DIFFERENCE?

COMPARISON SUBTRACTION: STORY PROBLEMS   **272**   WHAT'S THE DIFFERENCE?

TRY IT Solve Compare Problems

OFFLINE
15min

Objectives

- Use concrete objects to explain how to solve addition and subtraction problem-solving situations involving numbers up to 10.

Students will practice solving compare problems. Give students the cubes, Inch Grid Paper printout, and Solve Compare Problems activity page from their Activity Book. Read the directions with them.

1. Read Problem 1 aloud.

2. Have students use cubes or a sketch to solve the problem.

3. Have students write the answer.

4. Repeat Steps 1–3 with Problems 2–5. Although you should guide students through the problems and make sure they carefully align their 2 rows of cubes or sketches, students should use cubes and sketches to solve the problems on their own. Guide students to solve about half of the problems with cubes and the other problems with sketches.

Name: _____

What's the Difference?
Solve Compare Problems

Model the problem with cubes or sketches. Write the answer. **Check students' models or sketches**

1. There are 8 children. There are 7 fishing rods.

   How many more children than fishing rods are there? **See below.** ___1___ more child

2. Chad has 10 soccer balls. He also has 4 footballs.

   How many more soccer balls than footballs does Chad have? ___6___ more soccer balls

3. Hannah caught 8 butterflies. Bridget caught 1 butterfly.

   How many fewer butterflies did Bridget catch than Hannah? ___7___ fewer butterflies

4. There are 4 boys in the van. There is 1 girl in the van.

   How many more boys than girls are in the van? ___3___ more boys

COMPARISON SUBTRACTION: STORY PROBLEMS **273** WHAT'S THE DIFFERENCE?

T R Y I T

---

5. There are 3 ducks in the lake. There are 9 ducks on the shore.

   How many fewer ducks are in the lake than on the shore? ___6___ fewer ducks in the lake

Place a check mark next to the picture you would use to solve the problem.

6. Valerie baked 8 cakes. Helena baked 2 cakes.

   How many more cakes did Valerie bake than Helena?

   A.

   B.

   ✓ C.

COMPARISON SUBTRACTION: STORY PROBLEMS **274** WHAT'S THE DIFFERENCE?

T R Y I T

Additional Answers
1. **Sample sketch for Problem 1:** ○○○○○○○○◎ ○○○○○○○

7. Ellie had 9 balloons.
Carrie had 7 balloons.

How many fewer balloons did Carrie have than Ellie?

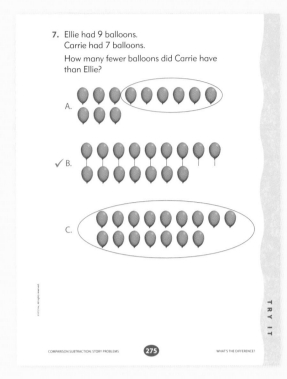

A.

✓ B.

C.

8. Laura baked 6 pies.
Debbie baked 2 pies.

How many fewer pies did Debbie bake than Laura?

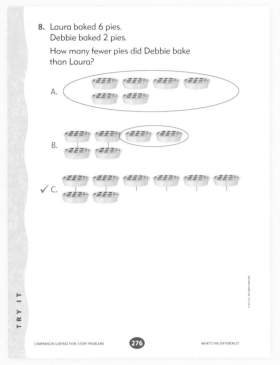

A.

B.

✓ C.

TRY IT

TRY IT

Add and Subtract Story Problems

▶ Lesson Objectives

Use concrete objects to explain how to solve addition and subtraction problem-solving situations involving numbers up to 10.

▶ Prerequisite Skills

Use concrete objects or sketches to model and solve addition or subtraction computation problems involving sums or minuends up through 20.

▶ Common Errors and Misconceptions

- Students might have difficulty seeing the connection between addition and subtraction situations.
- Students might have difficulty adding and subtracting with zero.

▶ Content Background

Students will solve addition and subtraction story problems.

Keywords

story problem – a word problem that represents a problem-solving situation

Materials to Gather

SUPPLIED

blocks – O (any two colors)

Solve Different Story Problems activity page

Checkpoint (printout)

ONLINE
20min

LEARN Picnic Addition and Subtraction

Students will explore strategies for solving combine, compare, and change story problems. They will also solve each of these types of problems. Encourage students to describe in their own words how the problem was solved, such as, "Amounts were put together by adding," or "An amount was changed by adding or subtracting," or "Amounts were compared, so I subtracted to find how many more (or fewer)."

Objectives

- Use concrete objects to explain how to solve addition and subtraction problem-solving situations involving numbers up to 10.

OFFLINE
10min

Objectives

Students will practice solving a mixed set of story problems. Give students the cubes and Solve Different Story Problems activity page from their Activity Book. Read the directions with them.

In addition problems, the number sentence can be written with addends in either order.

- Use concrete objects to explain how to solve addition and subtraction problem-solving situations involving numbers up to 10.

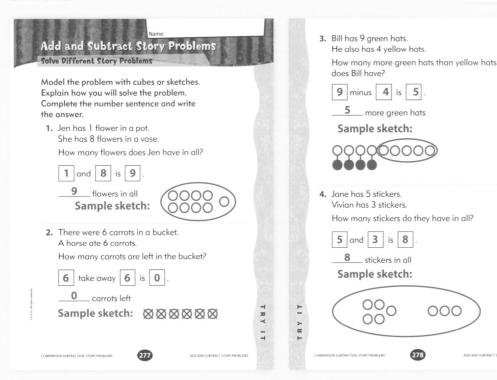

Additional Answers

1. Students could show a group of 1 cube and a group of 8 cubes. Then they could combine the groups and count how many cubes there are in all.

2. Students could make a train of 6 cubes. Then they could take 6 cubes off the train and see that no cubes are left.

3. Students could show a train of 9 cubes and a train of 4 cubes below it. They could count the unmatched cubes.

4. Students could show a group of 5 cubes and a group of 3 cubes. Then they could combine the groups and count how many cubes there are in all.

5. Students could make a train of 7 cubes and a train of 4 cubes below it. They could count the unmatched cubes.

6. Students could make a train of 10 cubes and remove 2 cubes. They could count the remaining cubes.

7. Students could make a train of 7 cubes and a train of 1 cube. They could count the unmatched spaces in the bottom train.

8. Students could make a train of 2 cubes and a train of 4 cubes, and combine them. They could count how many cubes in all.

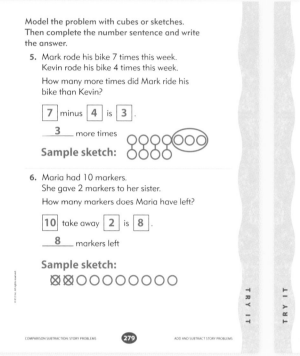

Model the problem with cubes or sketches. Then complete the number sentence and write the answer.

5. Mark rode his bike 7 times this week.
   Kevin rode his bike 4 times this week.

   How many more times did Mark ride his bike than Kevin?

   [7] minus [4] is [3].

   ___3___ more times

   Sample sketch:

6. Maria had 10 markers.
   She gave 2 markers to her sister.

   How many markers does Maria have left?

   [10] take away [2] is [8].

   ___8___ markers left

   Sample sketch:

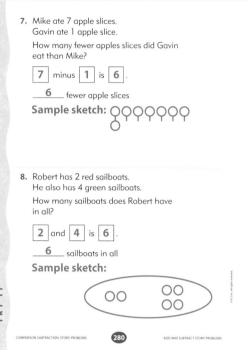

7. Mike ate 7 apple slices.
   Gavin ate 1 apple slice.

   How many fewer apples slices did Gavin eat than Mike?

   [7] minus [1] is [6].

   ___6___ fewer apple slices

   Sample sketch:

8. Robert has 2 red sailboats.
   He also has 4 green sailboats.

   How many sailboats does Robert have in all?

   [2] and [4] is [6].

   ___6___ sailboats in all

   Sample sketch:

TRY IT

CHECKPOINT

OFFLINE
10 min

Objectives

Print the Checkpoint and have students complete it on their own. Read the directions, problems, and answer choices to students, if necessary. Use the answer key to score the Checkpoint, and then enter the results online.

Give students the cubes for Problems 1–4.

- Use concrete objects to explain how to solve addition and subtraction problem-solving situations involving numbers up to 10.

○ Checkpoint   Math | Comparison Subtraction: Story Problems | Add and Subtract Story Problems

Name _____ Date _____

Checkpoint Answer Key

Use cubes to explain how to solve the problem. **See additional answers.**
(1 point)
1. There are 2 ducks in one pond.
   There are 5 ducks in another pond.

   How many ducks are there altogether?   ___7___ ducks altogether

(1 point)
2. Matt watched TV for 1 hour.
   Isabelle watched TV for 2 hours.

   How many hours was someone watching TV?   ___3___ hours altogether

(1 point)
Use cubes and then draw a sketch to show how to solve the problem.

3. Eloise put 8 marbles on the table.   **See additional answers.**
   1 marble rolled off onto the floor.

   How many marbles are still on the table?

   ___7___ marbles still on the table

   Sample sketch: ⊗○○○○○○○

1 of 3

Additional Answers

1. Students could show a group of 5 cubes and a group of 2 cubes. Then they could combine the groups and count how many cubes there are in all.

2. Students could show a group of 1 cube and a group of 2 cubes. Then they could combine the groups and count how many cubes there are in all.

3. Students could make a train of 8 cubes. Then they could take 1 cube off the train and count how many cubes are left.

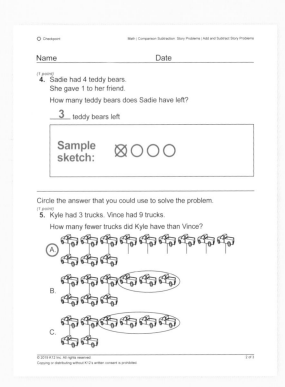

Name _____ Date _____

(1 point)
4. Sadie had 4 teddy bears.
She gave 1 to her friend.

How many teddy bears does Sadie have left?

___3___ teddy bears left

| Sample sketch: | ⊗ ○ ○ ○ |

Circle the answer that you could use to solve the problem.
(1 point)
5. Kyle had 3 trucks. Vince had 9 trucks.

How many fewer trucks did Kyle have than Vince?

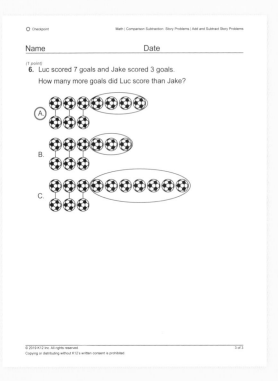

Name _____ Date _____

(1 point)
6. Luc scored 7 goals and Jake scored 3 goals.

How many more goals did Luc score than Jake?

Additional Answers

4. Explanations may vary. Students could make a train of 4 cubes.
Then they could take away 1 cube and count how many cubes
are left.

Compare Quantities to 10

Lesson Overview

Skills Update	5 minutes	ONLINE
GET READY Compare with JoJo	5 minutes	ONLINE
LEARN Match and Compare	15 minutes	ONLINE
LEARN Make a Mental Comparison	5 minutes	OFFLINE
TRY IT Compare Two Amounts	15 minutes	OFFLINE

▶ Lesson Objectives

Recognize and solve word problems involving numbers up to 10 in which two quantities are compared by the use of addition or subtraction.

▶ Prerequisite Skills

Demonstrate the meaning of subtraction as comparing two quantities to find the difference (with minuends up through 20).

▶ Content Background

Students will solve compare problems. They will identify the greater and lesser values in each problem.

In *compare problems*, students must compare two groups to determine how many more or fewer objects are in one group. To compare, they may subtract.

Students will first compare groups using models that are aligned so that the objects in the two groups match one-to-one. To find how many more or fewer, they will count the unmatched objects. When comparing greater numbers, counting isn't practical. Students will learn that they can subtract, rather than count, to solve compare problems.

Materials to Gather

SUPPLIED

blocks – O (red, blue)

Compare Two Amounts activity page

Keywords	
	compare problem – a problem in which two quantities are compared by finding the difference
	subtract – to take away objects from a group or to find a difference between two groups
	subtraction – the process of taking away objects from a group or finding the difference between two groups; a mathematical operation

GET READY Compare with JoJo

ONLINE 5 min

Students will review how to solve story problems that compare two amounts.

Objectives

- Demonstrate the meaning of subtraction as comparing two quantities to find the difference (with minuends up through 20).

LEARN Match and Compare

ONLINE 15 min

Students will model and solve compare problems.

Objectives

- Recognize and solve word problems involving numbers up to 10 in which two quantities are compared by the use of addition or subtraction.

Tips

Students may also use the red and blue blocks to model these problems.

LEARN Make a Mental Comparison

OFFLINE 5 min

Students will listen to story problems and identify the greater or lesser amount. There are no materials to gather for this activity.

1. **Say:** When solving compare problems, first decide which the greater number is and which is the lesser number. Let's practice doing this. I'll read some problems. Figure out the answer to each problem in your head—no models, pencils, or paper.

    Read each problem to students. Have them say the answer.

2. **Ask:** Annabelle bear has 3 pizzas and Buford bear has 4 pizzas. Which bear has more pizzas?
    Answer: Buford has more pizzas.

3. **Ask:** Annabelle bear has 3 pizzas and Buford bear has 4 pizzas. Which bear has fewer pizzas?
    Answer: Annabelle has fewer pizzas.

4. **Ask:** At the pizza party, 4 boxes of pizza were open and 2 were still closed. Were there more boxes open or more closed?
    Answer: There were more boxes open.

5. **Ask:** There were 6 plates on the table and 9 cups. Were there fewer plates or fewer cups?
    Answer: There were fewer plates.

6. **Ask:** Five of the cups were blue and 4 of the cups were green. Were there more blue cups or more green cups?
    Answer: There were more blue cups.

Objectives

- Recognize and solve word problems involving numbers up to 10 in which two quantities are compared by the use of addition or subtraction.

TRY IT Compare Two Amounts

Objectives

Students will practice solving compare problems by first identifying the greater and lesser number. Give students the cubes and Compare Two Amounts activity page from their Activity Book. Read the directions with them.

- Recognize and solve word problems involving numbers up to 10 in which two quantities are compared by the use of addition or subtraction.

Name: _____

Compare Quantities to 10
Compare Two Amounts

Circle the answer.

1. Carly has 8 books. Liz has 5 books.
   Who has more books?
   (A.) Carly has more books.
   B. Liz has more books.

2. Jason has 4 apples. Nick has 1 apple.
   Who has fewer apples?
   A. Jason has fewer apples.
   (B.) Nick has fewer apples.

3. David has 8 rocks in his collection.
   Paul has 4 rocks in his collection.
   Who has more rocks?
   (A.) David has more rocks.
   B. Paul has more rocks.

4. Mara ran 4 miles. Brendan ran 1 mile.
   Who ran fewer miles?
   A. Mara ran fewer miles.
   (B.) Brendan ran fewer miles.

COMPARISON SUBTRACTION: STORY PROBLEMS **281**

TRY IT

---

5. The chef made 8 pizzas. 1 bear came for a snack.
   Are there more pizzas or bears?
   (A.) There are more pizzas.
   B. There are more bears.

Circle the answer. You may use cubes to help you.

6. David wants 3 scoops of ice cream.
   Holly wants 2 scoops of ice cream.
   How many fewer scoops of ice cream does Holly want than David?
   A. 5   B. 2   (C.) 1

7. There are 3 people in Jane's family.
   Jane bought 5 ice cream sandwiches.
   If each person eats 1 sandwich, how many will be left over?
   A. 1   (B.) 2   C. 3

Circle the answer.

8. Summer bought 8 roses. Merrie bought 10 roses.
   How many fewer roses did Summer buy than Merrie?
   A. 9   (B.) 2   C. 6

9. Cameron read 5 pages. Eva read 10 pages.
   How many more pages did Eva read then Cameron?
   A. 6   (B.) 5   C. 15

TRY IT

COMPARISON SUBTRACTION: STORY PROBLEMS **282**   COMPARE QUANTITIES TO 10

Compare: More or Fewer?

Lesson Overview

Skills Update	5 minutes	ONLINE
LEARN How Many More?	15 minutes	ONLINE
LEARN How Many Fewer?	15 minutes	ONLINE
TRY IT Find More and Fewer	10 minutes	OFFLINE

▶ Lesson Objectives

Recognize and solve word problems involving numbers up to 10 in which two quantities are compared by the use of addition or subtraction.

▶ Prerequisite Skills

Demonstrate the meaning of subtraction as comparing two quantities to find the difference (with minuends up through 20).

▶ Content Background

Students will solve compare problems. They will answer the questions "How many more?" and "How many fewer?"

In *compare problems*, students must compare two groups to determine how many more or fewer objects are in one group. To compare, they may subtract.

Students will first compare groups using models that are aligned so that the objects in the two groups match one-to-one. To find how many more or fewer, they will count the unmatched objects. When comparing greater numbers, counting isn't practical. Students will learn that they can subtract, rather than count, to solve compare problems.

Keywords	**more** – a greater number or amount than another
	fewer – a lesser number than another

Materials to Gather

SUPPLIED

blocks – B (any two colors)

Find More and Fewer activity page

LEARN How Many More?

ONLINE 15min

Students will use online models and number sentences to solve compare problems that ask "How many more?"

Objectives

- Recognize and solve word problems involving numbers up to 10 in which two quantities are compared by the use of addition or subtraction.

Tips

Students may model the problems offline.

LEARN How Many Fewer?

ONLINE 15min

Students will use online models and number sentences to solve compare problems that ask "How many fewer?"

Objectives

- Recognize and solve word problems involving numbers up to 10 in which two quantities are compared by the use of addition or subtraction.

Tips

Students may model the problems offline.

TRY IT Find More and Fewer

OFFLINE 10min

Students will practice modeling and solving compare problems. Give students the circle blocks and Find More and Fewer activity page from their Activity Book. Read the directions with them.

In Problems 1–4, students should model with the circle blocks to solve. In Problems 5–8, students may use any method to solve.

Objectives

- Recognize and solve word problems involving numbers up to 10 in which two quantities are compared by the use of addition or subtraction.

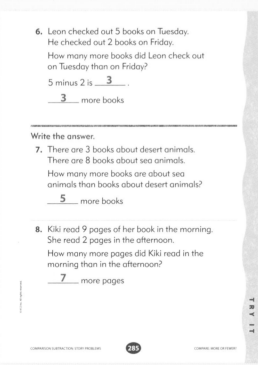

Compare: More or Fewer?
Find More and Fewer

Model the problem with circle blocks.
Write the answer. **Check students' models.**

1. The library has 6 animal magazines.
   It has 4 sports magazines.

   How many fewer sports magazines than
   animal magazines does the library have?

   6 minus 4 is __2__ .

   __2__ fewer sports magazines

2. A book about baseball has 9 pages.
   A book about soccer has 10 pages.

   How many more pages does the soccer
   book have than the baseball book?

   10 minus 9 is __1__ .

   __1__ more page

3. A shelf has 6 picture books.
   It has 9 chapter books.

   How many more chapter books than
   picture books are on the shelf?

   9 minus 6 is __3__ .

   __3__ more chapter books

4. On Monday, 7 children came to story hour.
   On Tuesday, 2 children came to story hour.

   How many fewer children came to story
   hour on Tuesday than on Monday?

   7 minus 2 is __5__ .

   __5__ fewer children

Choose how to solve the problem.
Write the answer.

5. The first poem in the book has 10 lines.
   The second poem has 8 lines.

   How many fewer lines does the second
   poem have than the first poem?

   10 minus 8 is __2__ .

   __2__ fewer lines

6. Leon checked out 5 books on Tuesday.
   He checked out 2 books on Friday.

   How many more books did Leon check out
   on Tuesday than on Friday?

   5 minus 2 is __3__ .

   __3__ more books

Write the answer.

7. There are 3 books about desert animals.
   There are 8 books about sea animals.

   How many more books are about sea
   animals than books about desert animals?

   __5__ more books

8. Kiki read 9 pages of her book in the morning.
   She read 2 pages in the afternoon.

   How many more pages did Kiki read in the
   morning than in the afternoon?

   __7__ more pages

Compare in Everyday Situations

Lesson Overview

Skills Update	5 minutes	ONLINE
LEARN Look for Compare Problems	10 minutes	ONLINE
LEARN Are You Comparing?	10 minutes	ONLINE
LEARN Make Up a Compare Story	10 minutes	OFFLINE
TRY IT Compare or Not?	10 minutes	OFFLINE

▶ Lesson Objectives

Recognize and solve word problems involving numbers up to 10 in which two quantities are compared by the use of addition or subtraction.

▶ Prerequisite Skills

Demonstrate the meaning of subtraction as comparing two quantities to find the difference (with minuends up through 20).

▶ Advance Preparation

Students will need household objects to compare. Gather 5 spoons, 3 forks, 6 cups, and 4 plates. The objects do not have to be alike and may be paper or plastic. For example, the spoons can be different kinds.

▶ Content Background

Students will recognize story problems that compare two amounts and solve problems that involve everyday situations. They will also create and solve problems of their own.

In *compare problems*, students must compare two groups to determine how many more or fewer objects are in one group. To compare, they may subtract.

Students will first compare groups using models that are aligned so that the objects in the two groups match one-to-one. To find how many more or fewer, they will count the unmatched objects. When comparing greater numbers, counting isn't practical. Students will learn that they can subtract, rather than count, to solve compare problems.

Keywords	
	change problem – a problem in which one quantity changes by having an amount added or taken away
	combine problem – an addition problem in which two numbers are put together to find a sum

Materials to Gather

SUPPLIED

blocks – O (any 2 colors)

Compare or Not? activity page

ALSO NEEDED

household objects – 5 spoons, 3 forks, 6 cups, 4 plates

LEARN Look for Compare Problems

ONLINE 10 min

Students will see combine, compare, and change story problems solved. Then they will decide whether the problem involved comparing to find the solution. Encourage students to describe in their own words how the problem was solved, such as "Amounts were combined by adding," or "An amount was changed by adding or subtracting," or "Amounts were compared, so I subtracted to find how many more (or fewer)."

Objectives

- Recognize and solve word problems involving numbers up to 10 in which two quantities are compared by the use of addition or subtraction.

LEARN Are You Comparing?

ONLINE 10 min

Students will see combine, compare, and change story problems. They will explain how they would solve the problem. Then students will decide whether the problem involved comparing to find the solution. Encourage students to describe in their own words how the problem was solved, such as "Amounts were put together, not compared," or "An amount changed, so I added more instead of comparing," or "I had to find how many more (or fewer), so I was comparing."

Objectives

- Recognize and solve word problems involving numbers up to 10 in which two quantities are compared by the use of addition or subtraction.

LEARN Make Up a Compare Story

OFFLINE 10 min

Students will create their own comparison story problems. Gather the 5 spoons, 3 forks, 6 cups, and 4 plates. Put the objects in groups.

1. Model for students how to create and solve a comparison story problem using the objects you have gathered.

   Step 1: State the problem: We are going on a picnic. We have 5 spoons and 3 forks. How many more spoons do we have than forks?

   Step 2: Ask (and train students to ask themselves) questions, such as:
   - How many spoons are in this group? (5)
   - How many forks are in this other group? (3)
   - What number sentence would solve this problem? 5 minus 3 is ? .
   - How many more spoons are there than forks? (2)

2. Have students create at least two of their own story problems to solve.

3. As students create and solve their own problems, have them ask themselves the questions above.

4. Check students' solutions to make sure that they have subtracted correctly. Answers will vary on the basis of items that students use in their story problems.

Objectives

- Recognize and solve word problems involving numbers up to 10 in which two quantities are compared by the use of addition or subtraction.

Tips

If students are struggling with solving their problems, have them match up their objects to compare. If the objects are difficult to match, students may use cubes to represent the objects.

TRY IT Compare or Not?

10 min

Objectives

- Recognize and solve word problems involving numbers up to 10 in which two quantities are compared by the use of addition or subtraction.

Students will practice deciding if a problem is a compare problem, solve the problem, and write a compare problem of their own. Give students the cubes and Compare or Not? activity page from their Activity Book. Read the directions with them.

For Question 9, write the problem for students, if necessary.

Compare in Everyday Situations
Compare or Not?

Name: _____

Write the answer.

1. Pat has 8 rocks in his collection.
   Chris has 4 rocks in her collection.
   How many rocks do they have together?
   __12__ rocks altogether

2. Jack has 4 apples. Nancy has 1 apple.
   How many fewer apples does Nancy have than Jack?
   __3__ fewer apples

3. Monty walked 4 blocks. Brenda walked 6 blocks.
   How many more blocks did Brenda walk?
   __2__ more blocks

4. Paula put 6 crackers on her plate.
   Max ate 2 of Paula's crackers.
   How many crackers does Paula have to eat now?
   __4__ crackers

COMPARISON SUBTRACTION: STORY PROBLEMS — 287 — COMPARE IN EVERYDAY SITUATIONS

TRY IT

---

5. The chef made 8 salads. He also made 5 pies.
   How many more salads did he make than pies?
   __3__ more salads

6. Len has 10 books. Carl has 8 books.
   How many fewer books does Carl have than Len?
   __2__ fewer books

Circle the answer.

7. Kevin bought 6 pens. Don bought 11 pens.
   How many fewer pens did Kevin buy than Don?
   (A) 5   B. 6   C. 11

8. Patty read 4 pages. Eva read 10 pages.
   How many more pages did Eva read than Patty?
   A. 4   (B) 6   C. 14

Make up a problem of your own that compares the numbers of animals. Solve your problem.

9. Pretend you have 2 dogs, 1 cat, and 3 hamsters. Make up a problem.
   The answer to your problem: **Check that the problem asks "how many more" or "how many fewer" and is solved correctly.**

COMPARISON SUBTRACTION: STORY PROBLEMS — 288 — COMPARE IN EVERYDAY SITUATIONS

TRY IT

COMPARE IN EVERYDAY SITUATIONS **385**

Estimate and Check Subtraction

Lesson Overview

Skills Update	5 minutes	ONLINE
GET READY Check Sums	5 minutes	ONLINE
LEARN Estimate Comparison Solutions	10 minutes	OFFLINE
LEARN Check Comparison Problems	10 minutes	OFFLINE
TRY IT Estimate and Check Comparisons	10 minutes	OFFLINE
CHECKPOINT	5 minutes	OFFLINE

▶ Lesson Objectives

- Make reasonable estimates for the solutions to subtraction problems with minuends up through 20.
- Check the accuracy of calculations for the solutions to subtraction problems with minuends up through 20.

▶ Prerequisite Skills

- Make reasonable estimates for the solutions to addition problems (for sums up through 20).
- Check the accuracy of calculations for the solutions to addition problems with sums up through 20.

▶ Advance Preparation

Make four trains of cubes to use as benchmarks: a 5-train, 10-train, 15-train, and 20-train. Make each benchmark train a different color.

▶ Content Background

Students will solve subtraction story problems and check the answers. They will also learn how to estimate to find the difference.

Estimates, or approximate calculations, are sufficient and appropriate in many everyday situations. One way to estimate sums or quantities is to choose the nearest target number, such as the nearest 5 or 10. This target number is called a *benchmark*.

This lesson uses the word *estimate* and the phrase *about how many* interchangeably. Students should understand that the term *estimate* is a mathematical term that means the same as *about how many*.

Materials to Gather

SUPPLIED

blocks – B (all colors)

blocks – O (all colors)

Check Comparison Problems activity page

Estimate and Check Comparisons activity page

Checkpoint (printout)

SUPPLIED

paper, drawing – 5 sheets

GET READY Check Sums

ONLINE 5 min

Students will use circles or sketches to check the solutions to addition story problems.

Gather the circle blocks and drawing paper.

Follow the directions on each screen. Students will model problems to see if a number sentence is correct or incorrect.

Objectives

- Check the accuracy of calculations for the solutions to addition problems with sums up through 20.

Tips

To make sure that students model the problems correctly, have them touch each object and count aloud.

LEARN Estimate Comparison Solutions

OFFLINE 10 min

Students will estimate the difference in a subtraction problem in which two amounts are compared.

Gather the cubes, the the benchmark cube trains, and a sheet of paper.

1. Show students the benchmark cube trains and have them count the cubes in each.

2. Line up the benchmark cube trains, putting one cube train under another. Align the left edges of each train.

   Ask: How many fewer is 10 than 15?
   ANSWER: 10 is 5 fewer than 15.

3. Have students review the differences between other pairs of benchmarks that have a difference of either 5 or 10 cubes.

4. Explain that you can use benchmarks like 5, 10, 15, and 20 to estimate how many more 11 apples is than 4 apples. Write the sentence "11 minus 4 is about" on a sheet of paper.

   To make sure that students model the problems correctly, have students touch each object and count aloud.

Objectives

- Make reasonable estimates for the solutions to subtraction problems with minuends up through 20.

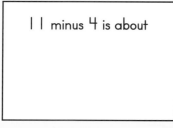

11 minus 4 is about

5. Have students make a train of 11 cubes. Have them compare the train of 11 cubes to the 10-cube and 15-cube benchmarks.

Ask: Is your cube train closer to the benchmark of 10 or the benchmark of 15? (10)

Write the number 10 on the paper below the number 11. Place the 10-cube train next to the paper.

11 minus 4 is about
10

6. Have students make a train of 4 cubes.

Ask: Is your cube train closer to the benchmark of 5 or the benchmark of 10? (5)

Write "minus 5 is" under "minus 4". Place the 5-cube train under the 10-cube train.

11 minus 4 is about
10 minus 5 is

7. Point to the numbers and the cube trains as you explain how to estimate.

Say: 11 is close to 10. 4 is close to 5. To find out about how much more 11 is than 4, we can compare 5 and 10.

Ask: How much more is 10 than 5? (5)

8. Have students put the train of 4 cubes under the train of 11 cubes with the left edges aligned.

Ask: About how much more is 11 than 4?

ANSWER: 11 is about 5 more than 4. So 11 apples is about 5 more than 4 apples.

9. Write the number 5 at the end of each sentence.

11 minus 4 is about 5
10 minus 5 is 5

LEARN Check Comparison Problems

OFFLINE 10 min

Objectives

- Check the accuracy of calculations for the solutions to subtraction problems with minuends up through 20.

Students will use models or sketches to check answers to subtraction problems. Give students the circle blocks, drawing paper, and Check Comparison Problems activity page from their Activity Book. Read the directions with them.

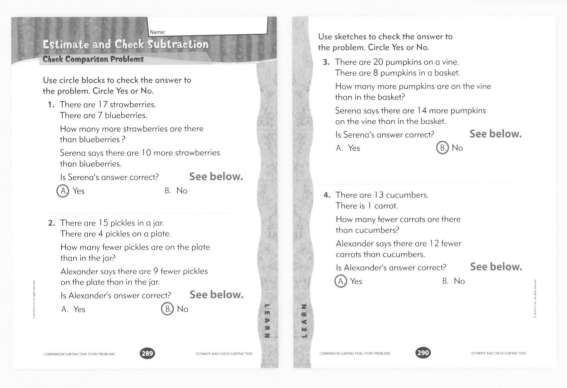

Estimate and Check Subtraction

Check Comparison Problems

Use circle blocks to check the answer to the problem. Circle Yes or No.

1. There are 17 strawberries.
   There are 7 blueberries.

   How many more strawberries are there than blueberries?

   Serena says there are 10 more strawberries than blueberries.

   Is Serena's answer correct?   **See below.**

   (A) Yes   B. No

2. There are 15 pickles in a jar.
   There are 4 pickles on a plate.

   How many fewer pickles are on the plate than in the jar?

   Alexander says there are 9 fewer pickles on the plate than in the jar.

   Is Alexander's answer correct?   **See below.**

   A. Yes   (B) No

Use sketches to check the answer to the problem. Circle Yes or No.

3. There are 20 pumpkins on a vine.
   There are 8 pumpkins in a basket.

   How many more pumpkins are on the vine than in the basket?

   Serena says there are 14 more pumpkins on the vine than in the basket.

   Is Serena's answer correct?   **See below.**

   A. Yes   (B) No

4. There are 13 cucumbers.
   There is 1 carrot.

   How many fewer carrots are there than cucumbers?

   Alexander says there are 12 fewer carrots than cucumbers.

   Is Alexander's answer correct?   **See below.**

   (A) Yes   B. No

COMPARISON SUBTRACTION: STORY PROBLEMS **289**   ESTIMATE AND CHECK SUBTRACTION

COMPARISON SUBTRACTION: STORY PROBLEMS **290**   ESTIMATE AND CHECK SUBTRACTION

Additional Answers

1. Students could make a row of 17 circles and a row of 7 circles below it. They could count the unmatched circles.

2. Students could make a row of 15 circles and a row of 4 circles below it. They could count the unmatched spaces in the bottom row.

3. **Sample sketch:** OOOOOOOO ⟨OOOOOOOOOOOO⟩
   OOOOOOOO

4. **Sample sketch:** OOOOOOOOOOOOO
   O

OFFLINE
10min

Students will practice estimating the answers to story problems using benchmarks. They will also model and solve subtraction story problems. Give students the benchmark cube trains, cubes, drawing paper, and Estimate and Check Comparisons activity page from their Activity Book. Read the directions with them.

- Make reasonable estimates for the solutions to subtraction problems with minuends up through 20.

Name:

Estimate and Check Subtraction

Estimate and Check Comparisons

Determine the benchmark for each number in the problem. Then circle the best estimate for the answer.

1. About how many more is 18 pears than 9 pears?

   A. about 5   **B. about 10**
   C. about 15   D. about 20

2. About how many more is 13 pineapples than 9 pineapples?

   A. about 5   B. about 10
   C. about 15   D. about 20

3. There are 16 cherries in a bowl, and 4 cherries on a table. About how many more cherries are in the bowl than on the table?

   A. about 5   **B. about 10**
   C. about 15   D. about 20

4. There are 3 birds in the tree and 9 birds on the fence. About how many fewer birds are in the tree than on the fence?

   A. about 5   B. about 10
   C. about 15   D. about 20

COMPARISON SUBTRACTION: STORY PROBLEMS   **291**   ESTIMATE AND CHECK SUBTRACTION

TRY IT

Use cubes or sketches to check the answer. Then circle Yes or No.

Check students' models or sketches.

5. There are 10 apples in a basket. There are 3 apples on a table. How many fewer apples are on the table than in the basket?

   Alexander says there are 5 fewer apples on the table than in the basket.

   Is Alexander's answer correct?

   A. Yes   **B. No**

6. There are 16 shells in a bowl, and 6 shells in a pail. There are 11 more shells in the bowl than in the pail.

   Is this answer correct?

   A. Yes   **B. No**

7. At the park, 12 girls rode on the swings and 5 girls went down the slide. So 7 more girls rode the swings than went down the slide.

   Is this answer correct?

   A. Yes   B. No

8. Wilma has 6 marbles. Jake has 8 marbles. Wilma has 2 fewer marbles than Jake.

   Is this answer correct?

   A. Yes   B. No

COMPARISON SUBTRACTION: STORY PROBLEMS   **292**   ESTIMATE AND CHECK SUBTRACTION

TRY IT

CHECKPOINT

Print the Checkpoint. In Part 1, students will complete the problems on their own. Read the directions, problems, and answer choices to students, if necessary. In Part 2, students will take a performance-based assessment. Use the answer key to score the Checkpoint, and then enter the results online.

Gather the blocks and drawing paper.

- Make reasonable estimates for the solutions to subtraction problems with minuends up through 20.
- Check the accuracy of calculations for the solutions to subtraction problems with minuends up through 20.

○ Checkpoint   Math | Comparison Subtraction: Story Problems | Estimate and Check Subtraction

Name _____ Date _____

Checkpoint Answer Key

Part 1

Circle the answer.
(1 point)
1. About how many more is 19 cupcakes than 3 cupcakes?
   - A. about 5
   - B. about 10
   - (C.) about 15
   - D. about 20

(1 point)
2. There are 11 leaves on the cherry tree. There are 4 leaves on the maple tree. About how many more leaves are on the cherry tree than the maple tree?
   - (A.) about 5
   - B. about 10
   - C. about 15
   - D. about 20

(1 point)
3. April has 14 flowers. Ann has 19 flowers. About how many fewer flowers does April have than Ann?
   - (A.) about 5
   - B. about 10
   - C. about 15
   - D. about 20

1 of 2

○ Checkpoint   Math | Comparison Subtraction: Story Problems | Estimate and Check Subtraction

Name _____ Date _____

Part 2

Use cubes or sketches to check each answer.
(1 point)
4. There are 9 cans on the shelf. There are 2 cans on the counter. How many fewer cans are on the counter than on the shelf? Alexander says there are 7 fewer cans on the counter. Is Alexander's answer correct?
   - (A.) Yes
   - B. No

(1 point)
5. There are 18 petals on the red flower. There are 16 petals on the yellow flower. There are 3 more petals on the red flower than on the yellow flower. Is this answer correct?
   - A. Yes
   - (B.) No

(1 point)
6. Rob put 5 of his toy cars in a basket. He put 9 of his toy cars in a box. Rob put 4 more toy cars in the box than in the basket. Is this answer correct?
   - (A.) Yes
   - B. No

2 of 2

Unit Review

Lesson Overview

UNIT REVIEW Look Back	15 minutes	**ONLINE**
UNIT REVIEW Checkpoint Practice	15 minutes	**OFFLINE**
▶ **UNIT REVIEW** Prepare for the Checkpoint		

▶ Unit Objectives

This lesson reviews the following objectives:

- Use concrete objects to explain how to solve addition and subtraction problem-solving situations involving numbers up to 10.
- Recognize and solve word problems involving numbers up to 10 in which two quantities are compared by the use of addition or subtraction.
- Make reasonable estimates for the solutions to subtraction problems with minuends up through 20.
- Check the accuracy of calculations for the solutions to subtraction problems with minuends up through 20.

▶ Advance Preparation

In this lesson, students will have an opportunity to review previous activities in the Comparison Subtraction: Story Problems unit. Look at the suggested activities in Unit Review: Prepare for the Checkpoint online and gather any needed materials.

Materials to Gather

SUPPLIED

blocks – O (any color)

Checkpoint Practice activity page

Keywords

benchmark	estimate (verb)
change problem	fewer
check	more
combine problem	story problem
compare	subtract
compare problem	subtraction
difference	take away
estimate (noun)	

UNIT REVIEW Look Back

Objectives

• Review unit objectives.

In this unit, students have learned to use concrete objects to explain how to solve addition and subtraction problem-solving situations involving numbers up to 10. They have also learned to recognize and solve story problems involving numbers up to 10 in which two quantities are compared. They have learned to make estimates for solutions to subtraction problems and to check the accuracy of those solutions. Students will review key concepts from the unit to prepare for the Unit Checkpoint.

UNIT REVIEW Checkpoint Practice

Objectives

• Review unit objectives.

Students will complete a Checkpoint Practice activity page to prepare for the Unit Checkpoint. If necessary, read the directions, problems, and answer choices to students. Have students answer the problems on their own. Review any missed problems with students.

Name:

Unit Review
Checkpoint Practice

Write the answer. You may use models or sketches to help you.

1. Tara did 6 word puzzles.
   She also did 3 number puzzles.

   Did Tara do more word puzzles or number puzzles?

   Circle the answer.

   (A) word puzzles   B. number puzzles

   How many more? ___3___ more

2. Cole has 4 sand buckets.
   Chad has 3 sand buckets.

   How many sand buckets do they have in all?

   ___7___ sand buckets

3. There were 8 lions resting in the sun, and then 5 of the lions moved under a tree.

   How many lions are still resting in the sun?

   ___3___ lions

COMPARISON SUBTRACTION: STORY PROBLEMS   293   UNIT REVIEW

---

4. Michael's Pet Store has 7 white kittens and 2 brown kittens.

   How many fewer brown kittens are there than white kittens?

   ___5___ fewer brown kittens

Circle the answer.

5. There are 4 fruit bars.
   There are 2 children.

   Are there more fruit bars or children?

   (A) fruit bars   B. children

6. If you take away 4 marbles from 12 marbles, do you have 6 marbles left?

   A. Yes   (B) No

7. Pat made 10 sandwiches and Lisa made 8 sandwiches. How many more sandwiches did Pat make than Lisa?

   A. 8   B. 6   (C) 2

COMPARISON SUBTRACTION: STORY PROBLEMS   294   UNIT REVIEW

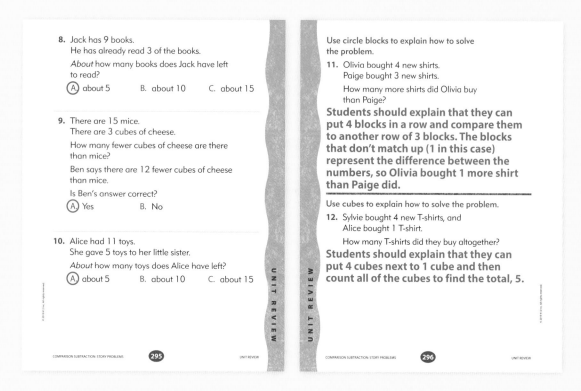

8. Jack has 9 books.
He has already read 3 of the books.

About how many books does Jack have left to read?

Ⓐ about 5   B. about 10   C. about 15

9. There are 15 mice.
There are 3 cubes of cheese.

How many fewer cubes of cheese are there than mice?

Ben says there are 12 fewer cubes of cheese than mice.

Is Ben's answer correct?

Ⓐ Yes   B. No

10. Alice had 11 toys.
She gave 5 toys to her little sister.

About how many toys does Alice have left?

Ⓐ about 5   B. about 10   C. about 15

Use circle blocks to explain how to solve the problem.

11. Olivia bought 4 new shirts.
Paige bought 3 new shirts.

How many more shirts did Olivia buy than Paige?

Students should explain that they can put 4 blocks in a row and compare them to another row of 3 blocks. The blocks that don't match up (1 in this case) represent the difference between the numbers, so Olivia bought 1 more shirt than Paige did.

Use cubes to explain how to solve the problem.

12. Sylvie bought 4 new T-shirts, and Alice bought 1 T-shirt.

How many T-shirts did they buy altogether?

Students should explain that they can put 4 cubes next to 1 cube and then count all of the cubes to find the total, 5.

⇥ **UNIT REVIEW** Prepare for the Checkpoint

What you do next depends on how students performed in the previous activity, Unit Review: Checkpoint Practice. If students had difficulty with any of the problems, complete the appropriate review activity listed in the table online.

Unit Checkpoint

Lesson Overview

| UNIT CHECKPOINT Offline | 45 minutes | OFFLINE |

▶ Unit Objectives

This lesson assesses the following objectives:

- Use concrete objects to explain how to solve addition and subtraction problem-solving situations involving numbers up to 10.

- Recognize and solve word problems involving numbers up to 10 in which two quantities are compared by the use of addition or subtraction.

- Make reasonable estimates for the solutions to subtraction problems with minuends up through 20.

- Check the accuracy of calculations for the solutions to subtraction problems with minuends up through 20.

Materials to Gather

SUPPLIED

Unit Checkpoint (printout)

blocks – O (red, blue)

UNIT CHECKPOINT Offline

Objectives

- Assess unit objectives.

Students will complete the Unit Checkpoint offline. Print the Checkpoint and have students complete it on their own. Read the directions, problems, and answer choices to students, if necessary. Use the answer key to score the Checkpoint, and then enter the results online.

Give students the cubes for Problem 8.

Checkpoint   Math | Comparison Subtraction: Story Problems | Unit Checkpoint

Name _____ Date _____

Unit Checkpoint Answer Key

Circle the answer.

(1 point)
1. Which picture shows how many pictures they painted in all?

   Yasmin painted 9 pictures and Gino painted 1 picture.
   How many pictures did they paint in all?

   A. ○○○○○○○○○

   B. ○○○○○○○○○○

   Ⓒ (○○○○○○○○○○)

(1 point)
2. Which picture could you use to solve this problem?

   George painted 8 pictures. Jenny painted 5 pictures.
   How many fewer pictures did Jenny paint than George?

   Ⓐ

   B.

   C.

© 2010 K12 Inc. All rights reserved.
Copying or distributing without K12's written consent is prohibited.
1 of 4

Checkpoint   Math | Comparison Subtraction: Story Problems | Unit Checkpoint

Name _____ Date _____

(1 point)
3. Which picture could be used to solve this problem?

   David has 8 marbles. Jasmin has 9 marbles.
   How many more marbles does Jasmin have than David?

   Ⓐ

   B.

   C.

(1 point)
4. Kristy's cake had 7 candles on it.
   Kyle's cake had 4 candles on it.

   How many fewer candles were on Kyle's cake than Kristy's?

   Ⓐ 3   B. 4   C. 11

(1 point)
5. There are 7 apples in the kitchen and 5 children.

   If each child gets 1 apple, how many apples will be left over?

   A. 12   B. 5   Ⓒ 2

(1 point)
6. Mason has 9 dolls. Ciera has 6 dolls.

   How many more dolls does Mason have than Ciera?

   A. 15   B. 8   Ⓒ 3

© 2010 K12 Inc. All rights reserved.
Copying or distributing without K12's written consent is prohibited.
2 of 4

Name _____ Date _____

Write the answer.
(1 point)
7. Jason has 3 pairs of tennis shoes. Lauren has 2 pairs.

   How many more pairs of tennis shoes does Jason have than Lauren?

   _____1_____ more pair

Use the cubes to help explain how to solve this problem.
(1 point)
8. There are 3 ducks on the lake and 9 ducks on the shore.

   How many fewer ducks are on the lake than on the shore?

   <u>Students should explain that they can put 9 cubes in a row and compare them to another row of 3 cubes. The spaces underneath the cubes that don't have a match (6 in this case) show the difference between the two numbers, so there are 6 fewer ducks on the lake than on the shore.</u>

Name _____ Date _____

Estimate to solve the problem and then circle the answer.
(1 point)
9. *About* how many is 10 take away 4?

   (A) about 5   B. about 10   C. about 15

(1 point)
10. Estimate the answer to 20 take away 9.

   A. about 5   (B) about 10   C. about 30

(1 point)
11. Sarah has 14 marbles.
   She gives Henry 10 marbles.

   About how many marbles does Sarah have left?

   (A) about 5   B. about 15   C. about 25

Circle the answer.
(1 point)
12. There are 19 apples on the tree. Jody picked 8 apples.

   About how many apples were left on the tree?

   (A) 10   B. 7   C. 4

(1 point)
13. Talia was given the problem 8 minus 3 is ? She solved it correctly.

   Which shows the correct solution to this problem?

   (A) 8 minus 3 is 5   B. 8 minus 3 is 11   C. 8 minus 3 is 6

(1 point)
14. Which math problem is correct?

   A. 9 minus 3 is 5   B. 10 minus 8 is 3   (C) 7 minus 3 is 4

(1 point)
15. If you take away 4 books from 6 books, do you have 2 left?

   (A) Yes   B. No

Add or Subtract: Problem Solving

▶ Unit Objectives

- Recognize and solve word problems involving sums or minuends up through 20 in which one quantity changes through addition or subtraction.

- Recognize and solve word problems involving sums up through 20 in which two quantities are combined.

- Recognize and solve word problems involving numbers up to 10 in which two quantities are compared by the use of addition or subtraction.

▶ Big Ideas

The use of letters, numbers, and mathematical symbols makes possible the translation of complex situations or long word statements into concise mathematical sentences or expressions.

▶ Unit Introduction

In this unit, students will learn to recognize and solve a variety of story problems in which

- Two quantities are combined,
- Two quantities are compared, or
- One quantity changes through addition or subtraction

Different Types of Problems

Skills Update	5 minutes	ONLINE
LEARN Recognize Different Problems	15 minutes	ONLINE
LEARN Understand Different Problems	10 minutes	ONLINE
TRY IT A Variety of Problems	15 minutes	OFFLINE

▶ Lesson Objectives

- Recognize and solve word problems involving sums or minuends up through 20 in which one quantity changes through addition or subtraction.
- Recognize and solve word problems involving sums up through 20 in which two quantities are combined.
- Recognize and solve word problems involving numbers up to 10 in which two quantities are compared by the use of addition or subtraction.

▶ Prerequisite Skills

- Demonstrate the meaning of subtraction as taking away an amount from a given quantity (with minuends up through 20).
- Demonstrate the meaning of subtraction as comparing two quantities to find the difference (with minuends up through 20).
- Demonstrate the meaning of addition as the combining of two sets (for sums up through 20).
- Use concrete objects or sketches to model and solve addition or subtraction computation problems involving sums or minuends up through 20.

▶ Common Errors and Misconceptions

Students might have difficulty seeing the connection between addition and subtraction situations.

▶ Content Background

Students will solve different types of story problems. They will learn to read a problem, explain what is happening, and decide whether they should add or subtract to solve it.

- In *change problems*, students must add to or take away from a group—the number of objects in the group changes.
- In *combine problems*, students must put together two or more groups to find the sum. In some combine problems, however, they will be given the sum and will need to find one of the addends.
- In *compare problems*, students must compare two groups to determine how many more or fewer objects are in one group. They will first compare groups using models that are aligned so that the objects in the two groups match one-to-one. To find how many more or fewer, they will count the

Materials to Gather

SUPPLIED

A Variety of Problems activity page

unmatched objects. When comparing greater numbers, counting isn't practical. Students will learn that they can subtract, rather than count, to solve compare problems.

Students do not need to memorize the types of story problems. Instead, they should gain the experience and confidence necessary to read a problem, create a mental image, and form a plan for solving the problem.

Keywords

change problem – a problem in which one quantity changes by having an amount added or taken away
combine problem – an addition problem in which two numbers are put together to find a sum
compare problem – a problem in which two quantities are compared by finding the difference

---

LEARN Recognize Different Problems

ONLINE 15 min

Students will learn that explaining what is happening in a story problem can help them figure out how to solve the problem. They will watch Alexander and Serena explain how to solve three problems. Then students will explain how to solve three similar problems.

After students explain how to solve each problem, click Check and listen to the model explanation together. Discuss how students' explanations compare to the model explanations.

Objectives

- Recognize and solve word problems involving sums or minuends up through 20 in which one quantity changes through addition or subtraction.
- Recognize and solve word problems involving sums up through 20 in which two quantities are combined.
- Recognize and solve word problems involving numbers up to 10 in which two quantities are compared by the use of addition or subtraction.

LEARN Understand Different Problems

ONLINE 10 min

Students will learn how to decide whether they need to add or subtract to solve problems. For each problem, have students tell you what information the problem gives them. Help students find the words in the question that indicate whether amounts should be combined, compared, or changed. Then have them explain why they should add or subtract.

Objectives

- Recognize and solve word problems involving sums or minuends up through 20 in which one quantity changes through addition or subtraction.
- Recognize and solve word problems involving sums up through 20 in which two quantities are combined.
- Recognize and solve word problems involving numbers up to 10 in which two quantities are compared by the use of addition or subtraction.

TRY IT A Variety of Problems

Objectives

Students will practice explaining how to solve story problems and deciding whether to add to subtract to solve. Give students the A Variety of Problems activity page from their Activity Book and read the directions with them. Use the answer key to check students' answers, and then enter the results online.

- Recognize and solve word problems involving sums or minuends up through 20 in which one quantity changes through addition or subtraction.

- Recognize and solve word problems involving sums up through 20 in which two quantities are combined.

- Recognize and solve word problems involving numbers up to 10 in which two quantities are compared by the use of addition or subtraction.

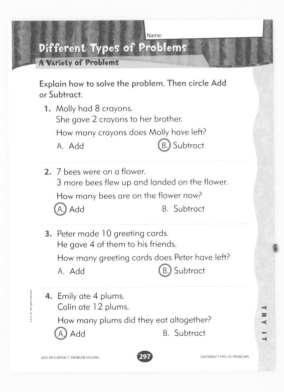

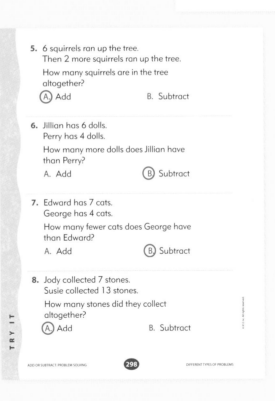

Combine and Change Problems

Lesson Overview

Skills Update	5 minutes	ONLINE
GET READY Choose the Correct Solution	5 minutes	ONLINE
LEARN Change Problems	10 minutes	ONLINE
LEARN Change or Combine to Solve	15 minutes	ONLINE
TRY IT More Problems	10 minutes	OFFLINE

▶ Lesson Objectives

- Recognize and solve word problems involving sums or minuends up through 20 in which one quantity changes through addition or subtraction.
- Recognize and solve word problems involving sums up through 20 in which two quantities are combined.

▶ Prerequisite Skills

- Demonstrate the meaning of subtraction as taking away an amount from a given quantity (with minuends up through 20).
- Demonstrate the meaning of addition as the combining of two sets (for sums up through 20).
- Use concrete objects or sketches to model and solve addition or subtraction computation problems involving sums or minuends up through 20.

▶ Common Errors and Misconceptions

Students might have difficulty seeing the connection between addition and subtraction situations.

▶ Content Background

Students will model or sketch to solve change and combine story problems.

- In *change problems*, students must add to or take away from a group—the number of objects in the group changes.
- In *combine problems*, students must put together two or more groups to find the sum. In some combine problems, however, they will be given the sum and will need to find one of the addends.

Students do not need to memorize the types of story problems. Instead, they should gain the experience and confidence necessary to read a problem, create a mental image, and form a plan for solving the problem.

Materials to Gather

SUPPLIED

More Problems activity page

GET READY **Choose the Correct Solution**

ONLINE 5 min

Story problems don't always explicitly state whether to add or subtract. Students will practice reading story problems and deciding how to solve them.

Objectives

- Recognize and solve word problems involving sums or minuends up through 20 in which one quantity changes through addition or subtraction.
- Recognize and solve word problems involving sums up through 20 in which two quantities are combined.

LEARN **Change Problems**

ONLINE 10 min

Students will solve story problems in which a beginning amount is changed either by addition or subtraction.

Objectives

- Recognize and solve word problems involving sums or minuends up through 20 in which one quantity changes through addition or subtraction.

LEARN **Change or Combine to Solve**

ONLINE 15 min

Students will solve story problems involving amounts that change. They will use online cubes and number sentences to help them find the solutions.

Guide students through the activity. In all three problems, they will be given the number sentence in words and asked to give the solution.

Objectives

- Recognize and solve word problems involving sums or minuends up through 20 in which one quantity changes through addition or subtraction.
- Recognize and solve word problems involving sums up through 20 in which two quantities are combined.

TRY IT **More Problems**

OFFLINE 10 min

Students will practice deciding whether to add or subtract when solving story problems and solving the problems. Give students the More Problems activity page from their Activity Book and read the directions with them.

Objectives

- Recognize and solve word problems involving sums or minuends up through 20 in which one quantity changes through addition or subtraction.
- Recognize and solve word problems involving sums up through 20 in which two quantities are combined.

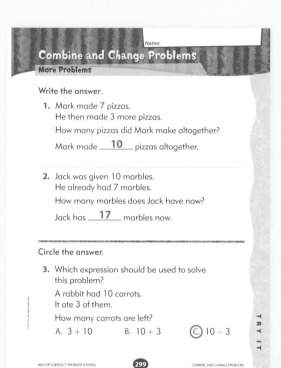

Name:

Combine and Change Problems
More Problems

Write the answer.

1. Mark made 7 pizzas.
   He then made 3 more pizzas.
   How many pizzas did Mark make altogether?

   Mark made __10__ pizzas altogether.

2. Jack was given 10 marbles.
   He already had 7 marbles.
   How many marbles does Jack have now?

   Jack has __17__ marbles now.

Circle the answer.

3. Which expression should be used to solve this problem?

   A rabbit had 10 carrots.
   It ate 3 of them.
   How many carrots are left?

   A. 3 + 10   B. 10 + 3   C. 10 − 3

TRY IT

Write the answer.

4. Shannon has 5 blue stones.
   Dylan has 5 red stones.
   How many stones do they have altogether?

   They have __10__ stones altogether.

5. Billy has 13 pears.
   Tommy has 3 pears.
   How many pears do they have altogether?

   They have __16__ pears altogether.

6. Hank has 12 baseball cards.
   Donnie has 8 baseball cards.
   How many baseball cards do they have altogether?

   They have __20__ baseball cards altogether.

7. Lucas has 3 teddy bears.
   Kevin has 5 teddy bears.
   How many teddy bears do they have altogether?

   They have __8__ teddy bears altogether.

TRY IT

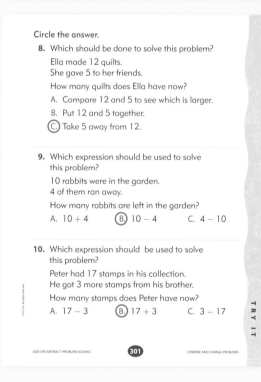

Circle the answer.

8. Which should be done to solve this problem?

   Ella made 12 quilts.
   She gave 5 to her friends.
   How many quilts does Ella have now?

   A. Compare 12 and 5 to see which is larger.
   B. Put 12 and 5 together.
   C. Take 5 away from 12.

9. Which expression should be used to solve this problem?

   10 rabbits were in the garden.
   4 of them ran away.
   How many rabbits are left in the garden?

   A. 10 + 4   B. 10 − 4   C. 4 − 10

10. Which expression should be used to solve this problem?

   Peter had 17 stamps in his collection.
   He got 3 more stamps from his brother.
   How many stamps does Peter have now?

   A. 17 − 3   B. 17 + 3   C. 3 − 17

TRY IT

Compare and Combine Problems

Skills Update	5 minutes	ONLINE
LEARN Compare on the Farm	15 minutes	ONLINE
LEARN Farm Combinations	15 minutes	OFFLINE
TRY IT Compare and Combine	10 minutes	OFFLINE

▶ Lesson Objectives

- Recognize and solve word problems involving numbers up to 10 in which two quantities are compared by the use of addition or subtraction.
- Recognize and solve word problems involving sums up through 20 in which two quantities are combined.

▶ Prerequisite Skills

- Demonstrate the meaning of subtraction as comparing two quantities to find the difference (with minuends up through 20).
- Demonstrate the meaning of addition as the combining of two sets (for sums up through 20).

▶ Common Errors and Misconceptions

Students might have difficulty seeing the connection between addition and subtraction situations.

▶ Content Background

Students will solve two different types of story problems: compare problems and combine problems.

- In *compare problems*, students must compare two groups to determine how many more or fewer objects are in one group. They will first compare groups using models that are aligned so that the objects in the two groups match one-to-one. To find how many more or fewer, they will count the unmatched objects. When comparing greater numbers, counting isn't practical. Students will learn that they can subtract, rather than count, to solve compare problems.

- In *combine problems*, students must put together two or more groups to find the sum. In some combine problems, however, they will be given the sum and will need to find one of the addends.

Students do not need to memorize the types of story problems. Instead they should gain the experience and confidence necessary to read a problem, create a mental image, and form a plan for solving the problem.

Materials to Gather

SUPPLIED

Farm Combinations activity page
Compare and Combine activity page

ALSO NEEDED

crayons

LEARN Compare on the Farm

ONLINE 15min

Objectives

Students will solve story problems in which two amounts are compared. Students will tell how many fewer or how many more one amount is than the other. They will fill in subtraction number sentences to show the difference.

- Recognize and solve word problems involving numbers up to 10 in which two quantities are compared by the use of addition or subtraction.

LEARN Farm Combinations

OFFLINE 15min

Objectives

Students will solve combine problems where they know the total amount that was combined and only one part that combines to make the total. They are to find the missing part. Guide students through each problem. Give students the crayons and the Farm Combinations activity page from their Activity Book. Read the directions with them.

- Recognize and solve word problems involving sums up through 20 in which two quantities are combined.

Tips

Be sure students understand that they don't have to color in the pictures perfectly.

1. Read the Problem 1 to students.

2. Reread only the first line of the problem. Have students count to see that the total number of roosters in the pictures is the same number that is in the written problem. (11)

3. Read only the second line of the problem. Have students color 9 of the roosters with a brown crayon.

4. Finally read the third line and the question the problem is asking. Tell students that as they color the rest of the roosters black, they should count to see how many there are. (2)

   The method students have just used is counting up to find the answer. However, with greater numbers, students should realize that they can subtract to find the answer.

5. As you read the worded number sentence to students and have them fill in the answer, point to the 11 roosters, the 9 brown roosters, and then the 2 black roosters.

6. Then as you read and have them write the missing portions of the symbolic number sentence, point to the parts of the worded number sentence above. Be sure students see the connection among the pictures, worded number sentence, and symbolic number sentence.

7. Repeat steps 1–6 for Problems 2–4.

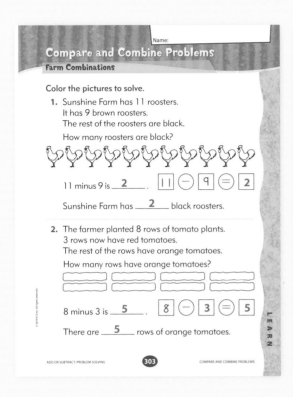

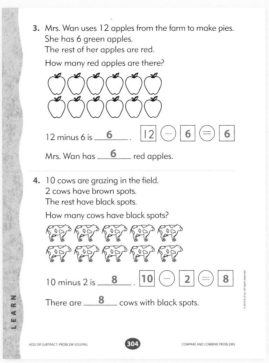

Compare and Combine Problems

Farm Combinations

Color the pictures to solve.

1. Sunshine Farm has 11 roosters.
   It has 9 brown roosters.
   The rest of the roosters are black.

   How many roosters are black?

   11 minus 9 is __2__ . | 11 | − | 9 | = | 2 |

   Sunshine Farm has __2__ black roosters.

2. The farmer planted 8 rows of tomato plants.
   3 rows now have red tomatoes.
   The rest of the rows have orange tomatoes.

   How many rows have orange tomatoes?

   8 minus 3 is __5__ . | 8 | − | 3 | = | 5 |

   There are __5__ rows of orange tomatoes.

3. Mrs. Wan uses 12 apples from the farm to make pies.
   She has 6 green apples.
   The rest of her apples are red.

   How many red apples are there?

   12 minus 6 is __6__ . | 12 | − | 6 | = | 6 |

   Mrs. Wan has __6__ red apples.

4. 10 cows are grazing in the field.
   2 cows have brown spots.
   The rest have black spots.

   How many cows have black spots?

   10 minus 2 is __8__ . | 10 | − | 2 | = | 8 |

   There are __8__ cows with black spots.

OFFLINE

10 min

TRY IT Compare and Combine

Students will practice deciding whether to add or subtract when solving story problems and solving the problems. Give students the Compare and Combine activity page from their Activity Book and read the directions with them. Use the answer key to check students' answers, and then enter the results online.

Objectives

- Recognize and solve word problems involving numbers up to 10 in which two quantities are compared by the use of addition or subtraction.

- Recognize and solve word problems involving sums up through 20 in which two quantities are combined.

Compare and Combine Problems
Compare and Combine

Write the answer.

1. Yubo wrote 9 stories. Cate wrote 3 fewer stories than Yubo.

   How many stories did Cate write?

   Cate wrote ___6___ stories.

2. Yuki practices judo 5 times per week. Sam practices judo 2 fewer times than Yuki.

   How many times does Sam practice judo a week?

   Sam practices judo ___3___ times a week.

3. Steven has 12 cats. 5 cats are brown and the rest are white.

   How many white cats does Steven have?

   Steven has ___7___ white cats.

4. Carrie ate 10 strawberries. Haley ate 1 strawberry.

   How many more strawberries did Carrie eat than Haley?

   Carrie ate ___9___ more strawberries than Haley.

T R Y   I T

Circle the answer.

5. Manuela has 14 stuffed animals. 10 of them are dogs and the rest are bears.

   How many stuffed bears does Manuela have?

   (A) 4   B. 5   C. 6

6. Katy has 15 dog treats. 12 of the dog treats are round and the rest are square.

   How many dog treats are square?

   (A) 3   B. 4   C. 5

7. Stephanie has 10 crayons. 6 crayons are yellow and the rest are black.

   How many black crayons does Stephanie have?

   (A) 4   B. 6   C. 16

8. Carol made 3 sandwiches. Margo made 8 sandwiches.

   Who made fewer sandwiches?

   (A) Carol   B. Margo

T R Y   I T

Change and Compare Problems

Lesson Overview

Skills Update	5 minutes	ONLINE
LEARN Beach Comparisons and Changes	15 minutes	ONLINE
LEARN What's Happening at the Beach	15 minutes	ONLINE
TRY IT Solving Problems	10 minutes	OFFLINE

▶ Lesson Objectives

- Recognize and solve word problems involving sums or minuends up through 20 in which one quantity changes through addition or subtraction.
- Recognize and solve word problems involving numbers up to 10 in which two quantities are compared by the use of addition or subtraction.

▶ Prerequisite Skills

- Demonstrate the meaning of subtraction as taking away an amount from a given quantity (with minuends up through 20).
- Demonstrate the meaning of subtraction as comparing two quantities to find the difference (with minuends up through 20).
- Demonstrate the meaning of addition as the combining of two sets (for sums up through 20).
- Use concrete objects or sketches to model and solve addition or subtraction computation problems involving sums or minuends up through 20.

▶ Common Errors and Misconceptions

Students might have difficulty seeing the connection between addition and subtraction situations.

▶ Content Background

Students will recognize various story problem types, with an emphasis on problems involving comparing amounts and amounts that change.

- In *change problems*, students must add to or take away from a group—the number of objects in the group changes.
- In *compare problems*, students must compare two groups to determine how many more or fewer objects are in one group. They will first compare groups using models that are aligned so that the objects in the two groups match one-to-one. To find how many more or fewer, they will count the unmatched objects. When comparing greater numbers, counting isn't practical. Students will learn that they can subtract, rather than count, to solve compare problems.

Students do not need to memorize the types of story problems. Instead, they should gain the experience and confidence necessary to read a problem, create a mental image, and form a plan for solving the problem.

Materials to Gather

SUPPLIED

Solving Problems activity page

LEARN Beach Comparisons and Changes

Students will choose the correct solution for a problem involving comparing amounts or an amount that changes as the problem is solved.

Objectives

- Recognize and solve word problems involving sums or minuends up through 20 in which one quantity changes through addition or subtraction.
- Recognize and solve word problems involving numbers up to 10 in which two quantities are compared by the use of addition or subtraction.

LEARN What's Happening at the Beach

Students will match story problems to a description of what is happening in the problem.

Objectives

- Recognize and solve word problems involving sums or minuends up through 20 in which one quantity changes through addition or subtraction.
- Recognize and solve word problems involving numbers up to 10 in which two quantities are compared by the use of addition or subtraction.

TRY IT Solving Problems

Students will practice deciding whether to add or subtract when solving story problems and solving the problems. Give students the Solving Problems activity page from their Activity Book and read the directions with them. Use the answer key to check students' answers, and then enter the results online.

Objectives

- Recognize and solve word problems involving sums or minuends up through 20 in which one quantity changes through addition or subtraction.
- Recognize and solve word problems involving numbers up to 10 in which two quantities are compared by the use of addition or subtraction.

Change and Compare Problems
Solving Problems

Write the answer.

1. Look at the two problems. Solve the problem that asks about changing the number of stamps that Harold has.

   Problem 1

   Harold has 6 stamps. Brent has 3 stamps.

   How many fewer stamps does Brent have than Harold?

   Problem 2

   Harold had 6 stamps.

   Brent gave him 3 more stamps.

   How many stamps does Harold have now?

   Which problem did you solve?

   A. Problem 1   (B.) Problem 2

   Answer: __9__ stamps

2. Frida had 7 books. James gave her some more books. Frida now has 10 books. How many books did James give Frida?

   James gave Frida __3__ more books.

Circle the answer.

3. Mason has 4 baseballs.
   Ciera has 10 baseballs.

   How many fewer baseballs does Mason have than Ciera?

   A. 4   B. 10   (C.) 6

4. Which choice best describes what is happening in this problem?

   Tanya had 9 crayons.
   She gave 3 crayons to Jackie. How many crayons does Tanya have left?

   A. Tanya now has more than 9 crayons.

   B. Tanya now has 9 crayons.

   (C.) Tanya now has fewer than 9 crayons.

5. Which problem asks about comparing the number of apples?

   (A.) Sharla has 6 apples. Jenny has 4 apples. How many fewer apples does Jenny have than Sharla?

   B. Sharla has 6 apples. Jenny has 4 apples. How many apples do they have altogether?

6. Which problem talks about something being taken away?

   (A.) Sam had 10 baseball cards.
   He gave 4 to his brother.
   How many cards does Sam have now?

   B. Anna has 7 candies.
   Maria has 6 candies.
   How many candies do they have altogether?

   C. There are 3 rabbits and 6 carrots.
   If each rabbit gets 1 carrot, how many carrots will be left over?

Write the answer.

7. Sophie had 6 pears.
   She gave 2 pears to Molly.

   How many pears does Sophie have left?

   Sophie has __4__ pears left.

8. Conner has 5 baseball hats and 3 visors.

   How many more baseball hats does Conner have than visors?

   Conner has __2__ more baseball hats than visors.

9. Look at the two problems. Solve the problem that asks you to compare the number of sailboats.

   Problem 1

   George saw 7 sailboats.
   Amanda saw 3 sailboats.

   How many sailboats did they see altogether?

   Problem 2

   George saw 7 sailboats.
   Amanda saw 3 sailboats.

   How many more sailboats did George see than Amanda?

   Which problem did you solve?

   A. Problem 1   (B.) Problem 2

   Answer: __4__ sailboats

10. Grant had painted 3 toy cars.
    He painted another 4 toy cars.

    How many toy cars did Grant paint altogether?

    Grant painted __7__ toy cars altogether.

TRY IT

Add or Subtract: More Exploration

Lesson Overview		
Skills Update	5 minutes	**ONLINE**
REVIEW Extend Your Understanding	10 minutes	**ONLINE**
CHECKPOINT	30 minutes	**OFFLINE**

▶ Lesson Objectives

- Recognize and solve word problems involving sums or minuends up through 20 in which one quantity changes through addition or subtraction.
- Recognize and solve word problems involving sums up through 20 in which two quantities are combined.
- Recognize and solve word problems involving numbers up to 10 in which two quantities are compared by the use of addition or subtraction.

▶ Prerequisite Skills

- Demonstrate the meaning of subtraction as taking away an amount from a given quantity (with minuends up through 20).
- Demonstrate the meaning of subtraction as comparing two quantities to find the difference (with minuends up through 20).
- Demonstrate the meaning of addition as the combining of two sets (for sums up through 20).
- Use concrete objects or sketches to model and solve addition or subtraction computation problems involving sums or minuends up through 20.

▶ Content Background

Students will have an opportunity for continued review. Then they will take a Checkpoint. If you wish, you may have students begin the next lesson after they complete the Checkpoint.

Materials to Gather

SUPPLIED
Checkpoint (printout)

REVIEW Extend Your Understanding

Objectives

To prepare for the Checkpoint, students will have a chance to practice skills they've learned in previous lessons.

- Recognize and solve word problems involving sums or minuends up through 20 in which one quantity changes through addition or subtraction.

- Recognize and solve word problems involving sums up through 20 in which two quantities are combined.

- Recognize and solve word problems involving numbers up to 10 in which two quantities are compared by the use of addition or subtraction

CHECKPOINT

Objectives

Print the Checkpoint and have students complete it on their own. Read the directions, problems, and answer choices to students, if necessary. Use the answer key to score the Checkpoint, and then enter the results online.

- Recognize and solve word problems involving sums or minuends up through 20 in which one quantity changes through addition or subtraction.

- Recognize and solve word problems involving sums up through 20 in which two quantities are combined.

- Recognize and solve word problems involving numbers up to 10 in which two quantities are compared by the use of addition or subtraction.

⚙ Checkpoint   Math | Add or Subtract: Problem Solving | Add or Subtract: More Exploration

Name _____   Date _____

Checkpoint Answer Key

Circe the answer.
(1 point)
1. Sandro had 14 baseball cards. He gave 9 to his brother.

   How many cards does Sandro have now?

   (A.) 5
   B. 9
   C. 14

(1 point)
2. Gino had 19 balloons. Then 5 of the balloons popped.

   How many balloons does Gino have now?

   A. 5
   (B.) 14
   C. 19

Solve.
(1 point)
3. Charles ate 4 carrots on Saturday morning. On Saturday afternoon he ate 5 more carrots.

   How many carrots did Charles eat altogether?

   Charles ate ___9___ carrots altogether.

(1 point)
4. Molly had some carrots. She gave 3 carrots to Anna. Now Molly has 3 carrots left.

   How many carrots did Molly have at the beginning?

   Molly had ___6___ carrots at the beginning.

Name _____ Date _____

(1 point)
5. Anna had 3 dolls.
Tina gave her 6 more dolls.

How many dolls does Anna have now?

Anna has __9__ dolls now.

(1 point)
6. Suzy has 11 rubber bands.
9 are red and the rest are blue.

How many blue rubber bands does Suzy have?

Suzy has __2__ blue rubber bands.

(1 point)
7. Parker has 16 dinosaurs.
8 are tall and the rest are short.

How many dinosaurs are short?

__8__ dinosaurs are short.

Circle the answer.
(1 point)
8. Jody has 7 carrots.
Susie has 13 carrots.

How many carrots do they
have altogether?

A. 6   B. 13   (C) 20

Name _____ Date _____

Solve.
(1 point)
9. Erin has 12 plates.
Megan has 7 plates.

How many plates do they have altogether?

They have __19__ plates altogether.

(1 point)
10. 7 children are playing on the jungle gym.
5 children are playing on the swing set.

How many children are playing in all?

__12__ children are playing in all.

(1 point)
11. Yuki grew 9 sunflowers.
Sam grew 5 sunflowers.

How many fewer sunflowers did Sam grow than Yuki?

Sam grew __4__ fewer sunflowers than Yuki.

(1 point)
12. Sanum had 10 pretzels for a snack.
Nick had 7 pretzels.

How many fewer pretzels did Nick have than Sanum?

Nick had __3__ fewer pretzels than Sanum.

Name _____ Date _____

Circle the answer.
(1 point)
13. There are 10 beanbags in the box and 8 children.

If each child gets 1 beanbag, how many extra beanbags
will there be?

(A) 2   B. 10   C. 18

(1 point)
14. Gabby put 6 pillows on her bed.
Jackie put 4 pillows on her bed.

How many more pillows did Gabby put on her bed than
Jackie?

A. 10   B. 6   (C) 2

(1 point)
15. Ben has 2 baseballs.
Patrick has 3 baseballs.

How many more baseballs does Patrick have than Ben?

(A) 1   B. 3   C. 5

Unit Review

Lesson Overview

UNIT REVIEW Look Back	15 minutes	ONLINE
UNIT REVIEW Checkpoint Practice	15 minutes	OFFLINE
▶ UNIT REVIEW Prepare for the Checkpoint		

▶ Unit Objectives

This lesson reviews the following objectives:

- Recognize and solve word problems involving sums or minuends up through 20 in which one quantity changes through addition or subtraction.
- Recognize and solve word problems involving sums up through 20 in which two quantities are combined.
- Recognize and solve word problems involving numbers up to 10 in which two quantities are compared by the use of addition or subtraction.

▶ Advance Preparation

In this lesson, students will have an opportunity to review previous activities in the Add or Subtract: Problem Solving unit. Look at the suggested activities in Unit Review: Prepare for the Checkpoint online and gather any needed materials.

Materials to Gather

SUPPLIED

Checkpoint Practice activity page

Keywords

change problem
combine problem

compare problem

UNIT REVIEW Look Back

ONLINE 15min

In this unit, students have learned to recognize and solve story problems in which two quantities are combined or compared and in which one quantity changes through addition or subtraction. Students will review key concepts from the unit to prepare for the Unit Checkpoint.

Objectives

- Review unit objectives.

UNIT REVIEW Checkpoint Practice

Students will complete a Checkpoint Practice activity page to prepare for the Unit Checkpoint. If necessary, read the directions, problems, and answer choices to students. Have students answer the problems on their own. Review any missed problems with students.

Objectives

- Review unit objectives.

Tips

Remind students to draw simple sketches (such as lines, circles, or dots) if they use models and sketches to solve problems in this activity.

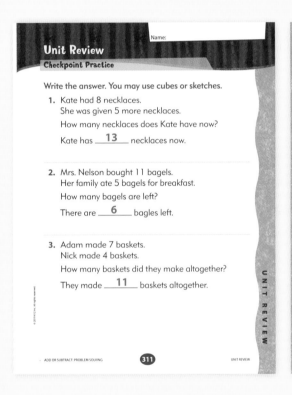

Name: _____

Unit Review
Checkpoint Practice

Write the answer. You may use cubes or sketches.

1. Kate had 8 necklaces.
   She was given 5 more necklaces.
   How many necklaces does Kate have now?

   Kate has __13__ necklaces now.

2. Mrs. Nelson bought 11 bagels.
   Her family ate 5 bagels for breakfast.
   How many bagels are left?

   There are __6__ bagles left.

3. Adam made 7 baskets.
   Nick made 4 baskets.
   How many baskets did they make altogether?

   They made __11__ baskets altogether.

ADD OR SUBTRACT: PROBLEM SOLVING   (311)   UNIT REVIEW

4. There are 12 juice boxes.
   There are 7 apple juice boxes and the rest are grape.
   How many juice boxes are grape?

   There are __5__ grape juice boxes.

5. There are 10 girls in the park.
   There are 9 boys in the park.
   How many fewer boys are there than girls?

   There is __1__ fewer boy.

6. There are 8 basketballs.
   There are 4 soccer balls.
   How many more basketballs are there than soccer balls?

   There are __4__ more basketballs than soccer balls.

7. Seth found 10 seashells at the beach.
   Rachel also found 10 seashells.
   How many seashells did they find altogether?

   They found __20__ seashells altogether.

ADD OR SUBTRACT: PROBLEM SOLVING   (312)   UNIT REVIEW

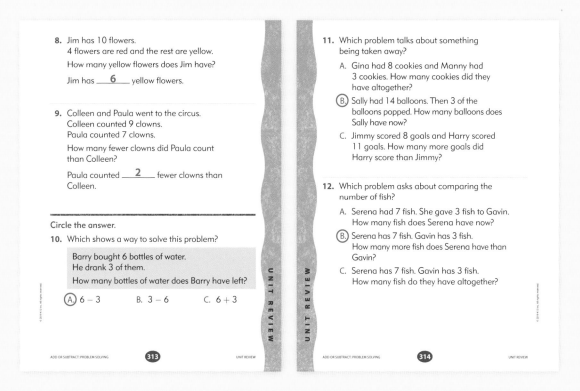

8. Jim has 10 flowers.
4 flowers are red and the rest are yellow.
How many yellow flowers does Jim have?

Jim has ___**6**___ yellow flowers.

9. Colleen and Paula went to the circus.
Colleen counted 9 clowns.
Paula counted 7 clowns.

How many fewer clowns did Paula count than Colleen?

Paula counted ___**2**___ fewer clowns than Colleen.

Circle the answer.

10. Which shows a way to solve this problem?

Barry bought 6 bottles of water.
He drank 3 of them.
How many bottles of water does Barry have left?

(A.) 6 − 3   B. 3 − 6   C. 6 + 3

11. Which problem talks about something being taken away?

A. Gina had 8 cookies and Manny had 3 cookies. How many cookies did they have altogether?

(B.) Sally had 14 balloons. Then 3 of the balloons popped. How many balloons does Sally have now?

C. Jimmy scored 8 goals and Harry scored 11 goals. How many more goals did Harry score than Jimmy?

12. Which problem asks about comparing the number of fish?

A. Serena had 7 fish. She gave 3 fish to Gavin. How many fish does Serena have now?

(B.) Serena has 7 fish. Gavin has 3 fish. How many more fish does Serena have than Gavin?

C. Serena has 7 fish. Gavin has 3 fish. How many fish do they have altogether?

➡ UNIT REVIEW Prepare for the Checkpoint

What you do next depends on how students performed in the previous activity, Unit Review: Checkpoint Practice. If students had difficulty with any of the problems, complete the appropriate review activity listed in the table online.

Unit Checkpoint

Lesson Overview

UNIT CHECKPOINT Offline	40 minutes	**OFFLINE**

▶ Unit Objectives

This lesson assesses the following objectives:

- Recognize and solve word problems involving sums or minuends up through 20 in which one quantity changes through addition or subtraction.
- Recognize and solve word problems involving sums up through 20 in which two quantities are combined.
- Recognize and solve word problems involving numbers up to 10 in which two quantities are compared by the use of addition or subtraction.

UNIT CHECKPOINT Offline

OFFLINE 40 min

Students will complete the Unit Checkpoint offline. Print the Checkpoint and have students complete it on their own. Read the directions, problems, and answer choices to students, if necessary. Use the answer key to score the Checkpoint, and then enter the results online.

Objectives

- Assess unit objectives.

Tips

Students may choose to use models or sketches to solve the story problems.

Name _____ Date _____

Unit Checkpoint Answer Key

Circle the answer.

(1 point)
1. Talya had 9 crayons. Her friend gave her 5 more. How many crayons does Talya have now?

   A. 4   B. 5   **C. 14**

(1 point)
2. Which best describes what is happening in this problem?

   Yasmin had 8 stickers. She bought 8 more stickers. How many stickers does she have now?

   A. Yasmin now has more than 8 stickers.
   B. Yasmin now has 8 stickers.
   C. Yasmin now has fewer than 8 stickers.

(1 point)
3. Which can be used to show what is happening in this problem?

   Tony had 11 crayons. He gave 5 of them to Jackie. How many crayons does he have left?

   A. 11 + 5
   B. 5 − 11
   C. 11 − 5

(1 point)
4. Jackson put 5 strawberries in his cereal. His mother put 3 more strawberries in his cereal. How many strawberries are now in Jackson's cereal?

   A. 10
   B. 8
   C. 2

(1 point)
5. Jillian has 9 dolls. Perri has 7 dolls. How many more dolls does Jillian have than Perri?

   A. 1   **B. 2**   C. 16

Name _____ Date _____

(1 point)
6. Dakota scored 5 goals in the soccer game. Mason scored 2 fewer goals than Dakota. How many goals did Mason score?

   A. 7   **B. 3**   C. 2

Solve.

(1 point)
7. Jim has 5 toy trucks. Hal has 4 toy trucks. How many toy trucks do they have altogether?

   They have __9__ toy trucks altogether.

(1 point)
8. Miguel has 15 fish in his aquarium. 7 fish are orange and the rest are green. How many fish are green?

   __8__ fish are green.

(1 point)
9. Cole has 9 toy train cars. 5 toy train cars are black and the rest are gray. How many toy train cars are gray?

   __4__ toy train cars are gray.

(1 point)
10. Dara had 9 oranges. She gave Jessica 3 oranges. How many oranges does Dara have left?

    Dara has __6__ oranges left.

(1 point)
11. Sarah has 4 pink purses and 7 purple purses. How many fewer pink purses does she have than purple purses?

    Sarah has __3__ fewer pink purses.

(1 point)
12. Justin can jump rope 10 times. Kyle can only jump rope 2 times. How many more times can Justin jump than Kyle?

    Justin can jump __8__ more times than Kyle.

Measurement

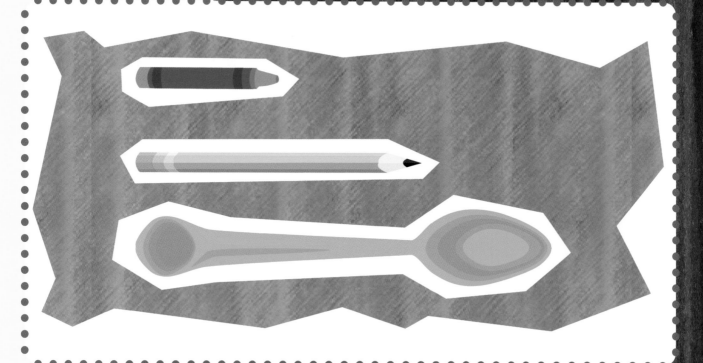

▶ Unit Objectives

- Measure the length of objects by using nonstandard units.
- Compare objects by length (for example, note which object is shorter, longer, or taller).
- Compare objects by weight (for example, note which object is heavier).
- Compare the capacity of objects by making direct comparisons between two objects (for example, note which object holds more).

▶ Big Ideas

- A quantity can be measured by identifying a unit of measure and repeating that unit over the quantity.
- The size of the unit used in measurement does not affect the quantity measured, but the larger the unit, the smaller the total number of units will be.
- Quantities can be compared, added, or subtracted if they have been measured by the same unit.

▶ Unit Introduction

Students will find the length of objects using nonstandard units of measure. They will compare the length of objects by finding which object is shorter or longer. Students will compare the weight of objects by finding which object is heavier or lighter. They will also compare the capacity of containers by finding which container holds more and which holds less.

Measure Objects

Lesson Overview

Skills Update	5 minutes	ONLINE
GET READY Numbers Through 20	5 minutes	ONLINE
LEARN Nonstandard Units	10 minutes	ONLINE
LEARN Measure with Cubes	15 minutes	OFFLINE
TRY IT Measure Length	5 minutes	OFFLINE
CHECKPOINT	5 minutes	OFFLINE

▶ Lesson Objectives

Measure the length of objects by using nonstandard units.

▶ Prerequisite Skills

Count aloud a number of objects up through 20.

▶ Advance Preparation

Cut 15 small pieces of paper, each about 1 square inch in size.

Gather the various household objects listed for students to measure. If these objects are not available, you may have students measure other objects, such as a paintbrush, book, sheet of paper, or glue stick.

▶ Safety

Remove the staples from the stapler before measuring it. When students are measuring the stapler, supervise them to make sure that they do not pinch their fingers.

▶ Content Background

Students will find the lengths of various objects using nonstandard units. All measurement involves a number of a certain unit, such as inches. Units can be standard or nonstandard. Standard units are ones that everyone knows and agrees are specific sizes, such as inches, centimeters, quarts, liters, pounds, or kilograms.

Nonstandard units also must each be the same size, but can be anything students choose to use. For example, some people will use their index finger to measure the length of an object when they don't have a ruler. Other nonstandard units for length might be a set of small paper clips, toothpicks, or craft sticks. Using nonstandard units to measure objects helps students understand that the number of units differs depending on the size of the unit of measure. They can then transfer this idea to standard units of measure.

Materials to Gather

SUPPLIED

blocks – O (any color)

Measure Length activity page

Checkpoint (printout)

ALSO NEEDED

paper – cut into 15 small, equal-sized pieces

household objects – crayons, eraser, stapler, marker, chalk, book, shoe

congruent – having exactly the same size and shape
length – the distance between two points
measure – to use standard units to find a distance, area, volume, capacity, temperature, or interval of time
measurement – the process of using units to find a quantity or size
nonstandard unit – any unit chosen to be used repeatedly to measure, such as a paper clip or triangular tile

ONLINE
5min

GET READY Numbers Through 20

Students will use the Counting Learning Tool to practice counting objects up through 20.

DIRECTIONS FOR USING THE COUNTING LEARNING TOOL

1. Select Problem Mode 1.
   - Choose the shape that students would like to count.
   - Click No to not use ten-frames.
   - Click Start.
2. Students should count aloud as they drag each object into a box.

Have students practice counting at least five numbers.

Objectives

- Count aloud a number of objects up through 20.

Tips

To prevent students from skipping an object or counting an object twice, have students touch each object online as they count it.

ONLINE
10min

LEARN Nonstandard Units

Students will practice measuring the length of objects in Serena's bathroom by using different nonstandard units of measurement.

Objectives

- Measure the length of objects by using nonstandard units.

Tips

Make sure that students count only the units of measure that fit within the vertical lines at the ends of the objects.

LEARN Measure with Cubes

OFFLINE 15min

Objectives
- Measure the length of objects by using nonstandard units.

Students will measure the length of objects by using cubes as a nonstandard unit of measure.

Gather the cubes and various school supplies such as a crayon, marker, stapler, eraser, and chalk for students to measure.

1. **Say:** Length is how long an object is from one end to the other end.
2. Give students the crayon and the cubes. Explain that to find the length of the crayon, they need to measure it from the end to the tip.
3. Show students how to line up the first cube with the flat end of the crayon to get an accurate measurement.

Tips

To help students measure accurately, make sure that they line up the end of the object being measured with the first cube.

For variety, use beads as a nonstandard unit of measure.

Ask: Is this crayon 1 cube long?
ANSWER: No, the crayon is longer than 1 cube.

4. Have students continue to add cubes until they measure the crayon's length.

Ask: About how many cubes long is the crayon?
A reasonable answer would be within 1 number of the correct number of cubes. For example, if the crayon is just short of 5 cubes long, an answer of 4 or 5 cubes long would be reasonable.

5. Line up 10 cubes under the crayon.

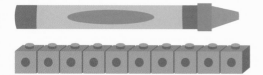

Ask: Is the crayon 10 cubes long? Why or why not?
ANSWER: No, 10 cubes are longer than the length of the crayon.

7. Follow Steps 3–5 to measure the other objects.

TRY IT Measure Length

OFFLINE 5min

Objectives
- Measure the length of objects by using nonstandard units.

Students will practice measuring objects using nonstandard units of measure. Give students the book, shoe, small squares of paper, and the Measure Length activity page from their Activity Book. Read the directions with them.

When students have completed the activity page, have them use the squares of paper to measure other objects.

Tips

For variety, use dried beans or paper clips for nonstandard units of measure.

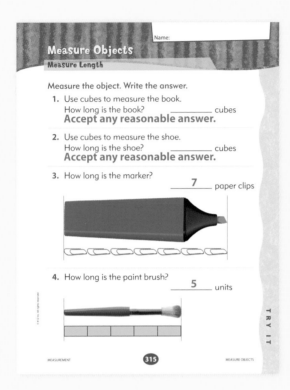

Measure Objects

Measure Length

Measure the object. Write the answer.

1. Use cubes to measure the book.
   How long is the book? _____ cubes
   Accept any reasonable answer.

2. Use cubes to measure the shoe.
   How long is the shoe? _____ cubes
   Accept any reasonable answer.

3. How long is the marker? ___7___ paper clips

4. How long is the paint brush? ___5___ units

TRY IT

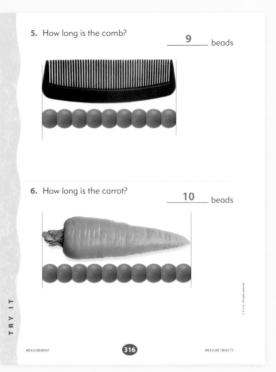

5. How long is the comb? ___9___ beads

6. How long is the carrot? ___10___ beads

TRY IT

CHECKPOINT

OFFLINE **5**min

Objectives

Print the Checkpoint. Students will take a performance-based assessment. Read the directions and problems to students, if necessary. Use the answer key to score the Checkpoint, and then enter the results online.

Gather the marker, stapler, and cubes.

- Measure the length of objects by using nonstandard units.

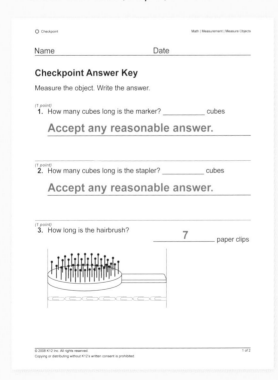

Checkpoint   Math | Measurement | Measure Objects

Name _____ Date _____

Checkpoint Answer Key

Measure the object. Write the answer.

(1 point)
1. How many cubes long is the marker? _____ cubes

   Accept any reasonable answer.

(1 point)
2. How many cubes long is the stapler? _____ cubes

   Accept any reasonable answer.

(1 point)
3. How long is the hairbrush? ___7___ paper clips

1 of 2

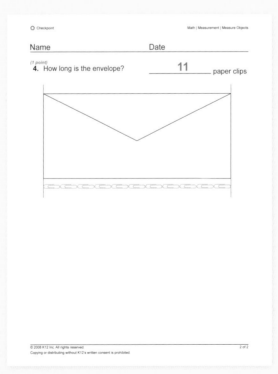

Checkpoint   Math | Measurement | Measure Objects

Name _____ Date _____

(1 point)
4. How long is the envelope? ___11___ paper clips

2 of 2

Compare Length

Skills Update	5 minutes	ONLINE
GET READY Attribute Match	5 minutes	ONLINE
LEARN Compare Length or Height of Objects	10 minutes	ONLINE
LEARN Shorter, Longer, and Taller	15 minutes	OFFLINE
TRY IT Compare Length of Objects	5 minutes	OFFLINE
CHECKPOINT	5 minutes	OFFLINE

▶ Lesson Objectives

Compare objects by length (for example, note which object is shorter, longer, or taller).

▶ Prerequisite Skills

Describe objects by their attributes, such as color, shape, and size.

▶ Advance Preparation

Gather the various household objects listed for students to measure. If these objects are not available, you may have students compare other objects, such as a paper towel roll and a toilet paper roll or a large jar and a small jar.

▶ Safety

Have students handle fragile objects carefully so that they do not break them.

▶ Content Background

Students will compare the length and height of objects by finding which is longer, shorter, or taller.

Materials to Gather

SUPPLIED

blocks – O (any color)

Compare Length of Objects activity page

Checkpoint (printout)

ALSO NEEDED

household objects – marker, crayon, 2 unsharpened pencils, eraser, spoon, place mat, picture frame, pen, clothespin, cup, mug, vase, bowl, can, cereal box

Keywords

compare – to find the similarities or differences among sizes, values, or amounts

height – the vertical distance from the base to the top of an object

longer – having a greater time or distance than another

opposite – being the other of two related things; for example, if the book is longer than the pencil, the opposite situation is that the pencil is shorter than the book

shorter – having a lesser time or distance than another

taller – a greater height than another

GET READY Attribute Match

Students will sort objects based on the attributes of color, shape, and size.

- Describe objects by their attributes, such as color, shape, and size.

LEARN Compare Length or Height of Objects

Students will use pictures to compare the length or height of objects.

Objectives

- Compare objects by length (for example, note which object is shorter, longer, or taller).

LEARN Shorter, Longer, and Taller

Students will compare the lengths of objects to find which object is shorter, longer, or taller than the other.

Gather the cubes, marker, crayon, pencils, eraser, spoon, place mat, picture frame, pen, clothespin, cup, mug, vase, bowl, can, and cereal box.

Objectives

- Compare objects by length (for example, note which object is shorter, longer, or taller).

DESCRIBE LENGTH AND HEIGHT

1. Show students the pen.

   Say: Length is the distance between the two ends of an object.

2. Have students use cubes to show how long the pen is.

3. Show students the cup.

   Say: Height is the distance from the bottom to the top of an object.

4. Have students stack cubes to show the height of the cup.

COMPARE LENGTH

5. Explain to students that you are going to compare the length of the marker and the crayon. (The marker must be longer than the crayon.)

   Say: We will use two pencils to help us line up the ends of our objects so that we can accurately compare the lengths.

6. Place one pencil vertically on the table. Place the crayon so that its end touches the pencil's edge. Guide students to line up the end of the marker against the side of the pencil, below the crayon. Place the second pencil vertically on the table at the other end of the marker.

   Say: You can see that the length of the marker goes past the length of the crayon. That means the marker is longer.

7. **Ask:** If the marker is longer than the crayon, how can we describe the length of the crayon compared to the marker?
   ANSWER: The crayon is shorter than the marker.

8. Explain that longer and shorter are opposite descriptions, but that both terms can be used to compare length.

9. Have students use the two pencils to compare the length of the pairs of objects:
   - a pen and an eraser
   - a spoon and a place mat
   - a picture frame and a clothespin

COMPARE HEIGHT

10. Explain to students that you are going to compare the height of the cup and the mug. Place the two objects side by side. (The cup must be taller than the mug.)

    Say: Comparing two objects to find which is taller is like finding the object that is longer, except now the objects are standing up.

11. **Ask:** Which object is taller?
    ANSWER: the cup

12. **Ask:** How can you tell the cup is taller?
    ANSWER: The cup stands higher than the mug.

13. **Ask:** If the cup is taller than the mug, how can we describe the mug compared to the cup?
    ANSWER: The mug is shorter than the cup.

14. Have students compare the height of the following pairs of objects:
    - a vase and a bowl
    - a can and a cereal box

OFFLINE
5min

TRY IT Compare Length of Objects

Objectives

Students will practice comparing objects to find which one is longer, shorter, or taller.

Give students the Compare Length of Objects activity page from their Activity Book and read the directions with them.

- Compare objects by length (for example, note which object is shorter, longer, or taller).

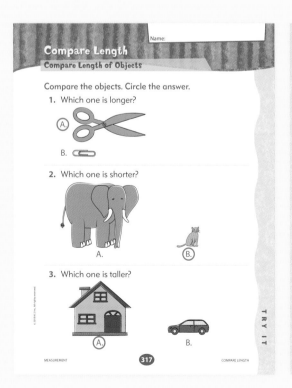

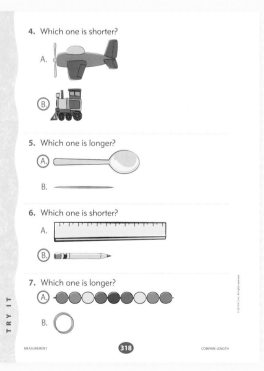

OFFLINE
5min

Objectives

- Compare objects by length (for example, note which object is shorter, longer, or taller).

Print the Checkpoint and have students complete it on their own. Read the directions and problems to students, if necessary. Use the answer key to score the Checkpoint, and then enter the results online.

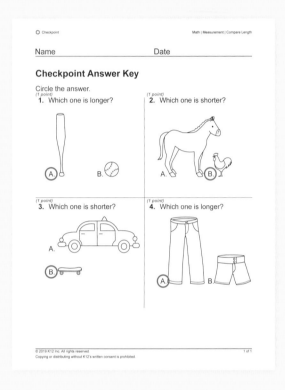

Compare Weight

Lesson Overview

Skills Update	5 minutes	ONLINE
LEARN Compare the Weight of Objects	15 minutes	ONLINE
LEARN Heavier or Lighter?	10 minutes	ONLINE
TRY IT Weight Comparison	10 minutes	OFFLINE
CHECKPOINT	5 minutes	OFFLINE

▶ Lesson Objectives

Compare objects by weight (for example, note which object is heavier).

▶ Advance Preparation

Gather the various household objects listed. If these objects are not available, you may gather other objects that are similar in weight.

▶ Content Background

Students will compare the weight of objects by finding which object is heavier or lighter.

Keywords

heavier – having a greater weight than another
lighter – having a lesser weight than another
weight – the measure of the heaviness of an object

Materials to Gather

SUPPLIED

blocks – O (1 of any color)
Weight Comparison activity page
Checkpoint (printout)

ALSO NEEDED

household objects – apple, paper clip,
    feather, pillow, ball, book, pencil,
    sheet of paper, 4 other objects
    students can hold

LEARN Compare the Weight of Objects

ONLINE 15min

Objectives

Students will compare the weights of objects to find which object is heavier. Gather the cubes, apple, paper clip, feather, pillow, and ball.

Follow the directions on each screen. Review the terms *heavier* and *lighter* with students before they start the activity. *Heavier* means that one object has a greater weight than another. *Lighter* means that one object has a lesser weight than another.

- Compare objects by weight (for example, note which object is heavier).

LEARN Heavier or Lighter?

ONLINE 10min

Objectives

Students will practice comparing the weight of objects by deciding which object in a pair is heavier or lighter.

- Compare objects by weight (for example, note which object is heavier).

TRY IT Weight Comparison

OFFLINE 10min

Objectives

Students will practice comparing objects to find which one is heavier or lighter. Give students a book, paper, pencil, assorted household items to compare, and the Weight Comparison activity page from their Activity Book. Read the directions with them.

- Compare objects by weight (for example, note which object is heavier).

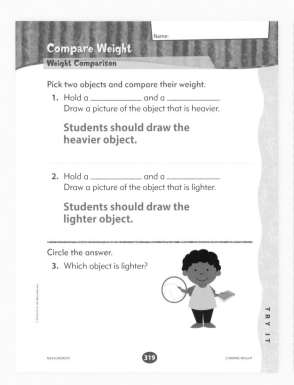

CHECKPOINT

Objectives

- Compare objects by weight (for example, note which object is heavier).

Print the Checkpoint and have students complete it on their own. Read the directions and problems to students, if necessary. Use the answer key to score the Checkpoint, and then enter the results online.

Compare Capacity

Lesson Overview

Skills Update	5 minutes	ONLINE
LEARN Fill to Capacity	15 minutes	OFFLINE
LEARN Check the Capacity	15 minutes	OFFLINE
TRY IT Fill and Compare	5 minutes	OFFLINE
CHECKPOINT	5 minutes	OFFLINE

▶ Lesson Objectives

Compare the capacity of objects by making direct comparisons between two objects (for example, note which object holds more).

▶ Advance Preparation

Label two index cards as follows: **holds more** and **holds less**.

Gather the various containers listed for students to use to compare capacities. If these types of containers are not available, you may have students use other types that are similar in size. If rice isn't available, you may use a different nonstandard unit of capacity, such as beans or macaroni.

▶ Safety

Have students handle fragile objects carefully so that they do not break them.

▶ Content Background

Students will compare the capacity of containers by finding which container holds more and which holds less.

Materials to Gather

SUPPLIED

Fill and Compare activity page

Checkpoint (printout)

ALSO NEEDED

index cards – labeled with **holds more** and **holds less**

household objects – bag of rice

containers – spoon, 1-cup measuring cup, 1 gallon of water, mug, pot, drinking glass, small bucket, bowl, teapot, watering can

Keywords

capacity – a measure indicating an amount a container can hold

container – an object that can be used to hold objects or liquids, such as a box, a cup, a pitcher, or a can

cup (c) – a unit for measuring capacity in the English system of measurement; 1 cup = 8 ounces

less – not as many as another

more – a greater number or amount than another

LEARN Fill to Capacity

Objectives

- Compare the capacity of objects by making direct comparisons between two objects (for example, note which object holds more).

Students will compare the capacity of two containers to find which holds more or less than the other. Gather the rice, water, measuring cup, mug, spoon, pot, glass, bucket, bowl, teapot, and watering can. Also gather the index cards.

1. Show students the mug and the spoon. Explain that students can compare capacity to find out if a container holds more or less than another container.

   Say: Capacity tells us how much a container holds.

2. Show students the bag of rice.

   Ask: Which container, the mug or spoon, do you think will hold more rice?

3. Show students how to scoop a cup of rice and pour it into mug. (The cup of rice should be level at the top, not overflowing.) Pour the rice until the mug is full.

   Ask: About how many cups of rice does the mug hold?

4. **Say:** Now let's see if the spoon will hold more rice than the mug or less rice than the mug.

5. Have students measure a cup of rice and pour rice into the spoon.

   Ask: How much rice does the spoon hold?

6. Put the mug and the spoon next to each other. Have students place the index card labeled "holds more" next to the container that holds more. Then have students place the index card labeled "holds less" next to the container that holds less.

   Ask: Which container has a greater capacity?

7. Explain that the mug has a larger capacity because it can hold more rice. The spoon holds less, so it has a smaller capacity than the mug.

8. Follow Steps 3–7 using the pot and the glass. Count aloud as you pour each cup of rice into the pot.

   Ask: Which container holds more? Which container holds less? How do you know?
   ANSWER: The pot holds more rice than the glass. The glass holds less rice than the pot. We poured rice into both containers.

9. Compare the bucket and bowl, and the teapot and watering can by using the measuring cup to fill them with water.

holds more

holds less

LEARN Check the Capacity

Objectives

- Compare the capacity of objects by making direct comparisons between two objects (for example, note which object holds more).

Students will compare capacities of different containers.
   Gather the measuring cup and the containers of varying shapes and sizes.

1. Show students two containers. Ask them to decide which one holds more or less.

2. Have students fill each container with water using the measuring cup to see which one holds more.

3. Continue with at least five more pairs of containers. At least one pair should consist of a short, wide container and a tall, thin container. Discuss the results with students.

TRY IT Fill and Compare

OFFLINE
5 min

Students will practice comparing capacity by filling pairs of containers with water and saying which holds more and which holds less.

Give students the measuring cup, water, four pairs of containers, and the Fill and Compare activity page from their Activity Book. Write the names of the containers for each problem on the activity page, and read the directions with students.

Objectives

- Compare the capacity of objects by making direct comparisons between two objects (for example, note which object holds more).

Tips

For variety, use flour, beans, or sand to compare capacity.

Place containers on a plate to minimize the mess from spills.

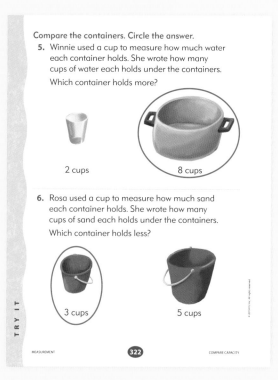

Compare Capacity
Fill and Compare

Name: _____

Pick two objects and compare their capacity.

1. Fill a _____ and _____.
   Draw a picture of the container that holds more.
   Students should draw the container that holds more.

2. Fill a _____ and _____.
   Draw a picture of the container that holds more.
   Students should draw the container that holds more.

3. Fill a _____ and _____.
   Draw a picture of the container that holds less.
   Students should draw the container that holds less.

4. Fill a _____ and _____.
   Draw a picture of the container that holds less.
   Students should draw the container that holds less.

MEASUREMENT 321 COMPARE CAPACITY

TRY IT

Compare the containers. Circle the answer.

5. Winnie used a cup to measure how much water each container holds. She wrote how many cups of water each holds under the containers.

   Which container holds more?

   2 cups   8 cups

6. Rosa used a cup to measure how much sand each container holds. She wrote how many cups of sand each holds under the containers.

   Which container holds less?

   3 cups   5 cups

MEASUREMENT 322 COMPARE CAPACITY

CHECKPOINT

Print the Checkpoint. Students will take a performance-based assessment. Read the directions and problems to students, if necessray. Use the answer key to score the Checkpoint, and then enter the results online.

Gather the measuring cup, water, and an assortment of containers to fill and compare. Fill in the names of the containers for each problem.

- Compare the capacity of objects by making direct comparisons between two objects (for example, note which object holds more).

⚙ Checkpoint   Math | Measurement | Compare Capacity

Name _____ Date _____

Checkpoint Answer Key

Compare the containers, and follow the directions.
(1 point)
1. Use the cup to fill a _____ and _____ with water. Point to the container that holds less.
   Students should point to the container that holds less.

(1 point)
2. Use the cup to fill a _____ and _____ with water. Point to the container that holds less.
   Students should point to the container that holds less.

(1 point)
3. Use the cup to fill a _____ and _____ with water. Point to the container that holds more.
   Students should point to the container that holds more.

(1 point)
4. Use the cup to fill a _____ and _____ with water. Point to the container that holds more.
   Students should point to the container that holds more.

1 of 1

Unit Review

Lesson Overview

UNIT REVIEW Look Back	15 minutes	ONLINE
UNIT REVIEW Checkpoint Practice	15 minutes	OFFLINE
⏩ UNIT REVIEW Prepare for the Checkpoint		

▶ Unit Objectives

This lesson reviews the following objectives:

- Measure the length of objects by using nonstandard units.
- Compare objects by length (for example, note which object is shorter, longer, or taller).
- Compare objects by weight (for example, note which object is heavier).
- Compare the capacity of objects by making direct comparisons between two objects (for example, note which object holds more).

▶ Advance Preparation

In this lesson, students will have an opportunity to review previous activities in the Measurement unit. Look at the suggested activities in Unit Review: Prepare for the Checkpoint online and gather any needed materials. You may use the suggested materials or substitute other household objects that can be compared.

Materials to Gather

SUPPLIED

block – B (1 red)

Checkpoint Practice activity page

ALSO NEEDED

containers – 1-cup measuring, 1 gallon of water, drinking glasses (1 large, 1 small), bowls (1 large, 1 small)

household objects – 10 paper clips, book, pencil, sheet of paper

Keywords

capacity	longer
compare	measure
congruent	measurement
container	more
cup	nonstandard unit
heavier	opposite
height	shorter
length	taller
less	weight
lighter	

UNIT REVIEW Look Back

Objectives
• Review unit objectives.

In this unit, students have learned to measure the length of objects by using nonstandard units. They have also learned to measure and compare length, weight, and capacity of objects. Students will review key concepts from the unit to prepare for the Unit Checkpoint.

UNIT REVIEW Checkpoint Practice

Objectives
• Review unit objectives.

In Part 1, students will measure and compare objects to prepare for the Unit Checkpoint. In Part 2, students will complete a Checkpoint Practice activity page. If necessary, read the directions, problems, and answer choices to students. Have students answer the problems on their own. Review any missed problems with students.

Gather the circle block, book, paper clips, paper, pencil, water, measuring cup, drinking glasses, and bowls.

PART 1

1. Have students hold the circle block in one hand and the book in the other.

   Ask: Which is lighter?
   ANSWER: The circle is lighter.

2. Have students use paper clips to measure the length of the piece of paper.

   Ask: How many paper clips long is the piece of paper?

   Accept any reasonable answer.

3. Have students use paper clips to measure the length of the pencil.

   Ask: How many paper clips long is the pencil?

   Accept any reasonable answer.

4. Make a chain of 2 paper clips by placing them end to end. Place another chain of 6 paper clips below the first.

   Ask: Which chain of paper clips is longer?
   ANSWER: The chain of 6 paper clips is longer.

5. Use the measuring cup to fill each glass with water. Have students compare the amount of water in the two glasses.

   Ask: Which glass holds more?

   Students should point to the glass that holds more.

6. Use the measuring cup to fill each bowl with water. Have students compare the amount of water in the two bowls.

   Ask: Which bowl holds less?

   Students should point to the bowl that holds less.

PART 2

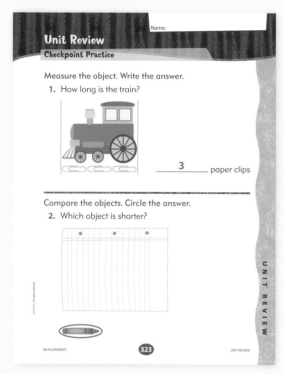

⮕ **UNIT REVIEW** Prepare for the Checkpoint

What you do next depends on how students performed in the previous activity,
Unit Review: Checkpoint Practice. If students had difficulty with any of the
problems, complete the appropriate review activity listed in the table online.

Unit Checkpoint

Lesson Overview

UNIT CHECKPOINT	40 minutes	OFFLINE

▶ Unit Objectives

This lesson assesses the following objectives:

- Measure the length of objects by using nonstandard units.
- Compare objects by length (for example, note which object is shorter, longer, or taller).
- Compare objects by weight (for example, note which object is heavier).
- Compare the capacity of objects by making direct comparisons between two objects (for example, note which object holds more).

Materials to Gather

SUPPLIED

Checkpoint (printout)

ALSO NEEDED

containers – 1-cup measuring cup, 1 gallon of water, drinking glasses (1 large, 1 small)

household objects – 10 paper clips, book, pencil, sheet of paper

OFFLINE
40 min

UNIT CHECKPOINT Offline

Objectives

- Assess unit objectives.

Students will complete the Unit Checkpoint offline. In Part 1, students will take a performance-based assessment. In Part 2, students will complete the problems on their own. Print the Unit Checkpoint. Read the directions, problems, and answer choices to students if necessary. Use the answer key to score the Unit Checkpoint, and then enter the results online.

Gather the paper clips, book, drinking glasses, water, and measuring cup. For Problem 4, use the measuring cup to fill the two glasses with water.

Name   Date

Unit Checkpoint Answer Key

Part 1
Say the answer.
(1 point)
1. Use the paper clips to measure. How many paper clips long is the book?

Students should use paper clips to measure the book. Accept any reasonable answer.

(1 point)
2. Make a chain of 7 paper clips by putting paper clips on the table next to each other horizontally, end to end. Below that, make a chain of 2 paper clips. Which chain of paper clips is longer?

Students should point to the chain of 7 paper clips.

(1 point)
3. Pick up a paper clip. Then pick up the book. Which one is lighter?

Students should say that the paper clip is lighter.

(1 point)
4. Look at these two containers of water. Which container holds more water?

Students should identify the container that holds more water.

Give students Part 2 of the assessment.

Name   Date

Part 2
Write the answer.
(1 point)
5. How long is the domino?   **2** paper clips

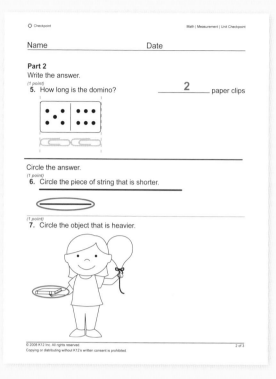

Circle the answer.
(1 point)
6. Circle the piece of string that is shorter.

(1 point)
7. Circle the object that is heavier.

Name   Date

(1 point)
8. Bror used a cup to measure how much water each container holds. He wrote how many cups of water each holds under the containers. Circle the container that holds less.

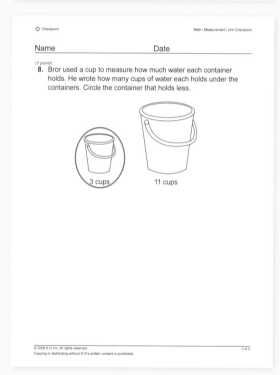

3 cups   11 cups

Numbers Through 30

23

▶ Unit Objectives

- Count aloud a number of objects up through 30.
- Use concrete objects or sketches to represent a quantity up through 30.
- Given two or more sets of 30 or fewer objects, identify which set has more or fewer objects than another set, or which sets have an equal number of objects.
- Write numerals from 1 through 30.
- Recognize that numbers with greater values describe sets with more objects in them than numbers with lesser values do (for sets of 30 or fewer objects).

▶ Big Ideas

Numbers can represent the results of counting.

▶ Unit Introduction

Students will count a number of objects up through 30. They will learn to represent amounts up through 30 with objects and with sketches. Students will compare two groups of objects to determine which group has more or fewer objects. They will compare three groups of objects to determine which group has the fewest or the most objects. Students will learn to identify groups that have the same number of objects. They will learn that numbers with greater values describe groups with more objects and numbers with lesser values describe groups with fewer objects. Finally, students will learn to write numbers from 1 through 30.

Count and Show Numbers Through 30

Lesson Overview

Skills Update	5 minutes	ONLINE
GET READY Count Stars	5 minutes	ONLINE
LEARN Count Through 30	5 minutes	ONLINE
LEARN Spill and Count	10 minutes	OFFLINE
LEARN Show Numbers	10 minutes	OFFLINE
TRY IT Count and Show Numbers	10 minutes	OFFLINE

▶ Lesson Objectives

- Count aloud a number of objects up through 30.
- Use concrete objects or sketches to represent a quantity up through 30.

▶ Prerequisite Skills

- Count aloud a number of objects up through 20.
- Use concrete objects or sketches to represent a quantity up through 20.

▶ Common Errors and Misconceptions

- Students might start counting before or after pointing to the first object in a group. Or they might stop counting before or after they point to the last object. Students should point to each object as they count it.
- Students might say more than one number for each object when counting objects in a group. Or they might skip objects. Students should point to each object and say exactly one number. Then they should point to the next object and say exactly one number, and so on.
- Students might use an incorrect counting sequence, such as "one, two, four, six, ten."

▶ Advance Preparation

Place 30 dried beans in a plastic cup that students can hold comfortably. Divide a sheet of drawing paper into 2 sections by folding or drawing lines. Number index cards 21 through 30.

▶ Content Background

In this lesson, students will learn to count up through 30. They will also use objects and sketches to represent quantities up through 30.

Materials to Gather

SUPPLIED

blocks – O (all colors)

Count and Show Numbers activity page

ALSO NEEDED

household objects – bag or cup, hand towel, 1 plastic cup, 30 dried beans

paper, drawing

crayons

index cards – numbered 21 through 30

Keywords

count – to say each number according to a defined sequence, such as consecutively, by 2s, or backward

represent – to symbolize or stand for something else

GET READY **Count Stars**

ONLINE
5min

Students will practice counting. They will count aloud to find the number of stars up through 20.

Objectives

- Count aloud a number of objects up through 20.

Tips

Make sure that students count in the correct sequence, starting with the number 1.

To prevent students from skipping an object or counting an object twice, have students touch each object online as they count it.

LEARN **Count Through 30**

ONLINE
5min

Students will practice counting up through 30. They will count beans with Serena.

Objectives

- Count aloud a number of objects up through 30.

LEARN **Spill and Count**

OFFLINE
10min

Objectives

- Count aloud a number of objects up through 30.

Students will count up through 30 objects in a group.

Gather the 30 dried beans in the plastic cup and the hand towel.

1. Spill all 30 beans onto a hand towel to prevent them from scattering. Explain to students that they are going to count the beans. Show students how to touch each bean and move it to the tabletop to indicate that it has been counted.

2. Count 10 beans together. Have students say what number comes after 10.

3. Continue counting beans from 11 to 19. Have students say what number comes after 19.

   Say: After 20, we count like we're starting with 1 again, but we say 20 before each number.

4. Continue counting beans from 21 to 29. Have students touch and say each number from 21 to 29 after you say it. Have them say what number comes after 29.

5. Have students count the 30 beans by themselves.

6. Place the beans back into the cup.

   Say: I'm going to spill out some beans. Then you can count them.

7. Spill most of the beans from the cup, leaving a few in the cup. Have students touch each bean as they count the numbers in sequence. Then return the beans to the cup.

8. **Say:** Now it's your turn to spill some beans and count them.

   Have students spill some beans and count them. Repeat the process until students have practiced counting at least five groups of beans.

Tips

For other counting objects, use beads, cubes, or circles.

LEARN Show Numbers

OFFLINE 10 min

Objectives

- Use concrete objects or sketches to represent a quantity up through 30.

Students will represent amounts up through 30 with cubes and drawings.

Gather the cubes, number cards, drawing paper, and crayons. Place the cubes in a container, such as a bag or cup.

1. Place the number cards for 21–30 face down in the workspace. Let students choose a card, and help them read the number if necessary.

2. Have students use cubes to show the number.

   Ask: What is another way that we can we show a number?
   ANSWER: We can draw a picture.

3. Have students draw dots or lines on one section of the paper to show the number.

4. When students have completed their drawing, have them count the objects that they drew. Write the number in the section with the drawing.

5. Repeat Steps 1–4.

Tips

To prevent students from counting the same cube twice, have them touch each cube as they count it.

To prevent students from counting the same object twice, have them cross out each object as they count it.

TRY IT Count and Show Numbers

OFFLINE 10 min

Objectives

- Count aloud a number of objects up through 30.
- Use concrete objects or sketches to represent a quantity up through 30.

Students will practice counting and showing numbers. Give students the cubes and the Count and Show Numbers activity page from their Activity Book. Read the directions with them.

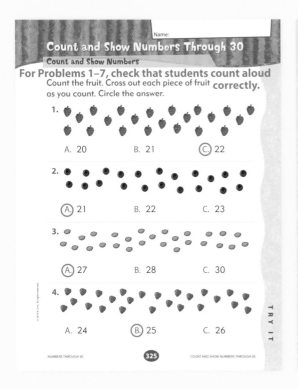

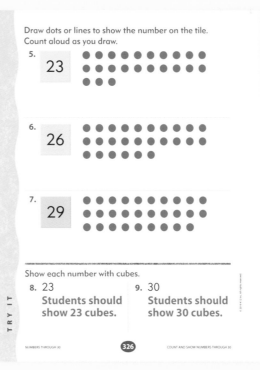

Count Objects Through 30

Lesson Overview

Skills Update	5 minutes	**ONLINE**
GET READY Count Beads	5 minutes	**ONLINE**
LEARN How Many Beads?	15 minutes	**ONLINE**
TRY IT Count Gems	10 minutes	**OFFLINE**
CHECKPOINT	10 minutes	**OFFLINE**

▶ Lesson Objectives

Count aloud a number of objects up through 30.

▶ Prerequisite Skills

Count aloud a number of objects up through 20.

▶ Common Errors and Misconceptions

- Students might start counting before or after pointing to the first object in a group. Or they might stop counting before or after they point to the last object. Students should point to each object as they count it.
- Students might say more than one number for each object when counting objects in a group. Or they might skip objects. Students should point to each object and say exactly one number. Then they should point to the next object and say exactly one number, and so on.
- Students might use an incorrect counting sequence, such as "one, two, four, six, ten."

▶ Content Background

Students will practice counting different objects up through 30.

GET READY Count Beads

ONLINE
5 min

Objectives

Students will practice counting a number of objects up through 20 by counting beads.

- Count aloud a number of objects up through 20.

LEARN How Many Beads?

ONLINE
15 min

Objectives

Students will practice counting objects up through 30. They will count beads on necklaces.

- Count aloud a number of objects up through 30.

TRY IT Count Gems

OFFLINE
10 min

Objectives

Students will practice counting objects. Give students the Count Gems activity page from their Activity Book and read the directions with them.

- Count aloud a number of objects up through 30.

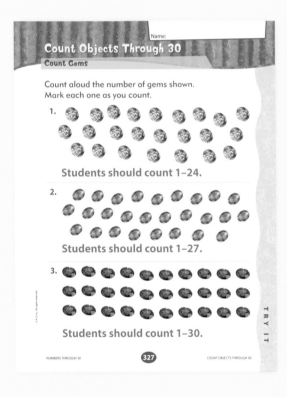

Name:

Count Objects Through 30
Count Gems

Count aloud the number of gems shown.
Mark each one as you count.

1. Students should count 1–24.

2. Students should count 1–27.

3. Students should count 1–30.

NUMBERS THROUGH 30 — 327 — COUNT OBJECTS THROUGH 30

TRY IT

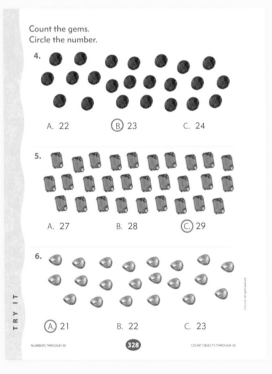

Count the gems.
Circle the number.

4.

A. 22   B. 23   C. 24

5.

A. 27   B. 28   C. 29

6.

A. 21   B. 22   C. 23

NUMBERS THROUGH 30 — 328 — COUNT OBJECTS THROUGH 30

TRY IT

Objectives

Print the Checkpoint. Students will take a performance-based assessment. Read the directions and problems to students, if necessary. Use the answer key to score the Checkpoint, and then enter the results online.

- Count aloud a number of objects up through 30.

Name _____ Date _____

Checkpoint Answer Key

Count aloud the number of objects shown. Write the answer.

(1 point)
1. How many triangles are there? _____ **30** _____ triangles

(1 point)
2. How many circles are there? _____ **25** _____ circles

Name _____ Date _____

(1 point)
3. How many rectangles are there? _____ **22** _____ rectangles

(1 point)
4. How many squares are there? _____ **27** _____ squares

Represent Amounts Through 30

Lesson Overview

Skills Update	5 minutes	ONLINE
GET READY Show an Amount Through 20	5 minutes	ONLINE
LEARN Show Amounts with Sticks	10 minutes	OFFLINE
LEARN Draw Amounts	10 minutes	OFFLINE
TRY IT Show and Draw Amounts	10 minutes	OFFLINE
CHECKPOINT	5 minutes	OFFLINE

▶ Lesson Objectives

Use concrete objects or sketches to represent a quantity up through 30.

▶ Prerequisite Skills

Use concrete objects or sketches to represent a quantity up through 20.

▶ Advance Preparation

Place the circle block, triangle block, and square block in a paper bag.
   Number index cards 1 through 30. Place the index cards numbered 15 through 30 in the other paper bag. Save cards for use in future lessons.
   Fold each sheet of drawing paper into 4 sections.

▶ Content Background

Students will use objects and drawings to represent amounts through 30.

Materials to Gather

SUPPLIED

Show and Draw Amounts activity page

blocks – A (1 red)

blocks – C (1 blue)

blocks – D (1 green)

blocks – O (15 blue, 15 yellow)

Checkpoint (printout)

ALSO NEEDED

household objects – paper cups or
   rubber bands, 2 paper lunch bags

craft sticks – 30

paper, drawing – 2 sheets

index cards – numbered 1 through 30

GET READY Show an Amount Through 20

Students will practice representing amounts up through 20 by counting objects and identifying the number that matches.

- Use concrete objects or sketches to represent a quantity up through 20.

LEARN Show Amounts with Sticks

Objectives

Students will represent amounts up through 30 by forming and counting groups of objects.

Gather the craft sticks and the paper cups or rubber bands.

- Use concrete objects or sketches to represent a quantity up through 30.

1. Have students form a group of 24 craft sticks. Tell them to count aloud as they put each craft stick in the group.

2. Have students move 10 sticks to the side as they count aloud from 1 to 10.

   Say: Let's keep this group of 10 together and form another group as we continue counting.

3. Have students begin with 11 and stop at 20. Keep the two groups of 10 separate. Tell students that there are 10 sticks in the first group and another 10 in the second group. Explain that so far there are 20 sticks.

4. Have students begin with 21 and continue counting the remaining sticks.

   Ask: How many sticks are in the group? How do you know that you have 24 craft sticks?
   ANSWER: I counted. The last number I counted was 24.

5. Show students that counting by 10s and then adding on the extra ones can make counting faster.

6. Repeat steps 1–5 using the following amounts: 28, 17, 25, 12, and 30.

Tips

To keep the sticks together, students may either use a rubber band or put the group of sticks in a paper cup.

LEARN Draw Amounts

Objectives

Students will represent amounts up through 30 by drawing sketches.

Gather the bag of numbered index cards, bag of blocks, and drawing paper.

- Use concrete objects or sketches to represent a quantity up through 30.

1. Have students pull a numbered index card out of one bag and tell you what the number is. Then have them pull a shape out of the other bag. Have students describe the shape by using the attributes of color, size, and name of the shape.

2. Have students draw as many of the chosen shape as the number on the index card. For example, if students pull the index card with the number 21 and a triangle block, they would draw 21 triangles. Students should use one section of a sheet of drawing paper for the drawing.

3. Have students count the objects that they drew.

4. Repeat Steps 1–3 until students have filled the sections of the drawing paper.

   Ask: How do drawings help you show an amount?
   ANSWER: They help me see the amount and I can count them.

Tips

To help students draw the correct number, encourage them to draw rows of 10 objects for numbers greater than 10.

To give students additional practice, leave the index cards out of the bag once they are removed, and have students draw sketches of different amounts.

TRY IT Show and Draw Amounts

Students will practice representing amounts through 30 by using drawings and cubes. Give students the cubes and the Show and Draw Amounts activity page from their Activity Book. Read the directions with them.

Objectives

• Use concrete objects or sketches to represent a quantity up through 30.

Tips

Have students point to the number in each problem and say it aloud before they start to draw.

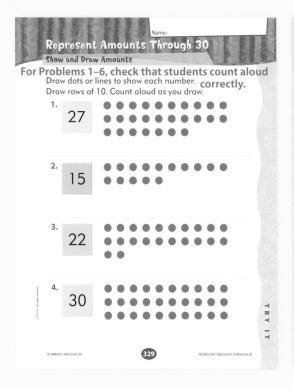

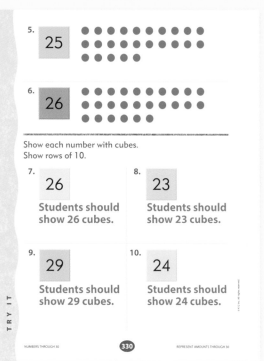

CHECKPOINT

Print the Checkpoint. Students will take a performance-based assessment. Read the directions and problems to students, if necessary. Use the answer key to score the Checkpoint, and then enter the results online.

Gather the cubes for Problems 3 and 4.

Objectives

- Use concrete objects or sketches to represent a quantity up through 30.

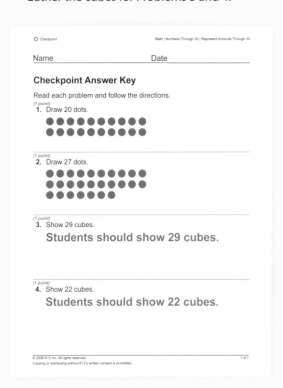

Compare Groups Through 30

Lesson Overview

Skills Update	5 minutes	ONLINE
GET READY Compare Groups of Fruit	5 minutes	ONLINE
TRY IT Compare Different Groups	5 minutes	ONLINE
LEARN Compare Groups of Cubes	10 minutes	OFFLINE
LEARN Compare Plant Groups	10 minutes	OFFLINE
TRY IT Compare Groups	10 minutes	OFFLINE

▶ Lesson Objectives

Given two or more sets of 30 or fewer objects, identify which set has more or fewer objects than another set, or which sets have an equal number of objects.

▶ Prerequisite Skills

Given two or more sets of 20 or fewer objects, identify which set has more or fewer objects than another set, or which sets have an equal number of objects.

▶ Advance Preparation

Gather three identical clear plastic containers with lids. The containers should be large enough to each hold 30 cubes. Place 22 cubes in one container, 27 in a second container, and 30 in the third container.

Number index cards 1 through 30, or gather the number cards you created previously. Label two index cards with the word **same** and four other index cards with the following words: **more, fewer, most, fewest**. Save cards for use in future lessons.

▶ Content Background

Students will compare groups of objects and identify which has more or fewer objects.

Keywords

compare – to find the similarities or differences among sizes, values, or amounts
equal – the relationship of expressions, numbers, or amounts that have the same value
fewer – a lesser number than another
fewest – the least number among three or more
more – a greater number or amount than another
most – the greatest number or amount among three or more

Materials to Gather

SUPPLIED
Compare Plant Groups activity page
Compare Groups activity page
blocks – O (all colors)

ALSO NEEDED
containers – 3, clear with plastic lids
index cards – two labeled **same;** four labeled **more, fewer, most, fewest**
index cards – numbered 1 through 30

GET READY Compare Groups of Fruit

ONLINE 5 min

Students will practice comparing two groups of fruit to identify which group has more and which group has fewer pieces of fruit. Then they will compare three groups to find the groups that have an equal number of pieces of fruit.

Objectives

- Given two or more sets of 20 or fewer objects, identify which set has more or fewer objects than another set, or which sets have an equal number of objects.

TRY IT Compare Different Groups

ONLINE 5 min

Students will answer questions online to demonstrate what they have learned about comparing groups.

Objectives

- Given two or more sets of 30 or fewer objects, identify which set has more or fewer objects than another set, or which sets have an equal number of objects.

LEARN Compare Groups of Cubes

OFFLINE 10 min

Students will compare groups of objects. They will identify if a group has more or fewer objects, the most or fewest objects, or the same number of objects.
Gather the containers of cubes, number cards, and index cards.

Objectives

- Given two or more sets of 30 or fewer objects, identify which set has more or fewer objects than another set, or which sets have an equal number of objects.

Tips

Use the same color cubes in each container. You can also place the cubes from each container on different colors of paper to keep the groups separate.
Encourage students to make trains of 10 cubes to count and compare each group.

MORE AND FEWER

1. Show students the containers with 22 cubes and 30 cubes. Give students the index cards labeled **more** and **fewer**. Read the words on the labeled cards aloud.

2. Have students guess which container has more cubes and place the card labeled **more** next to it. Have students place the card labeled **fewer** next to the other container.

3. Have students count the cubes in each container. Encourage them to make trains of 10 cubes as they count. Have them compare the two groups of cubes. Then have them place the correct number card next to each group.

4. **Ask:** Which container had fewer cubes?
   ANSWER: the container with 22 cubes

   Ask: How do you know?
   ANSWER: Each cube in the group of 22 had a match with each cube in the group of 30. There were cubes that were not matched in the group of 30.

5. Have students move the labeled cards to the correct group if necessary.

6. Repeat Steps 2–5 using the container with 27 cubes and the container with 30 cubes.

MOST AND FEWEST

7. Show students all three containers. Give them the index cards labeled **most** and **fewest**. Read the words on the labeled cards aloud.

   Ask: Which container do you think has the most cubes?

8. Have students place the labeled cards next to the containers with the most and the fewest cubes.

9. Have students count the cubes in each container. Have them compare the three groups of cubes. Then have them place the correct number card next to each group.

10. **Ask:** Which container has the most cubes?
    ANSWER: the container with 30 cubes

    Ask: How do you know?
    ANSWER: The group of 30 cubes had cubes that were not matched to the group of 22 or 27 cubes.

11. Have students move the labeled cards to the correct group if necessary.

SAME

12. Put 26 cubes in two containers and 19 cubes in the third container. Give students the two index cards labeled **same**.

    Ask: Which two containers do you think have the same number of cubes?

13. Have students place the labeled cards next to the containers that have the same number of cubes.

14. Have students count the cubes in each container. Have them compare the three groups of cubes.

    Ask: How do you know these two groups have an equal number of cubes?
    ANSWER: When I matched up the cubes from those two containers, all the cubes were matched with no cubes left over in either group.

15. Have students move the labeled cards to the correct group if necessary.

OFFLINE
10min

LEARN Compare Plant Groups

Students will compare two groups of objects and identify which group has more or fewer objects in it. They will compare three groups of objects to identify which group has the most or fewest. They will also identify the two groups that have an equal number of objects.

Give students the Compare Plant Groups activity page from their Activity Book and read the directions with them.

Objectives

- Given two or more sets of 30 or fewer objects, identify which set has more or fewer objects than another set, or which sets have an equal number of objects.

Tips

If students have difficulty comparing groups, have them represent each each group in the problem with circles of a different color. Then have students match the circles to determine which group has more or fewer, or most or fewest.

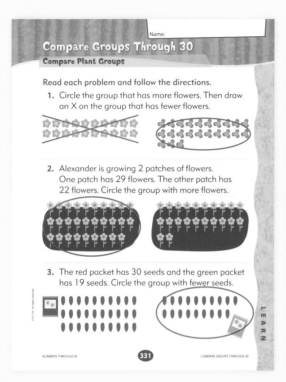

Compare Groups Through 30
Compare Plant Groups

Read each problem and follow the directions.

1. Circle the group that has more flowers. Then draw an X on the group that has fewer flowers.

2. Alexander is growing 2 patches of flowers. One patch has 29 flowers. The other patch has 22 flowers. Circle the group with more flowers.

3. The red packet has 30 seeds and the green packet has 19 seeds. Circle the group with fewer seeds.

L E A R N

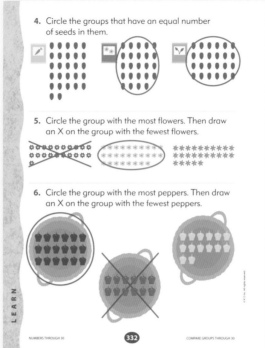

4. Circle the groups that have an equal number of seeds in them.

5. Circle the group with the most flowers. Then draw an X on the group with the fewest flowers.

6. Circle the group with the most peppers. Then draw an X on the group with the fewest peppers.

L E A R N

OFFLINE

10 min

TRY IT Compare Groups

Objectives

Students will practice identifying groups that have more or fewer and most or fewest. Give students the Compare Groups activity page from their Activity Book and read the directions with them.

- Given two or more sets of 30 or fewer objects, identify which set has more or fewer objects than another set, or which sets have an equal number of objects.

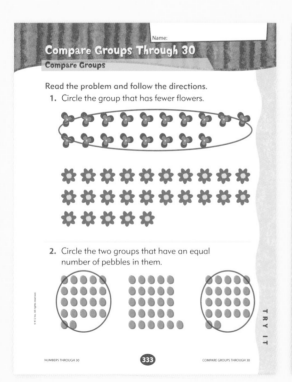

Compare Groups Through 30
Compare Groups

Read the problem and follow the directions.

1. Circle the group that has fewer flowers.

2. Circle the two groups that have an equal number of pebbles in them.

T R Y I T

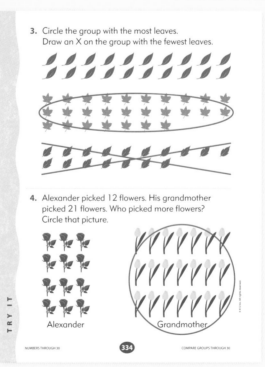

3. Circle the group with the most leaves. Draw an X on the group with the fewest leaves.

4. Alexander picked 12 flowers. His grandmother picked 21 flowers. Who picked more flowers? Circle that picture.

Alexander   Grandmother

T R Y I T

Groups in a Picture Graph

Lesson Overview

Skills Update	5 minutes	ONLINE
GET READY More, Fewer, and Same	5 minutes	ONLINE
LEARN Show More or Fewer	15 minutes	ONLINE
LEARN Use a Picture Graph to Compare	5 minutes	ONLINE
TRY IT Compare Sets	10 minutes	OFFLINE
CHECKPOINT	5 minutes	OFFLINE

▶ Lesson Objectives

Given two or more sets of 30 or fewer objects, identify which set has more or fewer objects than another set, or which sets have an equal number of objects.

▶ Prerequisite Skills

- Given two or more sets of 20 or fewer objects, identify which set has more or fewer objects than another set, or which sets have an equal number of objects.
- Use pictures and picture graphs to compare data (for example, find largest, smallest, most often, least often).

▶ Advance Preparation

Cut out the train cars on the Show More or Fewer activity page.

▶ Content Background

Students will use picture graphs to compare two groups of objects to identify the group with more or fewer and to compare three or more groups to find the group with the most or fewest number of objects. They will also identify groups that have an equal number of objects.

Materials to Gather

SUPPLIED

Show More or Fewer activity page

Compare Sets activity page

blocks – O (all colors)

Checkpoint (printout)

ALSO NEEDED

scissors, adult

GET READY More, Fewer, and Same

ONLINE 5 min

Students will practice comparing groups by using a balance to identify the group with more or fewer objects.

Objectives

- Given two or more sets of 20 or fewer objects, identify which set has more or fewer objects than another set, or which sets have an equal number of objects.

LEARN Show More or Fewer

ONLINE 15 min

Students will build paper trains and compare them to trains that are shown online. Gather the paper train cars from the Show More or Fewer activity page.

Follow the directions on each screen.

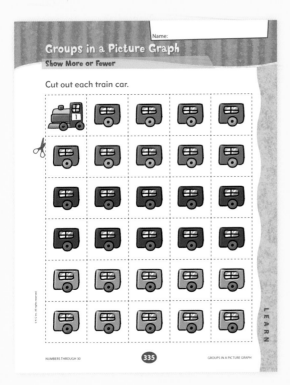

Objectives

- Given two or more sets of 30 or fewer objects, identify which set has more or fewer objects than another set, or which sets have an equal number of objects.

Tips

If students have difficulty comparing the train cars, have them make trains of cubes instead.

LEARN Use a Picture Graph to Compare

ONLINE 5 min

Students will compare data on a picture graph.

Objectives

- Given two or more sets of 30 or fewer objects, identify which set has more or fewer objects than another set, or which sets have an equal number of objects.

Tips

Have students place a finger on the two rows of the picture graph that are being compared and slide their finger to the ends of the rows to compare the data.

TRY IT Compare Sets

OFFLINE
10min

Objectives

Students will practice comparing groups of objects. Give students the cubes and the Compare Sets activity page from their Activity Book. Read the directions with them.

1. Make one group of 21 cubes, another group of 26 cubes, and a third group of 23 cubes. Have students identify the group that has the fewest cubes.

2. Make two groups of 20 cubes and one group of 23 cubes. Have students identify the groups that have the same number of cubes.

3. Have students complete the Compare Sets activity page.

- Given two or more sets of 30 or fewer objects, identify which set has more or fewer objects than another set, or which sets have an equal number of objects.

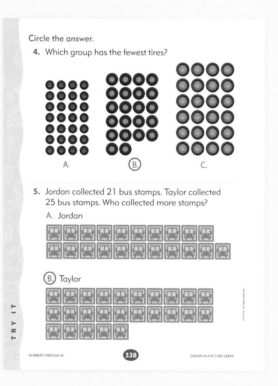

GROUPS IN A PICTURE GRAPH **459**

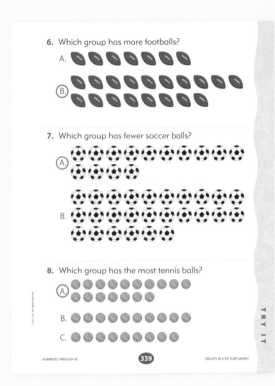

CHECKPOINT

OFFLINE 5 min

Print the Checkpoint and have students complete it on their own. Read the directions, problems, and answer choices to students, if necessary. Use the answer key to score the Checkpoint, and then enter the results online.

Objectives

- Given two or more sets of 30 or fewer objects, identify which set has more or fewer objects than another set, or which sets have an equal number of objects.

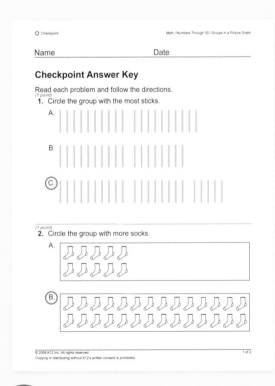

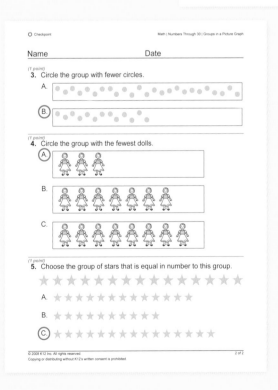

Write Numerals Through 30

Lesson Overview

Skills Update	5 minutes	ONLINE
GET READY Count, Draw, and Write	5 minutes	ONLINE
LEARN Write Numerals	15 minutes	OFFLINE
LEARN Count Beads and Write Numbers	10 minutes	OFFLINE
TRY IT Write 1 Through 30	10 minutes	OFFLINE

▶ Lesson Objectives

Write numerals from 1 through 30.

▶ Prerequisite Skills

Write numerals from 1 through 20.

▶ Advance Preparation

Print the Numeral Writing Guide.
   Prepare 6 resealable bags with the following numbers of counting objects: 30, 28, 27, 24, 23, and 21.

▶ Safety

Supervise students to make sure they do not choke on small objects.

▶ Content Background

Students will say and write the numerals 1 through 30.

Keywords

number – a quantity or value
numeral – a symbol that stands for a number

Materials to Gather

SUPPLIED
Write 1 Through 30 activity page
Numeral Writing Guide (printout)

ALSO NEEDED
household objects – 1 small towel, 6 resealable plastic bags
counting objects – 153
index cards – 6
paper, wide-line handwriting – 2 sheets
paper, drawing – 2 sheets

GET READY Count, Draw, and Write

ONLINE
5 min

Students will practice counting a group of objects through 20. Students will make a simple sketch to represent the same amount using Xs, dots, or squares. Then they will write the numeral that represents the group.

Gather the handwriting paper and drawing paper.

Objectives

- Write numerals from 1 through 20.

Tips

To make sure that students draw the correct number of objects, have them point to an object online with one hand and an object on the paper with the other hand.

LEARN Write Numerals

OFFLINE
15 min

Students will practice writing numbers through 30.

Gather the Numeral Writing Guide printout, handwriting paper, and drawing paper.

1. Review writing numerals using the Numeral Writing Guide printout.
2. Have students write the numbers 10 through 30. Use the online Numeral Writing Guide to help students if they have difficulty forming the numbers.

Objectives

- Write numerals from 1 through 30.

Tips

Remind students to start writing all numbers on the top line.

LEARN Count Beads and Write Numbers

OFFLINE
10 min

Students will count groups of beads or other objects and write the number that represents each amount.

Gather the prepared bags of beads, small towel, and index cards.

1. Give students the bag of 30 beads. Have them empty the bag onto the towel and count the beads. Have students touch each object once as they count. Explain that the last number they say tells how many objects are in the group.
2. Have students write the number of beads on an index card. Check to make sure students write the number correctly.
3. Have students return the beads to the bag with the index card. Seal the bag and place it to the side.
4. Repeat Steps 1–3 with the other 5 bags of beads.
5. Display all the bags of beads. Have students read the index card with the number of beads in each bag.

Objectives

- Write numerals from 1 through 30.

Tips

For counting objects, use beads or other small, durable household items (for example, dry macaroni, shells, or twists).

TRY IT Write 1 Through 30

OFFLINE 10 min

Students will practice counting objects and writing the numerals that represent the number of objects in the group. Give students the Write 1 Through 30 activity from their Activity Book and read the directions with them.

Objectives

- Write numerals from 1 through 30.

Tips

To prevent students from counting the same object twice, have them cross out each object as they count it.

Compare Groups and Numbers

Lesson Overview

Skills Update	5 minutes	ONLINE
GET READY Compare Numbers of Bugs	5 minutes	ONLINE
LEARN Compare Numbers of Cubes	10 minutes	OFFLINE
LEARN Compare Numbers on a Graph	10 minutes	OFFLINE
TRY IT Greater and Lesser Numbers	10 minutes	OFFLINE
CHECKPOINT	5 minutes	OFFLINE

▶ Lesson Objectives

Recognize that numbers with greater values describe sets with more objects in them than numbers with lesser values do (for sets of 30 or fewer objects).

▶ Prerequisite Skills

- Recognize that numbers with greater values describe sets with more objects in them than numbers with lesser values do (for sets of 20 or fewer objects).
- Use pictures and picture graphs to compare data (for example, find largest, smallest, most often, least often).

▶ Advance Preparation

Prepare bags with 20, 25, and 27 cubes. Use different color cubes in each bag. Prepare groups of 20 and 28 circles and groups of 22 and 19 circles to compare.
Number index cards 1 through 30, or gather the number cards you created previously.

▶ Content Background

Students will compare the number of objects in groups. They will identify the groups with greater or lesser numbers of objects.

Materials to Gather

SUPPLIED

Compare Numbers on a Graph activity page

Greater and Lesser Numbers activity page

Checkpoint (printout)

blocks – O (all colors)

blocks – B (all colors)

ALSO NEEDED

resealable plastic bags – 3

index cards – numbered 1 through 30

Keywords

greater – larger in number or amount than another
greatest – the largest in value of three or more numbers or amounts
least – the smallest in value of three or more numbers or amounts
lesser – smaller in number or amount than another

GET READY Compare Numbers of Bugs

ONLINE 5 min

Objectives

- Recognize that numbers with greater values describe sets with more objects in them than numbers with lesser values do (for sets of 20 or fewer objects).

Students will use numbers to describe the number of bugs in two groups up through 20. Then they will compare the groups and identify the group with the greater number or lesser number of bugs.

Tips

To prevent students from skipping an object or counting an object twice, have students touch each object online as they count it.

LEARN Compare Numbers of Cubes

OFFLINE 10 min

Objectives

- Recognize that numbers with greater values describe sets with more objects in them than numbers with lesser values do (for sets of 30 or fewer objects).

Students will compare groups of objects using cubes and number cards. They will learn that greater numbers are used to describe groups with more objects and lesser numbers are used to describe groups with fewer objects.

Gather the number cards and the bags filled with cubes.

1. Give students the bag of 20 cubes and have them count the cubes aloud. Have students place the matching number card (20) in the bag with the cubes.

2. Repeat Step 1 with the bag with 27 cubes.

   Ask: Which group has more cubes?
   ANSWER: the one with 27 cubes

3. Point to the number cards.

   Say: 27 is more than 20. 27 is a greater number than 20. 20 is a lesser number than 27.

4. Repeat Step 1 with the bag with 25 cubes.

5. Show students the bags with 27 and 25 cubes.

   Ask: Which is a lesser number: 25 or 27? How do you know?
   ANSWER: 25; There are fewer cubes in the bag with 25 cubes.

6. Show students the bags with 20, 25, and 27 cubes.

   Ask: Which group has the fewest cubes?
   ANSWER: the one with 20

7. Point to the number cards.

   Say: The number 20 is the least of the three numbers and describes the group with the fewest cubes.

8. Show students the bags with 25 and 20 cubes.

   Ask: Which is the greater number, 25 or 20? How do you know?
   ANSWER: 25; There are more cubes in the bag with 25 cubes.

Tips

If students have difficulty choosing the group with more cubes, align the cubes in each group so that they match one-to-one. Explain that the group with unmatched cubes has more objects in it.

LEARN Compare Numbers on a Graph

Students will compare groups of objects on a picture graph to identify which group has the most objects. Then they will compare two groups to identify the group that has a greater number of objects, the group with more objects, and the group with fewer objects.

Give students the Compare Numbers on a Graph activity page from their Activity Book and read the directions with them.

Objectives

- Recognize that numbers with greater values describe sets with more objects in them than numbers with lesser values do (for sets of 30 or fewer objects).

Tips

If students have difficulty determining which group has the most or the fewest, explain that the group with the longest line is the group with *most* objects and the group with the shortest line has the *fewest* objects.

Name: _____

Compare Groups and Numbers
Compare Numbers on a Graph

Count aloud the pictures in each row of the picture graph. Use the data for Problems 1–4. Circle the answer.

Jack's Aquarium

Each picture in the boxes equals 1.

1. Which row on the picture graph has the most objects?
   A. 🐢   B. 🐠   C. 🐟   D. 🐌

2. Does Jack have a greater number of goldfish or snails?
   A. 🐟   B. 🐌

3. Does Jack have fewer snails or turtles?
   A. 🐌   B. 🐢

4. Does Jack have more goldfish or turtles?
   A. 🐟   B. 🐢

Count aloud the pictures in each row of the picture graph. Use data for Problems 5–8. Circle the answer.

Things Lily Found on a Walk

Each picture in the boxes equals 1.

5. Which row on the picture graph has the most objects? How do you know?
   A. 🌰   B. 🪶   C. 🐚   D. 🪨
   Students should say 12 is more than 9, 5, or 10.

6. Which row on the picture graph has the fewest objects? How do you know?
   A. 🌰   B. 🪶   C. 🐚   D. 🪨
   Students should say 5 is fewer than 9, 12, or 10.

7. Does Lily have more pinecones or rocks?
   A. 🌰   B. 🪨

8. Does Lily have fewer pinecones or shells?
   A. 🌰   B. 🐚

Objectives

- Recognize that numbers with greater values describe sets with more objects in them than numbers with lesser values do (for sets of 30 or fewer objects).

Students will practice comparing groups to identify the group with more or fewer objects. They will also identify the greater and lesser number.

Gather the groups of circles you have prepared. Give students the Greater and Lesser Numbers activity page from their Activity Book and read the directions with them.

1. Place the group of 28 circles and the group of 20 circles on the table. Tell students that one group has 28 circles and the other has 20 circles.

   Ask: Which group has more circles?
   ANSWER: the group with 28 circles

2. Place the group of 22 circles and the group of 19 circles on the table.

   Ask: Which group has fewer circles?
   ANSWER: the group with 19 circles

3. Have students complete the Greater and Lesser Numbers activity page. Discuss the data in the picture graph with students before they answer the questions.

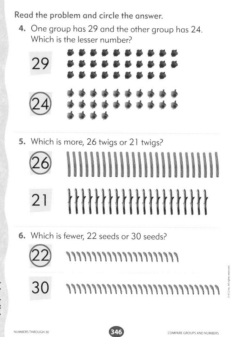

CHECKPOINT

Print the Checkpoint and have students complete it on their own. Read the directions, problems, and answer choices to students, if necessary. Use the answer key to score the Checkpoint, and then enter the results online.

Objectives

- Recognize that larger numbers describe sets with more objects in them than smaller numbers do (for sets of 30 or fewer objects).

Name _____ Date _____

Checkpoint Answer Key

Use the data on the picture graph for Problems 1–3.
Circle the answer.

Types of Animals Spotted in the Backyard

Each picture in the boxes equals 1.

(1 point)
1. Are there more frogs or more rabbits?

(A) 🐸   B. 🐰

(1 point)
2. Are there more mice or more birds?

A. 🐭   (B) 🐦

(1 point)
3. Are there fewer mice or fewer rabbits?

A. 🐭   (B) 🐰

Name _____ Date _____

Read the problem and circle the answer.
(1 point)
4. Jose has 15 crackers. Maria has 3 crackers.
Who has more crackers?

(A) Jose   B. Maria

(1 point)
5. Which flowerpot has fewer flowers?

(A)   B.

Name _____ Date _____

(1 point)
6. Maya has 10 marbles. Tuti has 5 marbles. Sam has 8 marbles.
Who has the fewest marbles?

A. Maya   (B) Tuti   C. Sam

Write Numerals From 1 Through 30

Lesson Overview

Skills Update	5 minutes	ONLINE
GET READY Count and Write Through 20	5 minutes	OFFLINE
LEARN Trace and Show Numbers	20 minutes	OFFLINE
TRY IT Count and Write Through 30	10 minutes	OFFLINE
CHECKPOINT	5 minutes	OFFLINE

▶ Lesson Objectives

Write numerals from 1 through 30.

▶ Prerequisite Skills

Write numerals from 1 through 20.

▶ Advance Preparation

Cut out the train cards on the Trace and Show Numbers activity page.

▶ Content Background

In this lesson, students will continue to practice saying and writing the numerals 1 through 30.

Materials to Gather

SUPPLIED

Trace and Show Numbers activity page

Count and Write Through 30 activity page

Checkpoint (printout)

ALSO NEEDED

household objects – 20 buttons, 1 bowl or bag

paper, wide-line handwriting – 1 sheet

scissors, adult

OFFLINE
5min

GET READY Count and Write Through 20

Students will count groups of buttons and write the number that represents each group.

Gather the buttons, container, and handwriting paper.

1. Put the buttons in the container.
2. Have students take a handful of buttons out of the container and count them. Encourage students to move each button from one location to another as they count.
3. Repeat Steps 1–2 four times with different numbers of buttons.

Objectives

- Write numerals from 1 through 20.

Tips

For other counting objects, use small, durable household items (for example, dry macaroni, shells, or twists).

LEARN Trace and Show Numbers

Objectives

- Write numerals from 1 through 30.

Students will trace each numeral from 19 through 30 and draw a sketch to show each amount. Then they will put the numbers in order.

Gather the cut-out train cards from the Trace and Show Numbers activity page.

1. Put the train cards on the table with the number-side down. Mix them up. Explain that each car on the train has a different number them on it.

2. Have students pick a card and turn it picture-side up. Have students trace the number with their fingers and then write the number on top of the dotted lines. Have them say the number.

3. Have students draw a simple sketch that represents the number on the train card.

4. Repeat Steps 1–3 with each card.

5. Mix up the train cards and form a stack with the picture-side up. For each card, have students say the number.

6. Have students put the train cars in order, starting with 19 and ending with 30.

Tips

If students need more practice, have them use buttons or other counting objects to show the number that they counted and drew.

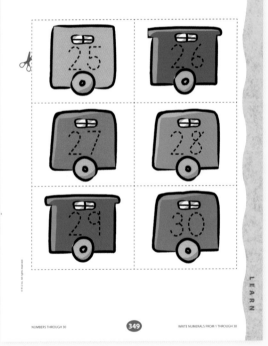

TRY IT Count and Write Through 30

Students will practice counting and writing numerals through 30. Give students the Count and Write Through 30 activity page from their Activity Book and read the directions with them.

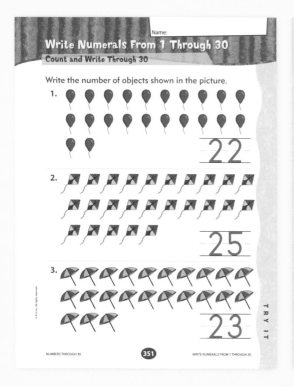

CHECKPOINT

Print the Checkpoint and have students complete it on their own. Read the directions and problems to students, if necessary. Use the answer key to score the Checkpoint, and then enter the results online.

- Write numerals from 1 through 30.

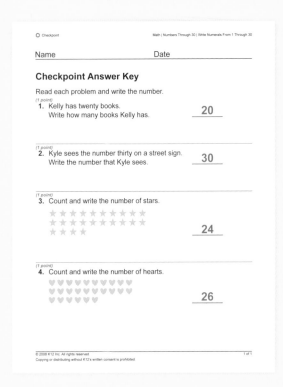

Unit Review

Lesson Overview

UNIT REVIEW Look Back	15 minutes	ONLINE
UNIT REVIEW Checkpoint Practice	15 minutes	OFFLINE
➡ UNIT REVIEW Prepare for the Checkpoint		

▶ Unit Objectives

This lesson reviews the following objectives:

- Count aloud a number of objects up through 30.
- Use concrete objects or sketches to represent a quantity up through 30.
- Given two or more sets of 30 or fewer objects, identify which set has more or fewer objects than another set, or which sets have an equal number of objects.
- Write numerals from 1 through 30.
- Recognize that numbers with greater values describe sets with more objects in them than numbers with lesser values do (for sets of 30 or fewer objects).

▶ Advance Preparation

In this lesson, students will have an opportunity to review previous activities in the Numbers Through 30 unit. Look at the suggested activities in Unit Review: Prepare for the Checkpoint online and gather any needed materials.

Materials to Gather

SUPPLIED

Checkpoint Practice activity page
blocks – O (10 blue, 10 yellow, 10 green)

Keywords	
compare	least
count	lesser
equal	more
fewer	most
fewest	number
greater	numeral
greatest	represent

ONLINE
15min

- Review unit objectives.

In this unit, students have learned to count a number of objects up through 30 and to represent amounts up through 30 with objects and with sketches. They have learned to compare two groups of objects to determine which group has more or fewer objects. They have also learned to compare three groups of objects to determine which group has the fewest or the most objects. Students have learned to identify groups that have the same number of objects. They have also learned that numbers with greater values describe groups with more objects and numbers with lesser values describe groups with fewer objects. Finally, students have learned to write numbers from 1 through 30. Students will review key concepts from the unit to prepare for the Unit Checkpoint.

OFFLINE
15min

- Review unit objectives.

Students will complete a Checkpoint Practice activity page to prepare for the Unit Checkpoint. If necessary, read the directions, questions, and answer choices to students. Have students answer the problems on their own. Review any missed problems with students.

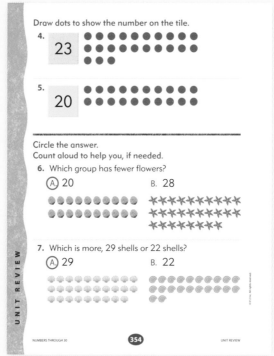

8. Which group of crayons is equal to the one below?

A.

B.

C.

9. Dave has 12 paintbrushes and Peg has 17.
Who has more paintbrushes?

A. Dave

B. Peg

10. Jana has 28 marbles. Sam has 17 marbles.
Who has more marbles?

Ⓐ Jana

B. Sam

11. Pam has a large group of buttons.
Mary has a small group of buttons.
One girl has 8 buttons. One girl has 30 buttons.
Who has 30 buttons?

Ⓐ Pam   B. Mary

Write the answer.

12. Write the number of fish.

27

13. Write the number twenty-six.

26

14. Write the number twenty-five.

25

⇥ UNIT REVIEW Prepare for the Checkpoint

What you do next depends on how students performed in the previous activity, Unit Review: Checkpoint Practice. If students had difficulty with any of the problems, complete the appropriate review activity listed in the table online.

Unit Checkpoint

UNIT CHECKPOINT Offline   40 minutes   **OFFLINE**

▶ Unit Objectives

This lesson assesses the following objectives:

- Count aloud a number of objects up through 30.
- Use concrete objects or sketches to represent a quantity up through 30.
- Given two or more sets of 30 or fewer objects, identify which set has more or fewer objects than another set, or which sets have an equal number of objects.
- Write numerals from 1 through 30.
- Recognize that numbers with greater values describe sets with more objects in them than numbers with lesser values (for sets of 30 or fewer objects).

Materials to Gather

SUPPLIED

blocks – O (15 blue, 15 yellow)

Unit Checkpoint (printout)

UNIT CHECKPOINT Offline

OFFLINE 40 min

Objectives

- Assess unit objectives.

Students will complete the Unit Checkpoint offline. Print the Checkpoint and have students complete it on their own. Read the directions, problems, and answer choices to students, if necessary. Use the answer key to score the Checkpoint, and then enter the results online.

Gather the cubes for Problem 3.

○ Checkpoint   Math | Numbers Through 30 | Unit Checkpoint

Name   Date

Unit Checkpoint Answer Key

Read each problem and follow the directions.
(1 point)
1. Count aloud the number of fish.

   Check that students count aloud from 1 through 10.

(1 point)
2. Count aloud the number of starfish.

   Check that students count aloud from 1 through 25.

(1 point)
3. Show 29 cubes in your workspace. Check that students have modeled 29 cubes.

(1 point)
4. Circle the group with the same number of triangles as the group below.

   A. △ △ △ △

   B. △ △ △ △ △ △ △ △

   C. △ △ △ △ △ △ △ △ △

1 of 2

○ Checkpoint   Math | Numbers Through 30 | Unit Checkpoint

Name   Date

(1 point)
5. Circle the group with the fewest apples.

   A. (apples)

   B. (apples)

   C. (apples)

(1 point)
6. Which group has the most toy cars?

   A. (cars)

   B. (cars)

   C. (cars)

(1 point)
7. Count and write how many dots are in this group.

   6

(1 point)
8. Write the number twenty-two.

   22

(1 point)
9. Sandee has 25 bottle caps. Raymond has 30 bottle caps.

   Who has more bottle caps?

   A. Sandee   B. Raymond

(1 point)
10. Thomas ate 10 lima beans. Jesse ate 15 lima beans.

    Who ate fewer lima beans?

    A. Thomas   B. Jesse

2 of 2

Solid Figures

▶ Unit Objectives

- Identify common solid figures, such as cube, sphere, and cone.
- Compare common solid figures according to attributes (e.g., position, shape, size, roundness, or number of corners).
- Given a set of solid figures, identify which figure does not belong according to color, shape, or size.

- Use concrete objects or sketches to show how two or more plane figures can be put together to create a different shape (circles, triangles, rectangles, and squares only).
- Show how two or more plane figures can be taken apart to create different shapes (circles, triangles, rectangles, and squares only).

▶ Big Ideas

Geometric figures can be described and classified by the shapes of their faces and by how many faces, sides, and vertices they have.

▶ Unit Introduction

In this unit, students will review plane figures. Students will be introduced to three solid figures: cubes, cones, and spheres. They will learn how to describe solid figures by their number and shape of faces and their number of edges. They will sort figures based on these characteristics. Lastly students will learn to identify which solid in a set of solids does **not** belong based on its color, size, or shape.

Identify Solid Figures

Lesson Overview

Skills Update	5 minutes	ONLINE
GET READY Identify Plane Figures	10 minutes	ONLINE
LEARN Sort Plane Figures and Solids	10 minutes	OFFLINE
LEARN Identify and Describe Solids	10 minutes	OFFLINE
TRY IT Identify Solids	10 minutes	OFFLINE

▶ Lesson Objectives

Identify common solid figures, such as cube, sphere, and cone.

▶ Prerequisite Skills

Identify common plane figures, such as circle, triangle, square, and rectangle.

▶ Common Errors and Misconceptions

- Students might have heard some geometric vocabulary words, but their definitions of these words might be incorrect.
- Students might not recognize that a shape might be positioned different ways. For example, students might not recognize that the second shape is a square.

- Students might inappropriately use converse reasoning when classifying shapes. For example, they might say, "All square have 4 sides. This shape has 4 sides, so it must be a square."

▶ Advance Preparation

For plane figures, gather objects such as paper plates, compact discs, picture frames, and buttons. For solid figures, gather objects such as balls, marbles, boxes, sugar cubes, and ice-cream cones.

   If you do not find cones, use the Making Paper Cones activity page. Save cones for use in future lessons.

▶ Safety

Supervise students when they are working with the geometric solid blocks. These blocks have sharp corners.

▶ Content Background

Students will review plane figures and will be introduced to solid figures. Two-dimensional figures or shapes are called *plane figures*. These figures have length and width. Three-dimensional figures, which have length, width, and height, are called *solid figures* or *solids*. This lesson will use the term *solid figures* as well as the word *solids* to describe 3-dimensional figures. Reinforce both terms with students.

Materials to Gather

SUPPLIED

blocks – P, Q, T, V

Identify Solids activity page

Making Paper Cones activity page (optional)

ALSO NEEDED

household objects – at least 6 objects shaped like solid figures (2 spheres, 2 cubes, 2 cones)

household objects – at least 8 objects resembling plane figures (2 circles, 2 squares, 2 triangles, 2 rectangles)

paper, construction – 1 sheet

crayons

ONLINE
10min

GET READY Identify Plane Figures

Students will practice identifying shapes. They will find objects of different shapes in a picture of a room.

Objectives

- Identify common plane figures, such as circle, triangle, square, and rectangle.

Tips

If students are not sure which shape is shown, give them helpful cues. For example, for a triangle, tell students to think about the name of the shape with three sides.

OFFLINE
10min

LEARN Sort Plane Figures and Solids

Students will sort objects into two groups: plane figures and solid figures.
   Gather the household objects and geometric solid blocks. Lay out the objects in random order.

1. Explain that students are going to sort the objects into two groups. Hold up one household object that is shaped like a plane figure.

   Ask: What shape does this object look like?
   ANSWER: triangle [or square, circle, rectangle]

2. **Say:** This looks like a [triangle]. We can also say that it is a plane figure. When you sort the objects, one group will be plane figures, and the other group will be solid figures.

3. Start the group of plane figures by placing the selected object away from the others.

4. Hand students a 3-dimensional household object.

   Say: This object is a solid figure. All solid figures have length, width, and height.

   Place the object away from the plane figure group and the collection of objects.

5. **Say:** Sort all the objects into two groups: plane figures and solid figures.

6. After the objects are sorted, point to the group of plane figures. Have students describe the shapes in the group (for example, circles, squares, triangles, or rectangles).

Objectives

- Identify common solid figures, such as cube, sphere, and cone.

Tips

If students are having difficulty sorting the plane figures, review circles, squares, rectangles, and triangles using blocks as models.

7. Point to the group of solid figures. Have students describe the figures in this group (for example, one figure is round or one figure has sides that look like squares).

8. Hold up each figure and introduce it by name. Describe each geometric solid:
   - A cube has sides that look like squares. It has 8 corners.
   - A cone has a point at one end and a side that looks like a circle at the other end.
   - A sphere looks like a circle and is round.

LEARN Identify and Describe Solids

OFFLINE 10 min

Objectives

- Identify common solid figures, such as cube, sphere, and cone.

Students will describe solid figures. Then they will identify the solid figure that a household object most closely resembles.

Gather the geometric solid blocks, construction paper, and household objects.

1. Give students the geometric solid blocks. Have students hold the sphere and look at it from different angles.

   Ask: What does this solid figure look like?
   ANSWER: a ball or an orange

2. **Say:** This solid figure is a sphere. It is round. It does not have any corners.

   Ask: What objects have you seen that are shaped like a sphere?
   ANSWER: a baseball, a marble

3. Have students hold the cube and look at it from different angles.

   Ask: What shape do you see on the sides of this solid?
   ANSWER: squares

   Ask: How many squares do you see?
   ANSWER: 6

4. **Say:** This solid figure is a cube. If we trace a side, it looks like a square.

   Show students how to trace one side on the construction paper. Then have students trace one side.

5. **Ask:** What objects have you seen that are shaped like a cube?

   ANSWER: sugar cube, box

6. Have students hold the cone and look at it from different angles.

   Ask: What shape do you see on this solid?
   ANSWER: a circle

   Ask: How many circles do you see?
   ANSWER: 1

7. **Say:** This solid figure is a cone. One side of the cone is a circle, and there is a point at the other end.

   Have students trace the side to see the circle.

8. **Ask:** What objects have you seen that are shaped like a cone?
   ANSWER: ice-cream cone, party hat, traffic cone

9. Display the household objects that you collected.

   Say: Objects that we use every day can be shaped like solid figures.

   Have students make a group of all the objects that are shaped like a cube.

   Ask: How are these objects alike?
   ANSWER: They all have square sides.

Tips

If students have difficulty counting the sides of the cube, hold it for them and help them count.

10. Have students make a group of all the objects that are shaped like a sphere.

Ask: How are all these objects alike?
ANSWER: They are all round.

11. Finally have students sort all the objects that are shaped like a cone.

Ask: How are all these objects alike?
ANSWER: They all have one pointed end and one end that is a circle.

12. Have students point to each group and say the name of the solid figure.

OFFLINE
10min

TRY IT Identify Solids

Students will practice identifying solid figures. Give students the crayons, geometric solid blocks, and Identify Solids activity page from their Activity Book. Read the directions with them.

Objectives

- Identify common solid figures, such as cube, sphere, and cone.

Tips

If students have difficulty identifying the pictures, have them compare the pictures to geometric solid blocks.

To help students remember which color to use for each solid, have them put the geometric solid blocks on corresponding pieces of colored paper.

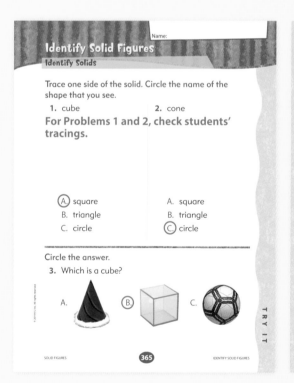

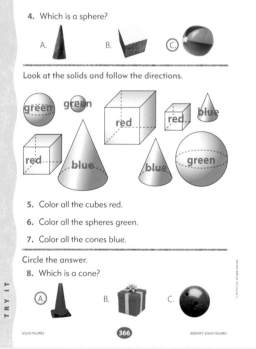

Solid Figures: More Exploration

Lesson Overview

Skills Update	5 minutes	ONLINE
REVIEW Extend Your Understanding	20 minutes	ONLINE
CHECKPOINT	20 minutes	OFFLINE

▶ Lesson Objectives

Identify common solid figures, such as cube, sphere, and cone.

▶ Prerequisite Skills

Identify common plane figures, such as circle, triangle, square, and rectangle.

▶ Content Background

In this lesson, students will have an opportunity for continued review. Then they will take a Checkpoint. If you wish, you may have students begin the next lesson after they complete the Checkpoint.

Materials to Gather

SUPPLIED

blocks – P, Q, R, T, U, V

Extend Your Understanding activity page

Checkpoint (printout)

ALSO NEEDED

crayons

REVIEW Extend Your Understanding

ONLINE 20min

In this activity, students will have an opportunity for continued review.
Gather the blocks, crayons, and Extend Your Understanding activity page.

Objectives

- Identify common solid figures, such as cube, sphere, and cone.

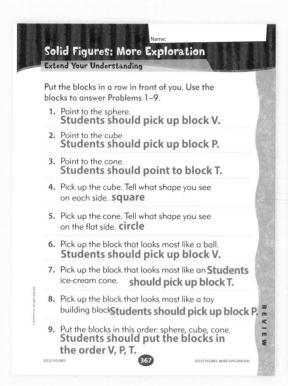

Solid Figures: More Exploration
Extend Your Understanding

Name:

Put the blocks in a row in front of you. Use the blocks to answer Problems 1–9.

1. Point to the sphere.
   Students should pick up block V.

2. Point to the cube.
   Students should pick up block P.

3. Point to the cone.
   Students should point to block T.

4. Pick up the cube. Tell what shape you see on each side. **square**

5. Pick up the cone. Tell what shape you see on the flat side. **circle**

6. Pick up the block that looks most like a ball.
   Students should pick up block V.

7. Pick up the block that looks most like an ice-cream cone. **Students should pick up block T.**

8. Pick up the block that looks most like a toy building block. **Students should pick up block P.**

9. Put the blocks in this order: sphere, cube, cone.
   Students should put the blocks in the order V, P, T.

SOLID FIGURES   367   SOLID FIGURES: MORE EXPLORATION

REVIEW

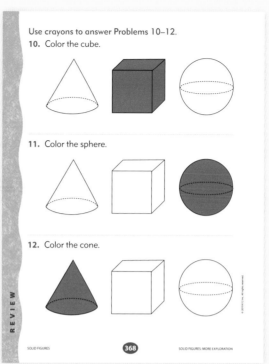

Use crayons to answer Problems 10–12.
10. Color the cube.

11. Color the sphere.

12. Color the cone.

REVIEW

SOLID FIGURES   368   SOLID FIGURES: MORE EXPLORATION

OFFLINE
20min

CHECKPOINT

Print the Checkpoint and have students complete it on their own. Read the directions, problems, and answer choices to students, if necessary. Use the answer key to score the Checkpoint, and then enter the results online.

Objectives

- Identify common solid figures, such as cube, sphere, and cone.

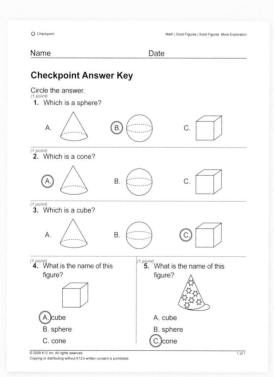

Checkpoint   Math | Solid Figures | Solid Figures: More Exploration

Name _____ Date _____

Checkpoint Answer Key

Circle the answer.
(1 point)
1. Which is a sphere?

   A.   (B.)   C.

(1 point)
2. Which is a cone?

   (A.)   B.   C.

(1 point)
3. Which is a cube?

   A.   B.   (C.)

(1 point)
4. What is the name of this figure?

   (A.) cube
   B. sphere
   C. cone

(1 point)
5. What is the name of this figure?

   A. cube
   B. sphere
   (C.) cone

Compare Figures by Shape or Size

Lesson Overview		
Skills Update	5 minutes	ONLINE
GET READY Sides and Corners	5 minutes	ONLINE
LEARN Compare Solids by Shape	15 minutes	OFFLINE
LEARN Compare Solids by Size	10 minutes	OFFLINE
TRY IT Compare Solids	10 minutes	OFFLINE

▶ Lesson Objectives

Compare common solid figures according to their attributes (e.g., position, shape, size, roundness, or number of corners).

▶ Prerequisite Skills

Compare plane figures by common attributes, such as number of sides and number of corners of triangles, rectangles, squares, pentagons, and circles.

▶ Common Errors and Misconceptions

- Students might have heard some geometric vocabulary words, but their definitions of these words might be incorrect.
- Students might inappropriately use converse reasoning when classifying shapes. For example, they might say, "All squares have 4 sides. This shape has 4 sides, so it must be a square."

▶ Advance Preparation

LEARN: COMPARE SOLIDS BY SHAPE

- Gather 3 cube-shaped objects, 3 cone-shaped objects, and 3 sphere-shaped objects. For example, gather balls, marbles, crates, cube-shaped tissue boxes, number cubes, bouillon cubes, party hats, and ice-cream cones.
- If you cannot find 3 cone-shaped objects, use the Making Paper Cones activity page, or gather the cones you made previously.

LEARN: COMPARE SOLIDS BY SIZE

- Gather 4 objects shaped like cubes. One object should be larger than all the others, 1 should be smaller than all the others, and 2 should be close in size. For example, gather 1 large box, 2 toy blocks, and 1 small number cube.
- Gather 4 objects shaped like spheres. One object should be larger than all the others, 1 should be smaller than all the others, and 2 should be close in size. For example, gather 1 basketball, 2 tennis balls, and 1 marble.

▶ Safety

Supervise students when they are working with the geometric solid blocks. These blocks have sharp corners.

Materials to Gather

SUPPLIED

blocks – P, T, V

Compare Solids by Size activity page

Compare Solids activity page

Making Paper Cones activity page (optional)

ALSO NEEDED

household objects – 9 objects shaped like solid figures (4 cubes, 3 cones, 4 spheres)

crayons

▶ Content Background

Students will compare the sizes and shapes of solid figures. Two-dimensional figures or shapes are called *plane figures*. Plane figures have length and width. Three-dimensional figures, which have length, width, and height, are called *solid figures* or *solids*. This lesson will use the terms *solid figures* as well as *solids* to describe 3-dimensional figures. Reinforce both terms with students.

GET READY Sides and Corners

Students will compare the number of sides and corners of plane figures.

Objectives

- Compare plane figures by common attributes, such as number of sides and number of corners of triangles, rectangles, squares, pentagons, and circles.

LEARN Compare Solids by Shape

Students will sort objects by shape. Then they will compare the objects in each group, discussing the attributes of that solid.

Gather the blocks and 9 household objects shaped like cubes, cones, and spheres (3 cubes, 3 cones, and 3 spheres).

Objectives

- Compare solid figures according to their attributes (e.g., position, shape, size, roundness, or number of corners).

1. Display the cube, cone, and sphere from the block set. Leave space around each block. Then show students the group of household objects.

2. Have students sort the household objects by shape, placing sphere-shaped objects in a group with the sphere block, cone-shaped objects in a group with the cone block, and cube-shaped objects in a group with the cube block. If students have difficulty sorting an object, have them hold it, describe its attributes, and find the block that is similar. For example, students might say, "This number cube has 6 square sides. All the sides are flat. It looks like the cube block."

3. Point to the group of cubes.

   Say: Tell what is the same about the objects in this group. Look at their corners and use your finger to trace around their sides.
   SAMPLE ANSWER: They have 8 corners. They have square sides.

   Ask: Will a cube roll smoothly like a ball?
   ANSWER: No

   Say: That's right. A cube won't roll like a ball because its sides are flat. Only solids with curved sides roll.

4. Point to the group of cones.

   Say: Tell what is the same about the objects in this group.
   SAMPLE ANSWER: They have 1 corner. They have 1 flat side that is a circle. They have a curved side.

   Ask: Can you roll a cone?
   ANSWER: Yes

   Say: That's right. A cone rolls in a funny way, but it will roll because it has a curved side. Solids with curved sides roll.

5. Point to the group of spheres.

   Say: Tell what is the same about the objects in this group.
   SAMPLE ANSWER: They have no corners. They are round.

   Ask: Can you roll a sphere?
   ANSWER: Yes

   Say: That's right. You can roll a sphere because it is curved. Solids with curved sides roll.

LEARN Compare Solids by Size

OFFLINE
10min

Objectives

Students will compare solid figures by size. They will identify the largest and smallest solid figures in a group. They will also identify any solid figures that are the same size.

Gather the 8 household objects shaped like cubes and spheres.

- Compare solid figures according to their attributes (e.g., position, shape, size, roundness, or number of corners).

1. **Say:** Let's compare solids to find which is largest, which is smallest, and which are about the same size.

2. Show students the cube-shaped objects.

   Ask: What is the name of this type of solid?
   ANSWER: cube

   Ask: How are these objects different?
   ANSWER: They are different sizes.

3. Tell students to pick up the largest object.

   Ask: How do you know this object is the largest?
   ANSWER: All the other objects are smaller.

4. Tell students to pick up the smallest object.

   Ask: How do you know this object is the smallest?
   ANSWER: All the other objects are larger.

5. Tell students to pick up the objects that are about the same size.

   Ask: Does size change the shape of the solids?
   ANSWER: No, all these objects are still cubes. They still have 6 flat, square sides. They still don't roll.

6. Have students arrange the 4 objects in a line, from smallest to largest (with objects about the same size next to each other).

7. Repeat Steps 2–6 with the sphere-shaped objects.

8. Give students the crayons and Compare Solids by Size activity page from their Activity Book. Read the directions with them. Have students complete the activity page. Guide them as necessary.

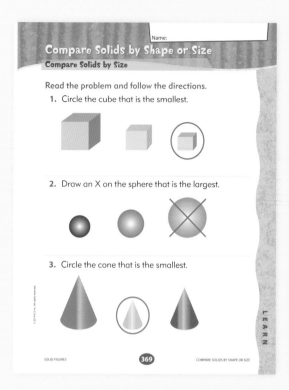

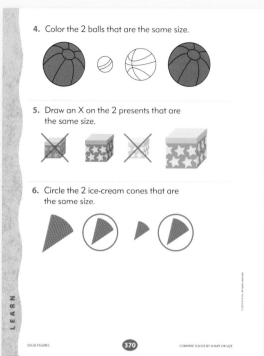

TRY IT Compare Solids

Students will practice comparing solids by size and shape. Give students the geometric solid blocks, crayons, and Compare Solids activity page from their Activity Book. Read the directions with them. Students may refer to the geometric solid blocks as they complete the activity page.

Objectives

- Compare solid figures according to their attributes (e.g., position, shape, size, roundness, or number of corners).

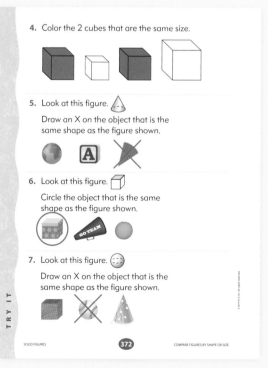

Attributes: More Exploration

Lesson Overview

Skills Update	5 minutes	ONLINE
REVIEW Extend Your Understanding	20 minutes	ONLINE
CHECKPOINT	20 minutes	OFFLINE

▶ Lesson Objectives

Compare solid figures according to attributes (e.g., position, shape, size, roundness, or number of corners).

▶ Prerequisite Skills

Compare plane figures by common attributes, such as number of sides and number of corners of triangles, rectangles, squares, pentagons, and circles.

▶ Content Background

In this lesson, students will have an opportunity for continued review. Then they will take a Checkpoint. If you wish, you may have students begin the next lesson after they complete the Checkpoint.

Materials to Gather

SUPPLIED

blocks – P, T, V

Extend Your Understanding activity page

Checkpoint (printout)

REVIEW Extend Your Understanding

ONLINE
20min

In this activity, students will have an opportunity for continued review. Gather the block and Extend Your Understanding activity page.

Objectives

- Compare solid figures according to their attributes (e.g., position, shape, size, roundness, or number of corners).

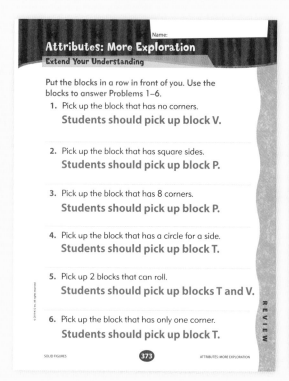

Put the blocks in a row in front of you. Use the blocks to answer Problems 1–6.

1. Pick up the block that has no corners.

Students should pick up block V.

2. Pick up the block that has square sides.

Students should pick up block P.

3. Pick up the block that has 8 corners.

Students should pick up block P.

4. Pick up the block that has a circle for a side.

Students should pick up block T.

5. Pick up 2 blocks that can roll.

Students should pick up blocks T and V.

6. Pick up the block that has only one corner.

Students should pick up block T.

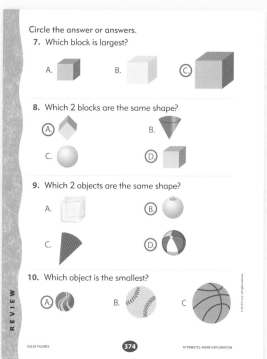

Circle the answer or answers.

7. Which block is largest?

A.   B.   Ⓒ

8. Which 2 blocks are the same shape?

Ⓐ.   B.   C.   Ⓓ

9. Which 2 objects are the same shape?

A.   Ⓑ   C.   Ⓓ

10. Which object is the smallest?

Ⓐ   B.   C

CHECKPOINT

OFFLINE 20min

Print the Checkpoint and have students complete it on their own. Read the directions, problems, and answer choices to students, if necessary. Use the answer key to score the Checkpoint, and then enter the results online.

Objectives

- Compare solid figures according to their attributes (e.g., position, shape, size, roundness, or number of corners).

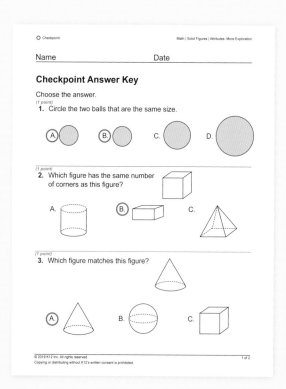

Checkpoint   Math | Solid Figures | Attributes: More Exploration

Name _____   Date _____

Checkpoint Answer Key

Choose the answer.

(1 point)
1. Circle the two balls that are the same size.

Ⓐ   Ⓑ   C.   D.

(1 point)
2. Which figure has the same number of corners as this figure?

A.   Ⓑ.   C.

(1 point)
3. Which figure matches this figure?

Ⓐ   B.   C.

1 of 2

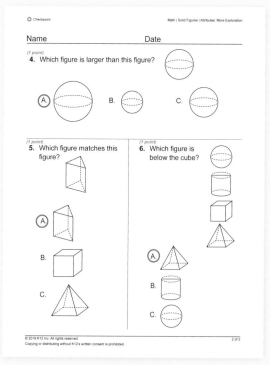

Checkpoint   Math | Solid Figures | Attributes: More Exploration

Name _____   Date _____

(1 point)
4. Which figure is larger than this figure?

Ⓐ   B.   C.

(1 point)
5. Which figure matches this figure?

Ⓐ   B.   C.

(1 point)
6. Which figure is below the cube?

Ⓐ   B.   C.

2 of 2

Sort Solid Figures

Lesson Overview

Skills Update	5 minutes	ONLINE
GET READY Which Shape Does Not Belong?	5 minutes	ONLINE
LEARN Identify Color, Shape, or Size of Solids	10 minutes	OFFLINE
LEARN Which Does Not Belong?	5 minutes	OFFLINE
TRY IT Identify the Different Solid Figure	10 minutes	OFFLINE
CHECKPOINT Online	5 minutes	ONLINE
CHECKPOINT Offline	5 minutes	OFFLINE

▶ Lesson Objectives

Given a set of solid figures, identify which figure does not belong according to color, shape, or size.

▶ Prerequisite Skills

Given a group of plane figures, identify which figure does not belong according to color, shape, or size.

▶ Common Errors and Misconceptions

- Students might have heard some geometric vocabulary words, but their definitions of these words might be incorrect.
- Students might not recognize that a shape might be positioned different ways. For example, students might not recognize that the second shape is a cube.

- Students might inappropriately use converse reasoning when classifying shapes. For example, they might say, "All square have 4 sides. This shape has 4 sides, so it must be a square."

▶ Advance Preparation

For solid figures, gather objects such as balls, marbles, boxes, sugar cubes, party hats, and ice-cream cones.

If you do not find cones, use the Making Paper Cones activity page, or gather the cones you made previously.

▶ Safety

Supervise students when they are working with the geometric solid blocks. These blocks have sharp corners.

Materials to Gather

SUPPLIED

blocks – P, T, V

blocks – O (3 of each color)

Which Does Not Belong? activity page

Identify the Different Solid Figure activity page

Making Paper Cones activity page (optional)

Checkpoint (printout)

ALSO NEEDED

household objects – 3 or more each of objects shaped like cubes, cones, and spheres

crayons

▶ Content Background

Students will identify the solid figure that does not belong in a group based on its color, shape, or size. Two-dimensional figures or shapes are called *plane figures*. These figures have length and width. Three-dimensional figures, which have length, width, and height, are called *solid figures* or *solids*. This lesson will use the term *solid figures* as well as *solids* to describe 3-dimensional figures. Reinforce both terms with students.

GET READY Which Shape Does Not Belong? [ONLINE 5 min]

Students will identify which plane figure does not belong based on its color, shape, or size.

Objectives

- Given a group of plane figures, identify which figure does not belong according to color, shape, or size.

LEARN Identify Color, Shape, or Size of Solids [OFFLINE 10 min]

Students will identify the solid figure that does not belong in a group based on its color, shape, or size.

Gather the cubes, household objects, and geometric solid blocks. Display the blocks so that students can refer to them throughout the activity.

1. Lay out a set of 4 cubes (3 red, 1 blue).

2. **Ask:** How are the solids in this group the same?
   ANSWER: They are all cubes. They are all the same size.

3. **Ask:** Which cube does **not** belong in this group?
   (Check to see that students choose the blue cube.)

4. **Ask:** Why doesn't this cube belong?
   ANSWER: Because it is a different color. This cube is blue and the rest of the cubes in the group are red.

5. Repeat Steps 1–4 with the following groups of objects:
   - Objects that are the same shape and color, but one is a different size
   - Objects that are the same size and color, but one is a different shape

6. Have students create the following groups:
   - 4 objects that are the same color and 1 object that is a different color
   - 3 objects that are the same size and 1 object that is a different size
   - 2 objects that are the same shape and 1 object that is a different shape

Objectives

- Given a set of solid figures, identify which figure does not belong according to color, shape, or size.

Tips

Have students hold the geometric solids and everyday objects to compare the color, size, and shape of the solids.

LEARN Which Does Not Belong?

Students will identify which solid does not belong to a group based on its size, color, or shape.

Give students the crayons and the Which Does Not Belong? activity page from their Activity Book. Read the directions with them.

- Given a set of solid figures, identify which figure does not belong according to color, shape, or size.

1. **Ask:** What attributes should we look at when finding an object in the picture that does not belong in the group?
   ANSWER: shape, size, and color

2. Have students complete the activity page. Guide students by asking questions such as the following:

   - What makes this object different from the others?

   - Why does this object **not** belong with the other objects?

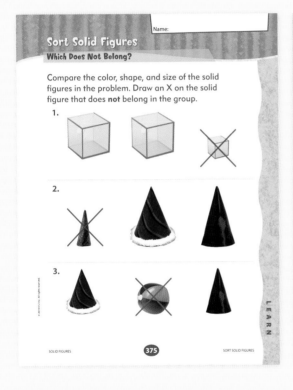

Name:

Sort Solid Figures

Which Does Not Belong?

Compare the color, shape, and size of the solid figures in the problem. Draw an X on the solid figure that does **not** belong in the group.

1.

2.

3.

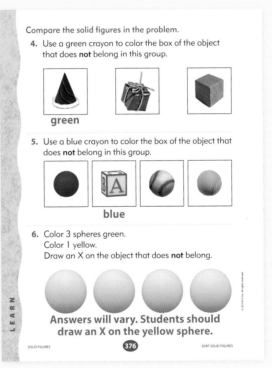

Compare the solid figures in the problem.

4. Use a green crayon to color the box of the object that does **not** belong in this group.

   green

5. Use a blue crayon to color the box of the object that does **not** belong in this group.

   blue

6. Color 3 spheres green.
   Color 1 yellow.
   Draw an X on the object that does **not** belong.

   Answers will vary. Students should draw an X on the yellow sphere.

Objectives

- Given a set of solid figures, identify which figure does not belong according to color, shape, or size.

Students will practice identifying a solid figure that is different from the others in a group. Give them the geometric solid blocks, household objects, and Identify the Different Solid Figure activity page from their Activity Book. Read the directions with them.

1. Give students a group of 3 objects shaped like a cube and 1 object shaped like a sphere.

   Ask: Which item does not belong in this group?
   ANSWER: The sphere does not belong in the group.

2. Give students a group of 3 objects shaped like a cube and 1 object shaped like a cone.

   Ask: Which item does not belong in this group?
   ANSWER: The cone does not belong in the group.

3. Give students a group of 3 objects shaped like a cone and 1 object shaped like a sphere.

   Ask: Which item does not belong in this group?
   ANSWER: The sphere does not belong in the group.

4. Give students a group of 3 objects shaped like a cone and 1 object shaped like a cube.

   Ask: Which item does not belong in this group?
   ANSWER: The cube does not belong in the group.

Have students complete the activity page. Display the blocks so that students can refer to them while they complete the activity page.

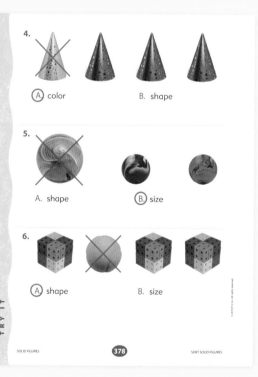

CHECKPOINT Online

Objectives

Students will complete this part of the Checkpoint online. If necessary, read the directions, problems, and answer choices to students and help them with keyboard or mouse operations.

- Given a set of solid figures, identify which figure does not belong according to color, shape, or size.

CHECKPOINT Offline

Objectives

Students will complete this performance-based assessment offline. Print the Checkpoint. Use the answer key to score the Checkpoint, and then enter the results online.

- Given a set of solid figures, identify which figure does not belong according to color, shape, or size.

    Gather the household objects and blocks. Display the blocks so that students can refer to them while they complete the Checkpoint. Give students 3 spherical items and 1 cube-shaped item for Problem 1. Give students a group of 4 items, one of which is much larger than the others, for Problem 2.

◇ Checkpoint   Math | Solid Figures | Sort Solid Figures

Name   Date

Checkpoint Answer Key

Read the question and follow the directions.

(1 point)
1. Look at the items. Which item does not belong in this group?

Students should respond that the cube-shaped object does not belong in the group.

(1 point)
2. Look at the objects. Which of the objects in this group is larger than the others?

Students should choose the largest object.

Put Together Shapes

Skills Update	5 minutes	ONLINE
LEARN Make a New Shape	15 minutes	OFFLINE
LEARN Piece Together Shapes	15 minutes	OFFLINE
TRY IT Create Different Shapes	10 minutes	OFFLINE

▶ Lesson Objectives

Use concrete objects or sketches to show how two or more plane figures can be put together to create a different shape (circles, triangles, rectangles, and squares only).

▶ Prerequisite Skills

Compare plane figures by common attributes, such as number of sides and number of corners of triangles, rectangles, squares, pentagons, and circles.

▶ Advance Preparation

Print the Circle Pieces. Cut around the shapes and on each line. Save the circle pieces for future lessons. You may wish to use an envelope or resealable bag to store the circle pieces.

▶ Content Background

Students will show how two or more plane figures can be put together to create a different shape. Two-dimensional figures or shapes are called *plane figures*. Plane figures have length and width. They can be put together to make other plane figures.

Materials to Gather

SUPPLIED

blocks – E (4 red)

blocks – K (6)

blocks – F, G, H, I, J

Circle Pieces (printout)

Create Different Shapes activity page

ALSO NEEDED

scissors, adult

LEARN Make a New Shape

OFFLINE 15 min

Students will put together two or more blocks to make larger shapes and different shapes. Gather the square (E) and triangle (K) blocks.

1. Show students how to put together 2 squares (E) to make a rectangle.

   Ask: What parts of the squares are touching?
   ANSWER: the sides

2. **Say:** Put together some squares to make a larger square.

   Observe as students find that they need at least 4 squares to make a larger square. You may need to remind students that all sides of a square must be the same length.

Objectives

- Use concrete objects or sketches to show how two or more plane figures can be put together to create a different shape (circles, triangles, rectangles, and squares only).

Tips

Tell students that they may need to rotate shapes to create the new shapes.

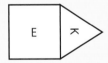

3. **Say:** Put together more than 2 squares to make a rectangle.

   Ask: How do you know you made a rectangle?
   ANSWER: My shape has 4 sides and 4 corners. It has 2 longer sides and 2 shorter sides.

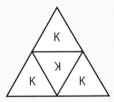

4. Have students put together a square and a triangle (K).

   Ask: How many sides does your new shape have?
   ANSWER: 5

   Say: Your shape is a pentagon.

5. **Say:** Put together some triangles to make a larger triangle.

   Observe as students put together triangles to make a larger triangle.

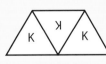

6. Have students put together triangles to make other shapes, such as the following:

7. Allow students to experiment, creating more shapes as time allows.

LEARN Piece Together Shapes

Objectives

- Use concrete objects or sketches to show how two or more plane figures can be put together to create a different shape (circles, triangles, rectangles, and squares only).

Tips

Use the larger blocks as a base on which students can lay smaller pieces when forming new shapes. For example in Step 5, have students use a larger triangle (H) as a base—they can lay the square and smaller triangles on top of it.

Students will put together the blocks and circle pieces to make other shapes, such as squares, rectangles, triangles, and circles.

Gather the blocks (F, G, H, I, J) and cut-out circle pieces.

1. Show the students the blocks. Have students put together two of the triangles to make a square. If students choose one large and one small triangle, ask them if they can make a square with the two different sizes. (No)

   Ask: How are the triangles you used alike?
   ANSWER: They are the same size.

   Ask: How many sides and how many corners does the square have?
   ANSWER: 4 sides and 4 corners

2. Have students put together other blocks pieces to make larger or smaller squares.

3. Have students put together two or more shapes to make a rectangle. Guide them to find more than one way to make a rectangle.

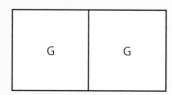

2 squares

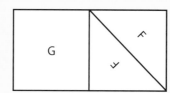

1 square and 2 triangles

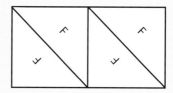

4 triangles

   Have students tell how many sides and corners the rectangles have.
   ANSWER: 4 sides, 4 corners

4. **Ask:** What two shapes can you put together to make a triangle?
   ANSWER: 2 triangles

   Have students put together 2 of the smaller triangles to make a larger triangle.

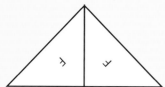

5. **Say:** Now start with a square and add other pieces to make a triangle.

Guide students to help them see that they can use a square and two small triangles to make a larger triangle.

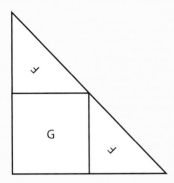

6. Clear the work area. Display the circle pieces.

7. **Say:** Put together 2 pieces to make a circle.

Guide students in joining the straight edges of two semicircles to form a circle.

8. **Say:** Now put together 4 pieces to make a circle.

9. As a challenge, have students use 3 pieces to make a circle.

OFFLINE
10 min

Students will practice putting together shapes to make different or larger shapes. Give students the blocks, cut-out circle pieces, and Create Different Shapes activity page from their Activity Book. Read the directions with them.

- Use concrete objects or sketches to show how two or more plane figures can be put together to create a different shape (circles, triangles, rectangles, and squares only).

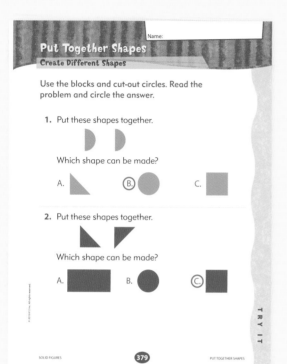

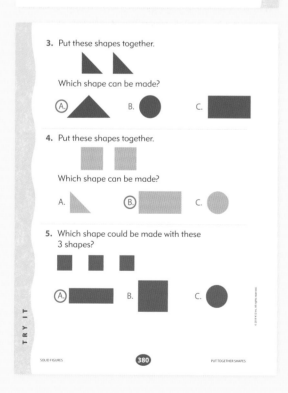

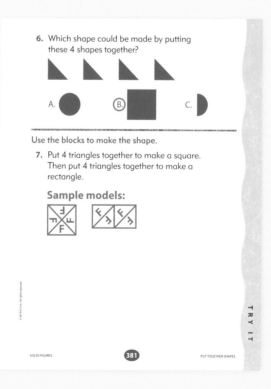

Combine Shapes: More Exploration

Skills Update	5 minutes	ONLINE
REVIEW Extend Your Understanding	30 minutes	ONLINE
CHECKPOINT	10 minutes	OFFLINE

▶ Lesson Objectives

Use concrete objects or sketches to show how two or more plane figures can be put together to create a different shape (circles, triangles, rectangles, and squares only).

▶ Prerequisite Skills

Compare plane figures by common attributes, such as number of sides and number of corners of triangles, rectangles, squares, pentagons, and circles.

▶ Content Background

In this lesson, students will have an opportunity for continued review. Then they will take a Checkpoint. If you wish, you may have students begin the next lesson after they complete the Checkpoint.

Materials to Gather

SUPPLIED

Checkpoint (printout)

blocks – F (4), G (2), J (2)

REVIEW Extend Your Understanding

ONLINE 30min

Objectives

- Use concrete objects or sketches to show how two or more plane figures can be put together to create a different shape (circles, triangles, rectangles, and squares only).

To prepare for the Checkpoint, students will have a chance to practice skills they've learned in previous lessons.

DIRECTIONS FOR USING THE PATTERN BLOCKS LEARNING TOOL

1. Click Same Shape.
2. Read the instructions, and click Start.
3. Have students drag shapes to the canvas to make the given shape. Show students how to rotate and flip shapes using the Rotate and Flip arrows.
4. After students create each shape, have them tell you what shapes they could break the shape apart into.
5. Continue as time allows.

CHECKPOINT

Objectives

- Use concrete objects or sketches to show how two or more plane figures can be put together to create a different shape (circles, triangles, rectangles, and squares only).

Print the Checkpoint and have students complete it on their own. Read the directions, problems, and answer choices to students, if necessary. Use the answer key to score the Checkpoint, and then enter the results online.

Give students the blocks for Problems 3–5.

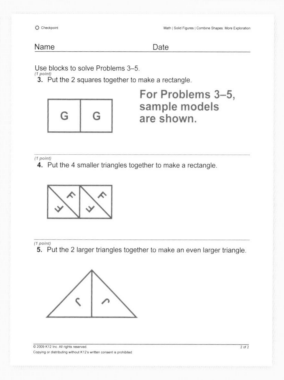

Take Apart Shapes

▶ Lesson Objectives

Show how two or more plane figures can be taken apart to create different shapes (circles, triangles, rectangles, and squares only).

▶ Prerequisite Skills

Use concrete objects or sketches to show how two or more plane figures can be put together to create a different shape (circles, triangles, rectangles, and squares only).

▶ Common Errors and Misconceptions

Students might not recognize that a shape might be positioned different ways. For example, students might not recognize that the second shape is a square.

▶ Advance Preparation

Gather the cut-out circles pieces from the Put Together Shapes lesson. If you don't have the circle pieces, print the Circle Pieces. Cut around the shapes and on each line. You may wish to use an envelope or a resealable bag to store the circle pieces.

Cut along the outside line of each shape on the Cut Up Shapes activity page. Place the shapes in a numerically ordered stack with shape 1 at the top.

▶ Safety

Supervise students to make sure they use their scissors safely and stay seated.

▶ Content Background

Students will show how two or more plane figures can be taken apart to create a different shape. Two-dimensional figures or shapes are called *plane figures*. Plane figures have length and width. They can be put together or taken apart to make other plane figures.

Materials to Gather

SUPPLIED

blocks – F, G, K

Circle Pieces (printout)

Cut Up Shapes activity page

Separate Shapes with Lines activity page

Shapes Within Shapes activity page

ALSO NEEDED

scissors, adult

scissors, round-end safety

ruler or straightedge

OFFLINE
5min

Objectives

- Use concrete objects or sketches to show how two or more plane figures can be put together to create a different shape (circles, triangles, rectangles, and squares only).

Students will put together blocks and circle pieces to make other shapes, such as squares, rectangles, triangles, and circles.

Gather the blocks and cut-out circle pieces.

1. Have students make a square using two blocks.

Ask: What shapes did you use?
ANSWER: 2 triangles

2. Have students make a triangle using two or more blocks.

Ask: What shapes did you use?
ANSWER: 2 triangles, 1 square and 2 triangles, or 4 triangles

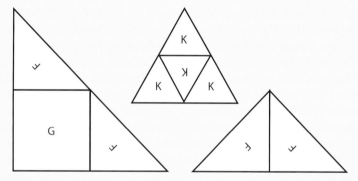

3. Have students show two ways to make a circle using two or more pieces.

Ask: How many pieces did you use?
ANSWER: 2, 3, or 4

4. Say: There are many different ways to put together two or more shapes to make a different shape.

Have students put together two or more shapes to make a rectangle. Challenge students to show you two different ways.

Ask: What shapes did you use?
ANSWER: 2 squares ,1 square and 2 triangles, or 4 triangles

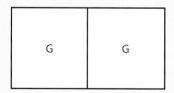 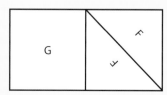 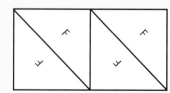

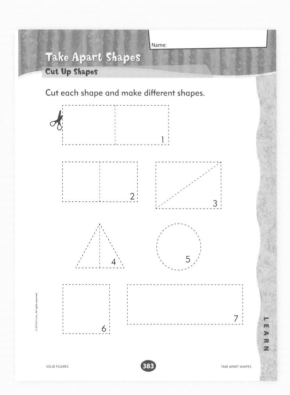

LEARN Cut Up Shapes

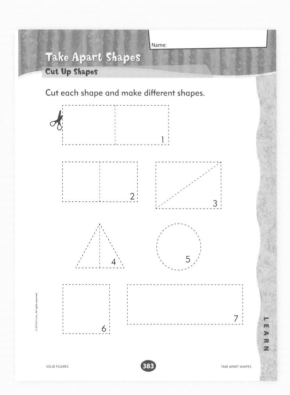

ONLINE
10min

Students will follow an online learning activity where they will be shown how to take apart plane figures to create two or more different shapes.

Gather the prepared paper shapes and scissors.

Read the instructions on-screen and guide students through the online activity.

Objectives

- Show how two or more plane figures can be taken apart to create different shapes (circles, triangles, rectangles, and squares only).

Tips

If students have difficulty cutting along fold lines, have them draw a line along the fold line and then cut along the line they drew.

Take Apart Shapes
Cut Up Shapes

Name:

Cut each shape and make different shapes.

1

2

3

4

5

6

7

L E A R N

SOLID FIGURES   **383**   TAKE APART SHAPES

LEARN Separate Shapes with Lines

Objectives

- Show how two or more plane figures can be taken apart to create different shapes (circles, triangles, rectangles, and squares only).

Students will draw lines to show how a shape can be separated to make two or more different shapes.

Give students a ruler or straightedge and the Separate Shapes with Lines activity page from their Activity Book.

1. **Say:** You can draw lines to show how you would take apart a shape to make different shapes.

2. Read the directions and Problem 1.

   Say: A triangle has 3 sides. Tell how to draw a line through the square to make two 3-sided shapes.

   ANSWER: Draw a line from one of the top corners to the bottom corner on the other side (diagonal line).

3. Position the ruler so that it touches 2 opposite corners of the square. Show students how to hold the ruler with one hand and draw with the other hand.

4. Have students try to complete Problem 2 on their own. Assist as needed.

5. Read Problem 3 and then point to students' answer to Problem 2.

   Ask: Where can we draw 1 more line to create 4 squares? (Students should indicate a horizontal line across the middle.)

6. Guide students to position their ruler at the marks on the sides of the square. Have them draw the first line.

7. Have students try to draw the second line on their own. Guide them as needed.

8. Have students try to complete Problem 4 on their own. Assist as needed.

9. Read Problem 5. Guide students to use the dot in the center of the circle to help them draw the line.

10. Read Problem 6.

    Ask: In which other problem did you draw 2 lines to make 4 shapes the same size?
    ANSWER: Problem 3

    Say: Use the work you did in Problem 3 to help you make 4 new shapes here.

11. Have students complete Problems 7 and 8 on their own. Assist as needed.

Tips

If students have difficulty visualizing the different shapes, have them use cut-out shapes and experiment with folding them in half different ways. For example, give students a cut-out square and have students fold it so that they make two triangles.

Make sure students do not become frustrated when using the straightedge to draw a line. If students have fine motor difficulties, you may have them show you where to draw the line. Then draw the line for them.

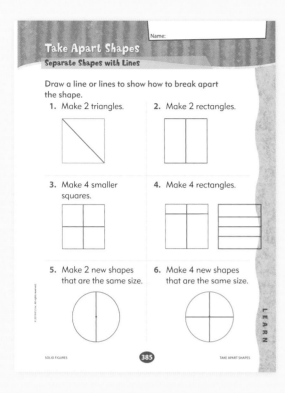

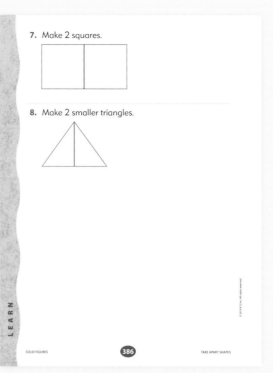

TRY IT Shapes Within Shapes

OFFLINE 10 min

Students will practice showing how to separate shapes to make new shapes. Give students the ruler or straightedge, scissors, and Shapes Within Shapes activity page from their Activity Book. Read the directions with them.

Objectives

- Show how two or more plane figures can be taken apart to create different shapes (circles, triangles, rectangles, and squares only).

Tips

Make sure students do not become frustrated when using the straightedge to draw a line. If students have fine motor difficulties, have them show you where to draw the line and then draw the line for them.

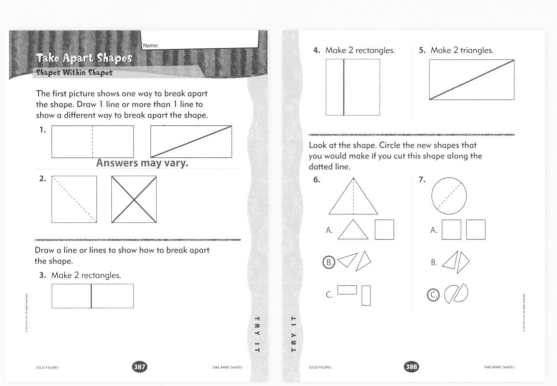

Take Apart Shapes
Shapes Within Shapes

The first picture shows one way to break apart the shape. Draw 1 line or more than 1 line to show a different way to break apart the shape.

1.

Answers may vary.

2.

Draw a line or lines to show how to break apart the shape.

3. Make 2 rectangles.

4. Make 2 rectangles.   **5.** Make 2 triangles.

Look at the shape. Circle the new shapes that you would make if you cut this shape along the dotted line.

6.

A.

(B.)

C.

7.

A.

B.

(C.)

TRY IT

TRY IT

Use scissors to answer the problem.

8. Cut apart the square to make 4 smaller shapes. Tell what shapes you made.

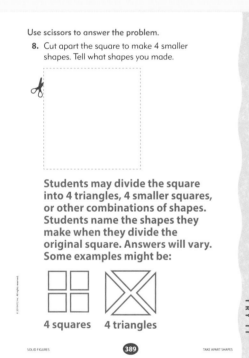

Students may divide the square into 4 triangles, 4 smaller squares, or other combinations of shapes. Students name the shapes they make when they divide the original square. Answers will vary. Some examples might be:

4 squares   4 triangles

TRY IT

Take Apart Shapes: More Exploration

Lesson Overview

Skills Update	5 minutes	ONLINE
REVIEW Extend Your Understanding	20 minutes	ONLINE
CHECKPOINT	20 minutes	OFFLINE

▶ Lesson Objectives

Show how two or more plane figures can be taken apart to create different shapes (circles, triangles, rectangles, and squares only).

▶ Prerequisite Skills

Use concrete objects or sketches to show how two or more plane figures can be put together to create a different shape (circles, triangles, rectangles, and squares only).

▶ Content Background

In this lesson, students will have an opportunity for continued review. Then they will take a Checkpoint. If you wish, you may have students begin the next lesson after they complete the Checkpoint.

Materials to Gather

SUPPLIED
Checkpoint (printout)

ALSO NEEDED
ruler or straightedge

REVIEW Extend Your Understanding

ONLINE 20min

To prepare for the Checkpoint, students will have a chance to practice skills they've learned in previous lessons.

DIRECTIONS FOR USING THE PATTERN BLOCKS LEARNING TOOL

1. Click Same Shape.
2. Read the instructions, and click Start.
3. Have students drag shapes to the canvas to make the given shape. Show students how to rotate and flip the shapes using the Rotate and Flip arrows.
4. Continue as time allows.

Objectives

- Show how two or more plane figures can be taken apart to create different shapes (circles, triangles, rectangles, and squares only).

CHECKPOINT

OFFLINE 20min

Print the Checkpoint and have students complete it on their own. Read the directions, problems, and answer choices to students, if necessary. Use the answer key to score the Checkpoint, and then enter the results online.

Give students the ruler or straightedge for Problems 4 and 5.

Objectives

- Show how two or more plane figures can be taken apart to create different shapes (circles, triangles, rectangles, and squares only).

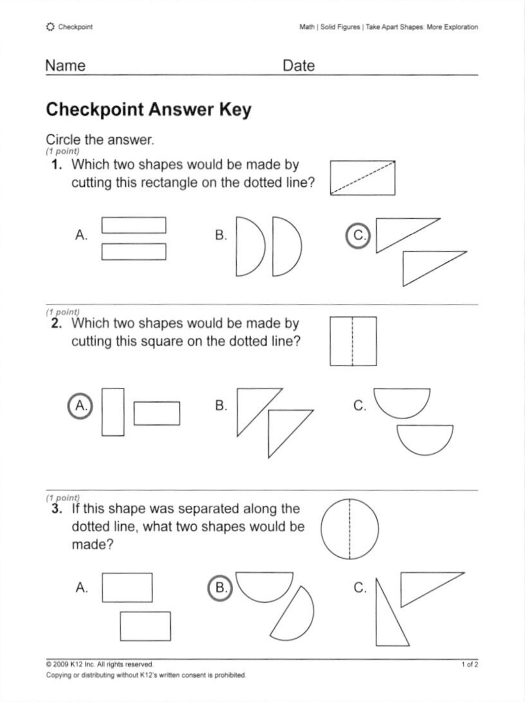

Name _____ Date _____

Checkpoint Answer Key

Circle the answer.

(1 point)
1. Which two shapes would be made by cutting this rectangle on the dotted line?

   A.   B.   **C.**

(1 point)
2. Which two shapes would be made by cutting this square on the dotted line?

   A.   B.   C.

(1 point)
3. If this shape was separated along the dotted line, what two shapes would be made?

   A.   **B.**   C.

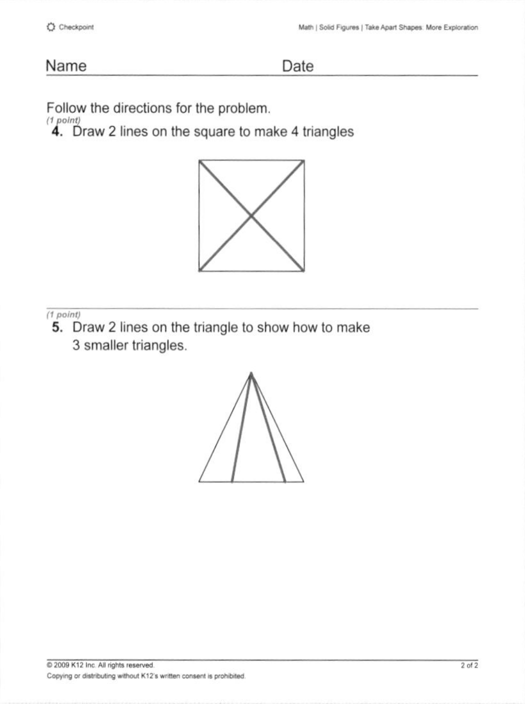

Name _____ Date _____

Follow the directions for the problem.

(1 point)
4. Draw 2 lines on the square to make 4 triangles

(1 point)
5. Draw 2 lines on the triangle to show how to make 3 smaller triangles.

Unit Review

UNIT REVIEW Look Back	15 minutes	**ONLINE**
UNIT REVIEW Checkpoint Practice	15 minutes	**OFFLINE**
⏵ **UNIT REVIEW** Prepare for the Checkpoint		

▶ Unit Objectives

This lesson reviews the following objectives:

- Identify common solid figures, such as cube, sphere, and cone.
- Compare common solid figures according to attributes (e.g., position, shape, size, roundness, or number of corners).
- Given a set of solid figures, identify which figure does not belong according to color, shape, or size.
- Use concrete objects or sketches to show how two or more plane figures can be put together to create a different shape (circles, triangles, rectangles, and squares only).
- Show how two or more plane figures can be taken apart to create different shapes (circles, triangles, rectangles, and squares only).

▶ Advance Preparation

In this lesson, students will have an opportunity to review previous activities in the Solid Figures unit. Look at the suggested activities in Unit Review: Prepare for the Checkpoint online and gather any needed materials. You may use the suggested materials or substitute other household objects that can be compared.

Materials to Gather

SUPPLIED

blocks – E (3), K (2), L (1)
Checkpoint Practice activity page

ALSO NEEDED

ruler or straightedge

Keywords	cone	solid figure
	cube	sphere
	plane figure	

UNIT REVIEW Look Back

Objectives

- Review unit objectives.

In this unit, students have reviewed plane figures. They have been introduced to three solid figures: cubes, cones, and spheres. They have learned how to describe solid figures by their number and shape of faces and their number of edges. They have sorted figures based on these characteristics. Students have learned to identify which solid in a set of solids does **not** belong based on its color, size, or shape. Lastly students learned how to take apart and put together shapes to create other shapes. Students will review key concepts in the unit to prepare for the Unit Checkpoint.

UNIT REVIEW Checkpoint Practice

Objectives

- Review unit objectives.

Students will complete a Checkpoint Practice activity page to prepare for the Unit Checkpoint. If necessary, read the directions, questions, and answer choices to students. Have students answer the problems on their own. Carefully review the answers with students.

Give students the blocks and ruler or straightedge for Problems 12–14.

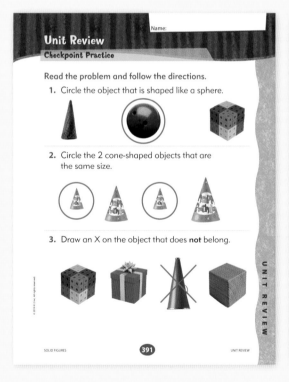

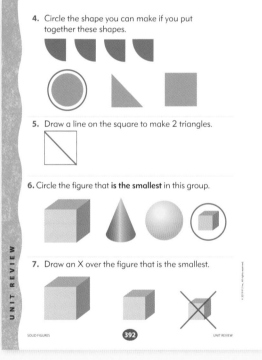

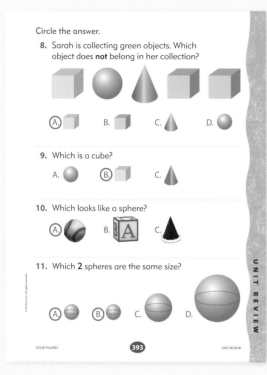

Circle the answer.

8. Sarah is collecting green objects. Which object does **not** belong in her collection?

A.   B.   C.   D.

9. Which is a cube?

A.   B.   C.

10. Which looks like a sphere?

A.   B.   C.

11. Which **2** spheres are the same size?

A.   B.   C.   D.

U N I T   R E V I E W

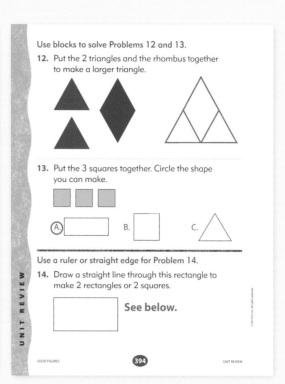

Use blocks to solve Problems 12 and 13.

12. Put the 2 triangles and the rhombus together to make a larger triangle.

13. Put the 3 squares together. Circle the shape you can make.

A.   B.   C.

Use a ruler or straight edge for Problem 14.

14. Draw a straight line through this rectangle to make 2 rectangles or 2 squares.

See below.

Additional Answers

14. Sample answers:

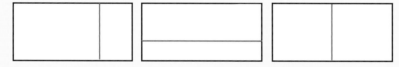

⇥ **UNIT REVIEW** Prepare for the Checkpoint

What you do next depends on how students performed in the previous activity, Unit Review: Checkpoint Practice. If students had difficulty with any of the problems, complete the appropriate review activity listed in the table online.

Unit Checkpoint

▶ Unit Objectives

This lesson assesses the following objectives:

- Identify common solid figures, such as cube, sphere, and cone.
- Compare solid figures according to attributes (e.g., position, shape, size, roundness, or number of corners).
- Given a set of solid figures, identify which figure does not belong according to color, shape, or size.
- Use concrete objects or sketches to show how two or more plane figures can be put together to create a different shape (circles, triangles, rectangles, and squares only).
- Show how two or more plane figures can be taken apart to create different shapes (circles, triangles, rectangles, and squares only).

▶ Advanced Preparation

Gather the cut-out circle pieces from the Put Together Shapes lesson. If you don't have the circle pieces, print the Circle Pieces. Cut around the shapes and on each line. You may wish to use an envelope or a resealable bag to store the circle pieces.

▶ Safety

Supervise students to make sure they use their scissors safely and stay seated.

Materials to Gather

SUPPLIED
Unit Checkpoint (printout)
blocks – G (3), K (1), M (1)
Circle Pieces (printout)

ALSO NEEDED
scissors, round-end safety

UNIT CHECKPOINT Offline

OFFLINE 45 min

Objectives

- Assess unit objectives.

Students will complete the Unit Checkpoint offline. Print the Checkpoint and have students complete it on their own. Read the directions, problems, and answer choices to students, if necessary. Use the answer key to score the Checkpoint, and then enter the results online.

Give students the blocks and cut-out circle pieces. For Problems 12–14, allow students to use these materials. For Problems 16–18, give students the scissors.

Name _____   Date _____

Unit Checkpoint Answer Key

Circle the answer.

(1 point)
1. Which object does **not** belong in the group?

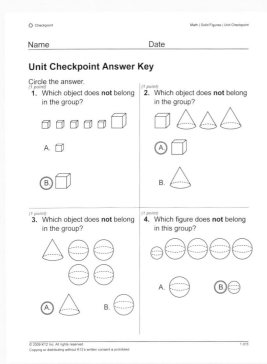

A. ▱

B. (circled) cube

(1 point)
2. Which object does **not** belong in the group?

A. (circled) cube

B. cone

(1 point)
3. Which object does **not** belong in the group?

A. (circled) cone

B. sphere

(1 point)
4. Which figure does **not** belong in this group?

A. sphere

B. (circled) small sphere

Name _____   Date _____

(1 point)
5. What is the name of this figure?

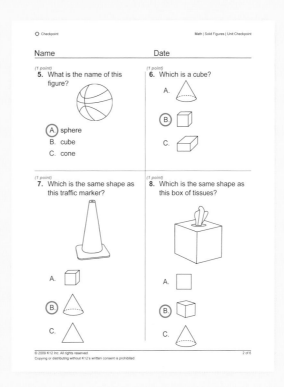

A. (circled) sphere
B. cube
C. cone

(1 point)
6. Which is a cube?

A. cone
B. (circled) cube
C. rectangular prism

(1 point)
7. Which is the same shape as this traffic marker?

A. cube
B. (circled) cone
C. triangle

(1 point)
8. Which is the same shape as this box of tissues?

A. square
B. (circled) cube
C. cone

Name _____   Date _____

(1 point)
9. Which object is the same shape as this object?

A. (circled) sphere
B. cube
C. cone

(1 point)
10. Which object is the same size as this object?

A. (circled) cone
B. cone
C. cone

(1 point)
11. Which 2 shapes would be made by cutting this triangle on the dotted line?

A. two triangles
B. (circled) triangle and smaller shape
C. two squares

Name _____   Date _____

(1 point)
12. Which shape could be made by putting these 3 shapes together?

A. rectangle
B. circle
C. (circled) rectangle

(1 point)
13. Which shape could be made by putting these 2 shapes together?

A. square
B. (circled) triangle
C. rectangle

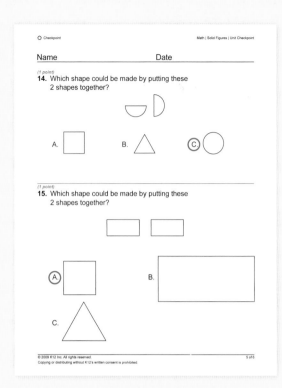

Name _____ **Date** _____

(1 point)

14. Which shape could be made by putting these 2 shapes together?

A. ☐   B. △   Ⓒ ○

(1 point)

15. Which shape could be made by putting these 2 shapes together?

Ⓐ ☐   B. ▭

C. △

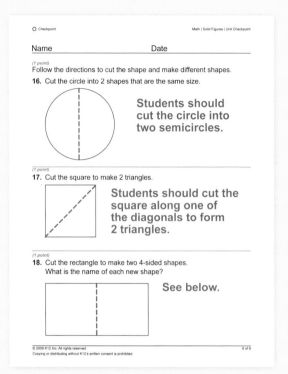

Name _____ **Date** _____

(1 point)

Follow the directions to cut the shape and make different shapes.

16. Cut the circle into 2 shapes that are the same size.

Students should cut the circle into two semicircles.

(1 point)

17. Cut the square to make 2 triangles.

Students should cut the square along one of the diagonals to form 2 triangles.

(1 point)

18. Cut the rectangle to make two 4-sided shapes. What is the name of each new shape?

See below.

Additional Answers

18. Students should cut the paper rectangle to form two new shapes. Students should name their new shapes. Depending on where students cut the rectangle, the two new shapes may be rectangles or squares.